A series of student texts in

Contemporary

General Editors:
Professor Arthur J. Willis
Professor Michael A. Sleigh

The Biology of Symbiosis

D.C. Smith

Department of Plant Sciences
University of Oxford

and

A.E. Douglas

John Innes Institute
Norwich

Edward Arnold

© D.C. Smith and A.E. Douglas 1987

First published in Great Britain 1987 by
Edward Arnold (Publishers) Ltd, 41 Bedford Square, London WC1B 3DQ

Edward Arnold (Australia) Pty Ltd, 80 Waverley Road, Caulfield East,
Victoria 3145, Australia

Edward Arnold, 3 East Read Street, Baltimore, Maryland 21202, U.S.A.

British Library Cataloguing in Publication Data

Smith, D.C.
    The biology of symbiosis.——(Contemporary biology)
    1. Symbiosis
    I. Title II. Douglas, A.E.   III. Series
    574.5′2482   QH548

    ISBN 0-7131-2939-5

Text set in 10/11pt Times Compugraphic
by Colset Private Limited, Singapore
Made and printed in Great Britain by Richard Clay Ltd, Bungay, Suffolk

Preface

Symbiosis was once regarded as a curiosity, remote from the mainstream of biology. The different associations were each considered as isolated phenomena, unconnected with each other. Indeed, the first major conference on symbiosis as a general topic, with botanists, zoologists and microbiologists coming together to discuss the different types of association, was not held until 1963 (by the Society of General Microbiology, in London). The second major conference was in 1974 (by the Society for Experimental Biology, in Bristol).

In the interval between these two conferences, a number of events had occurred which began to bring symbiosis to the notice of biologists as a phenomenon of more central importance. The seminal paper of Lynn Sagan (Margulis) in 1967, presenting detailed arguments for the symbiotic origin of a number of eukaryotic cell organelles, initiated a progressive and major change in the views of biologists about the origin and evolution of eukaryotes. This in its turn directed attention to the study of modern intracellular symbionts as an aspect of cell biology. Meanwhile, similarities between associations as different as lichens and corals were discovered in the way in which products of photosynthesis moved from algal symbionts to their heterotrophic hosts; this encouraged further comparative studies between different symbioses, not only in nutrient movement but also in other aspects such as recognition mechanisms.

The ecological importance of symbiosis has also come to be more appreciated in recent years, especially with the growing realization that the roots of the great majority of plants are mycorrhizal; it is now clear that mycorrhizas are the major organs of mineral nutrient uptake in natural vegetation. In the search to increase crop productivity yet reduce the use of chemical fertilizers, considerable attention has been paid to the fact that much more nitrogen is fixed by rhizobia in legume root nodules than by non-symbiotic, nitrogen-fixing bacteria in the soil. There is much current interest in the possibility of using modern techniques of genetic manipulation to enhance symbiotic nitrogen fixation. Improved methods of studying anaerobic microorganisms have allowed substantial advances in our understanding of rumen fermentation. Apart from the significance of this for increasing production of domestic animals such as cattle, it has also shown that many insect pests whose diet is cellulose and lignin digest these

v

compounds with the aid of gut symbionts in a fashion remarkably similar to that in ruminants.

All these various intertwining events have resulted in symbiosis becoming a much more prominent component of undergraduate curricula in biology, and increasing numbers of universities are offering general courses in symbiosis. A serious disadvantage for student and teacher alike is that the literature on symbiosis is very dispersed, and there is no single modern text on which to base a comprehensive course.

This book attempts to fill this gap. It is primarily aimed at students, and it is not intended as a research monograph. One of its objectives is to compare different types of association, in order to highlight similarities and differences in the interactions between organisms in symbiosis.

As will be explained in the opening chapter, the term 'symbiosis' means different things to different biologists. This book largely confines itself to associations which are considered to be mutualistic and not parasitic, and where one of the partners is a microorganism. Although, for obvious reasons, much greater attention has been paid in the past to parasitic associations, we hope that this book shows that mutualistic associations are also profoundly important.

Oxford   D.C.S.
Norwich   A.E.D.
1987

Acknowledgements

We are deeply grateful to colleagues who have read and commented upon various parts of the book: Professor J.E. Beringer (Chapter 4), Dr R. Robins (Chapter 5), Professor J.L. Harley FRS (Chapter 7), Dr A. McAllan and Dr M. Theodorou (Chapter 8), Drs A. and E. Southward (Chapter 9), and Professor D.H. Lewis (Chapters 1, 7, 10 and 11). Dr J.B. Searle read the book from the viewpoint of the general biologist. All were responsible for considerable improvements to the text. The residual errors are entirely our own responsibility.

We are very much indebted to the following for generously providing us with illustrations: Dr V. Ahmadjian, Dr N.J. Brewin, Dr G.S. Coleman, Dr J.A. Downie, Dr Jane Duddridge, Dr I. Gibson, Professor D.O. Hall, Dr Kay Hardie, Professor J.L. Harley, Dr C.R. Hawes, Mr F.J. Hill, Dr R. Honegger, Dr A. Johnston, Dr P. McAuley, Professor D.E. Mullins, Dr E. Peveling, Dr R. Robins, Dr D.-J. Shi, Dr R.K. Trench, Mr J.R. Turner, Dr C.R. Wilkinson and Dr E.A. Wood.

This book could not have been completed without efficient secretarial assistance. Early drafts were prepared by Suzy Oakes, while Mrs Gladys Roper devoted considerable time, effort and patient good humour to producing numerous later drafts. The photographic assistance of John Baker is deeply appreciated.

Finally, we are especially grateful for the forbearance, help and encouragement of our families.

Contents

1
Introduction: the concept of symbiosis

1.1 Definitions of symbiosis

In 1879, de Bary coined the termed *symbiosis*, which he defined in the phrase '. . . des Zusammenlebens ungleichnamiger Organismen . . .', the living together of differently named organisms. He clearly considered symbiosis to include both *mutualistic* associations (in which all the organisms involved are believed to derive benefit) and *parasitic* associations (in which one organism benefits to the detriment of other members of the association). Nevertheless, many biologists have subsequently equated symbiosis with mutualistic associations, and this is the meaning of symbiosis which has entered our everyday language. However, this more restrictive use of the term is frequently difficult to apply to real associations. It can sometimes be difficult to identify precisely what is meant by 'benefit', and certain associations are both parasitic and mutualistic at different stages or under different environmental circumstances. For such reasons, de Bary's original definition of symbiosis is preferred by a number of biologists (Lewis, 1973; Smith *et al.*, 1969; Stanier *et al.*, 1977), and is adopted in this book.

It is important to distinguish between *mutualism* which includes brief interactions such as pollination (and are not considered here), and *mutualistic symbiosis*, where the term 'symbiosis' implies living together, and hence some degree of permanence (see 1.3.4).

1.2 Scope of book

Most symbioses described in this book are traditionally regarded as mutualistic although, as will be discussed in 11.10, the evidence for this view is frequently circumstantial. The scope of the book is further limited to associations in which there is intimate contact between the partners, at least one of which is a microorganism (see 1.5), and in which it is particularly appropriate for interactions to be investigated at the cellular level. Interactions at other levels, e.g., behavioural or genic, are not considered in detail.

1.3 Characteristics of symbioses

The concepts of harm and benefit feature prominently in most discussions of

Table 1.1   Characteristics used in the description of symbiosis. (Modified from Starr, 1975.)

Characteristics	Principal features involved
1 Relative size of the partners	The partners in most symbioses are of unequal size; the larger is the *host*, and the smaller the *symbiont*.
2 Relative position of the partners	Symbionts are either external to the host (*ectosymbiotic*), or within it (*endosymbiotic*). Endosymbionts are either within host cells (*intracellular*) or external to them (*extracellular*).
3 Necessity of symbiosis to the organisms involved	Symbiosis is *obligate* for an organism if it cannot survive without its partner, and *facultative* if it is not dependent on the symbiosis.
4 Duration and stability of the symbiosis	All symbioses persist for an appreciable time relative to the life-spans of the partners. The processes which maintain the normally stable proportion of symbiont to host are termed *regulation*.
5 Perpetuation of the symbiosis	A host acquires its complement of symbionts either by *direct transmission* from another host, or from the external environment.
6 Specificity and recognition in symbiosis	*Specificity* refers to the degree of taxonomic difference between partners with which an organism associates; *recognition* refers to the discrimination and selection amongst potential partners which lead to the observed specificity.
7 Modes of interaction between the partners	The partners may interact in a range of ways, including genetic, metabolic, behavioural. Nutritional interactions are very common.
8 Integration in the symbiosis	Characteristics (e.g. structure, functions) which organisms display in symbiosis but not in isolation.
9 Significance of symbiosis to the well-being of the partners	An organism may derive benefit or harm or be unaffected by symbiosis.

symbiosis, for example, Boucher *et al.* (1982) and Whitfield (1979). However a range of other characteristics is also important in the description of a symbiosis, and these are summarized in Table 1.1. In this section, each characteristic is discussed and the various terms and concepts used in this book are introduced. For simplicity, a symbiosis is considered in the following discussion to comprise two species although in nature many associations involve three or more partners.

1.3.1   Relative size of the partners

The organisms involved in most associations are of unequal size. In this book, the larger will be known as the ***host***, and the smaller as the ***symbiont***.

In contrast to its vernacular meaning, the 'host' is not necessarily the 'provider'.

1.3.2 Relative position of the partners

The partners in the symbioses described in this book are in direct physical contact. The symbionts are either external to the host (*ectosymbiotic*) or within it (*endosymbiotic*). If they are endosymbiotic, then they occur within host cells (*intracellular*), or outside them (*extracellular*). Extracellular

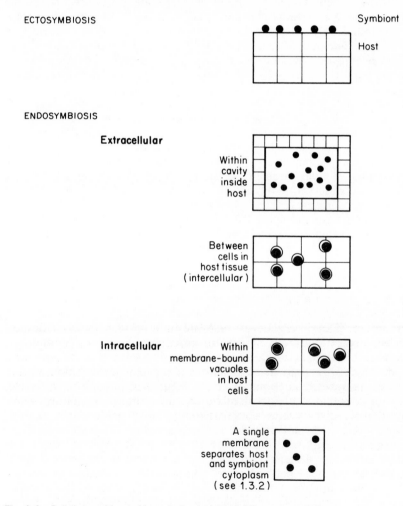

Fig. 1.1 Relative positions of host and symbiont in different associations.

symbionts may be either between cells of a host tissue (*intercellular*), or in an internal cavity (Fig. 1.1). Intracellular symbionts are almost always enclosed by a host membrane; in a very few associations only a single membrane separates host from symbiont cytoplasm and, in these cases, it is uncertain whether the membrane is of host or symbiont origin.

1.3.3   Necessity of symbiosis to the partners

Symbiosis is *obligate* for an organism which cannot survive and reproduce in the absence of its partner, and *facultative* if it is not dependent on the association. However, this simple dichotomy is complicated by the fact that some organisms, such as certain fungi, can be grown in isolation in the laboratory, but are found only in symbiosis in nature. This has led to a distinction between *physiological obligacy*, an absolute dependence on a partner, and *ecological obligacy*, the inability to survive in the natural environment in isolation from the partner (Brian, 1966). Thus, the fungi mentioned above are ecologically obligate but physiologically facultative.

Although obligacy is a useful concept, it is difficult to demonstrate conclusively that symbiosis is obligate for any organism. For example, failure to grow in isolation may be due to inappropriate techniques rather than to physiological obligacy. Sometimes, therefore, the distinction is made between symbiotic microorganisms which are *culturable* and those which are *unculturable*. Similar problems arise with ecological obligacy, because sampling and observation methods in the field may be inadequate to detect organisms growing away from symbiosis.

A symbiont growing apart from its host – whether in nature or in the laboratory – is said to be *free-living*. Hosts which have been artificially freed of their symbionts are termed *aposymbiotic*.

1.3.4   Duration and stability

Some authors (Starr, 1975; Lewis, 1985) are of the opinion that even the most transient associations are symbioses, provided the relationship is significant to the 'well-being' of at least one of the partners; by this definition, symbiosis would include insect pollination of plants and predator-prey relationships. In contrast, many authors (Boucher *et al.*, 1982; Margulis, 1976; Whitfield, 1979) consider that symbiosis should refer only to those associations where contact between the partners persists for 'an appreciable length of time' relative to the life span of the organisms involved. This second view is adopted in this book.

Most symbioses described in this book are stable in the sense that the relative biomass of the partners is constant or varies in a predictable manner with environmental circumstances or developmental stage of the partners. The mechanisms maintaining this stability are termed *regulation*.

1.3.5 Perpetuation of the symbiosis

The complement of symbionts acquired by a host may be derived either from the surrounding environment, or directly from another host with no significant intervening free-living phase. The latter will be called *direct transmission* and, in sexually reproducing hosts, it may involve mechanisms by which symbionts are smeared on to fertilized eggs or included in the cytoplasm of oocytes prior to fertilization.

1.3.6 Specificity and recognition

Most organisms can usually form a symbiosis with a number of taxonomically distinct partners. The *specificity* of a symbiosis refers to the degree of taxonomic difference between acceptable partners, and may vary from very low (where an organism can associate with members of more than one class or even phylum) to high or very high, where only a single species or 'strain' is acceptable (Table 1.2). Organisms which can enter into symbiosis are termed *symbiotic* while related taxa which do not form a symbiosis are *nonsymbiotic*. In some texts, nonsymbiotic forms are called 'free-living', but this can be confusing since the term is also used to describe symbionts living apart from their hosts, see 1.3.3.

Table 1.2 Levels of specificity in symbioses.

Level of specificity	Range of acceptable partners
Very high	Within the same strain (or subspecific taxon)
High	Within the same species
Moderate	Within the same genus
Low	Within the same family or order
Very low	Within the same class, phylum or larger grouping

During the establishment of a symbiosis, a wide variety of processes may be involved in the selection of partners and discrimination against inappropriate organisms. These are collectively known as *recognition* (Smith, 1981). Recognition mechanisms may include specific chemical interactions, tolerance or suppression of host defences, and metabolic, morphological or behavioural interactions. In discussions of certain aspects of biology (e.g., fusion of gametes, cell agglutination), 'recognition' is used in a much narrower sense to refer to the stereospecific interaction between surface molecules at initial contact between cells, but this restricted meaning is not very useful in the context of symbiosis.

1.3.7 Modes of interaction

There are many categories of interactions between the partners of a symbiosis, e.g., genetic, metabolic, behavioural (Starr, 1975).

For most associations discussed in this book, nutritional interactions play a key role, and the usual mode of nutritional interaction is *biotrophy*, in which an organism obtains nutrients from the living cells of its partner. In some associations, phases of *necrotrophy* may occur, in which an organism first engenders the death of cells of its partner and then derives nutrients from the dead cells.

The flow of nutrients between the partners may be unidirectional or bidirectional. For any particular nutrient, it is convenient to describe the partner from which nutrients originate as the *donor* and the other as the *recipient*.

1.3.8   Integration

Starr (1975) comments that most symbioses 'result at least temporarily, in something more than the sum of the parts', and describes this feature as *integration*. Recently, Lewis (1985) has defined integration more precisely as 'the display of structures, functions, etc., which are more than, and different from, those of which the participants are capable as individuals'. Examples of integration are the formation of a lichen thallus (Chapter 6) and the production of leghaemoglobin by the combined synthetic capabilities of legumes and their rhizobium symbionts (4.2.4.3).

1.3.9   Significance of symbiosis to the well-being of the partners

Many discussions of symbiosis (and especially mutualism) place great emphasis on the concept that a partner may derive 'benefit' or 'harm', although a clear and consistent definition of these terms is rarely provided. A variety of interactions may occur between the partners, some of which can sensibly be interpreted as advantageous (e.g., receiving scarce nutrients from a partner), some as disadvantageous (e.g., losing scarce nutrients to a partner), but many others cannot be so easily evaluated (e.g., the permanent loss of features present in nonsymbiotic relatives). Usually, it is the net outcome of the interactions which is assessed as 'beneficial' or 'harmful' to a partner, but because there is no agreed method of assessment, it becomes a matter of opinion for the author concerned, and conflicting or confusing views can arise. In lichens, for example, Hale (1983) suggested that the symbiont gains overall benefit especially because it is mechanically protected by the fungus against adverse environmental conditions. By contrast, Ahmadjian and Jacobs (1983) considered the fungus to be parasitic (i.e., harmful) because it does not seem to provide the symbiont with nutrients and tends to destroy some symbiont cells during the early stage of laboratory synthesis of lichens.

Such problems can be reduced if 'harm' and 'benefit' are defined in a biologically meaningful way. Organisms can be said to 'benefit' if they produce more offspring in the associated than in the unassociated state (Margulis, 1981). This idea was expressed more precisely by Law and Lewis (1983) who considered that associations are mutualistic if the *fitness* of the associating organisms is greater together than when apart.

Two further points concerning the meaning of benefit require consideration. The first is semantic. It is often written that an organism 'confers benefit' on its partner. This phrase might be taken to imply altruism, but as Droop (1963) commented, 'no . . . (organism) . . . is there for the benefit of the other partner'. Secondly, an organism deriving benefit from an association need not do so from all the interactions with its partner; some interactions may be disadvantageous and represent a *cost*. The observed benefit is a *net benefit*, a balance between gross benefits and gross costs.

1.4 The experimental study of symbiosis

1.4.1 The experimental material

Ideally, material for biological experiments should be derived from populations of organisms of known genetic constitution previously maintained under controlled environmental conditions. Unfortunately, hardly any associations offer such amenable material; examples of the few which can be maintained in permanent laboratory culture include the symbioses of *Chlorella* with hydra and *Paramecium bursaria* (Chapter 2). Some of the plant root symbioses (mycorrhizas, legume/rhizobium associations) can be synthesized from stocks of isolated host and symbiont, but this is often inconveniently slow. Studies of most other symbioses have to rely on material collected in nature, with the attendant difficulties of high experimental variability and, in many cases, limited availability. The relationship between host and symbiont often varies with season and other environmental conditions, and because of the need to conserve organisms in nature, it may not always be possible to collect material in quantities large enough for certain kinds of experiment; this is especially true of slow-growing associations such as lichens.

1.4.2 Study of the intact association

The interface between the partners of many symbioses is intimate and often complex, and it poses a formidable obstacle to experimental investigations of interactions between host and symbiont. For example, isotopes (e.g., ^{14}C, ^{15}N, ^{32}P) are widely used to study nutritional interactions, in particular to demonstrate the movement of nutrients between the partners. However, these methods provide little information about events at the interface. The chemical form in which isotopes cross the boundary between partners and the mechanism of transfer can rarely be identified directly. Inhibitors which selectively affect only one of the partners are very valuable in these studies, but are available for very few associations. Examples include: 3-(3,4-dichlorophenyl)-1,1-dimethyl urea (DCMU), which inhibits photosynthesis in a range of autotrophic symbionts without significantly affecting their heterotrophic hosts; and digitonin, which does not affect cyanobacterial symbionts but inactivates membrane function in their eukaryotic hosts (see 5.3.3 and 6.4.1.2).

Microscopy has proved very useful, particularly in the analysis of the development of symbioses. When combined with the use of radioactive isotopes in microautoradiography, further insights into interactions between the partners can often be gained.

1.4.3 Separation of host and symbiont

Partly because of the intrinsic difficulties of studying the intact symbiosis, many investigations focus on the isolated partners, or, frequently, solely on the symbiont. However, many symbionts isolated into long-term culture differ from their condition in symbiosis by a number of characteristics (e.g., gross morphology, growth rate, metabolic properties including release of nutrients, surface characteristics and reproductive behaviour). Many symbionts are therefore studied immediately after separation from the host even though such preparations are often contaminated with adhering host material which is difficult to remove.

A valuable approach for the study of nutrient interactions is to separate the host into symbiont-containing and symbiont-free regions. This has provided useful information for hydra/*Chlorella* (2.2.2.2.), legume/*Rhizobium* (4.2.4.2.), bryophyte/cyanobacteria (5.3.4.2.), lichen (6.4.1.1.), ectomycorrhizal (7.4.1.1.) and insect/mycetocyte (9.10.3.) associations.

1.5 Classification of organisms

A wide variety of organisms is discussed in this book. The major taxonomic groupings are therefore outlined here.

The most fundamental distinction among living organisms is that between *prokaryotes* and *eukaryotes*, which 'probably represents the single greatest evolutionary discontinuity in the present day world' (Stanier *et al.*, 1977). The basic difference between prokaryotes and eukaryotes is the organization of the genetic material. In *prokaryotes*, the DNA is usually in the form of a single filament or loop and lies free in the cell. By contrast, the DNA of *eukaryotes* is contained within a membrane-bound nucleus and is usually packaged together with histones and other proteins into one to many chromosomes. Correlated with this is a number of other differences between prokaryotes and eukaryotes (Table 1.3).

The traditional division of living organisms into two kingdoms, 'Plantae' and 'Animalia', is generally agreed to be invalid because it does not recognize the distinction between prokaryotes and eukaryotes, but none of the several

Table 1.3 Some differences between prokaryotes and eukaryotes (after Margulis, 1981; Stanier *et al.*, 1977).

Character	Prokaryotes	Eukaryotes
Size and general form.	Most are small cells (1–10 μm diam.). Usually unicellular or simple filaments. Sometimes with cellular differentiation, but no tissue differentiation.	Most have large cells (10–100 μm diam.). May be unicellular, colonial or filamentous, but most are multicellular with tissue differentiation.
Membrane-bound organelles.	Absent.	Present (e.g. mitochondria, chloroplasts).
Organisation of DNA.	DNA not associated with proteins; no nucleus.	DNA associated with proteins (usually including histones) and packaged into several to many chromosomes; defined nucleus bounded by double membrane.
Segregation of DNA.	Occurs without microtubules.	Chromosomes segregated on microtubules, usually arranged as a mitotic spindle.
Sexual systems.	Where present, unidirectional transfer of genetic material from donor to recipient.	Present in most forms, with equal participation of genomes of two partners at fertilization.
Phagocytosis and/or pinocytosis.	Absent.	Present, but not universal (e.g., absent in fungi).

modern schemes of classification has obtained universal acceptance. In this book, one of the schemes proposed by Whittaker and Margulis (1978) will be followed. Five kingdoms are recognized.

MONERA – all prokaryotes; the eubacteria (including the classically recognized bacteria and cyanobacteria – the 'blue-green algae') and the archaebacteria (e.g., halobacteria and methanogenic bacteria).

PROTOCTISTA – protozoa, algae, slime moulds and flagellate fungi. (Many schemes have a somewhat different arrangement and assign all single-celled eukaryotes to the phylum Protista, but this is a less satisfactory grouping than the Protoctista because, for example, it excludes the multicellular relatives of unicellular algae).

FUNGI – Zygomycotina, Ascomycotina, Basidiomycotina and Deuteromycotina.

PLANTAE – Bryophyta, Pteridophyta, Gymnospermae and Angiospermae.

ANIMALIA – Porifera, Metazoa.

Following common practice (e.g., Stanier *et al.*, 1977), members of the Monera, Protoctista and Fungi which are partners in the associations described in this book are known as **microorganisms**.

Members of the Protoctista will be referred to in the text as **protists**, which, following the approach of Taylor (1979) in a different context, is 'more euphonious than the etymologically correct term protoctists'.

2
Algae in symbiosis I. With freshwater hosts (animals and protists)

2.1 Introduction

A range of aquatic protists and animals possess unicellular photosynthetic symbionts. The symbionts have traditionally been classified by their colour as 'zoochlorellae' (green), 'zooxanthellae' (yellow or brown) or 'cyanellae' (blue-green). However this practice should be avoided because colour is not always a good index of taxonomic position. Although all 'cyanellae' are cyanobacteria, 'zooxanthellae' and 'zoochlorellae' each comprise a variety of different taxa (Table 2.1).

The survey of associations in Table 2.1 reveals several general features.

(a) By and large, each host species contains only one species or genus of algal symbiont. The few exceptions include certain marine foraminifera, which have both the dinoflagellate *Symbiodinium microadriaticum* and the chlorophycean *Chlorella*, (see 3.4.1), and the marine coelenterate *Anthopleura xanthogrammica*, which may contain *S. microadriaticum* and/or '*Chlorella*-like' algae (O'Brien, 1978).

(b) Symbiosis with algae is common among various groups of protists, e.g. the larger foraminifera and freshwater ciliates, and 'lower' invertebrate phyla, especially the coelenterates. By contrast, there are few examples of symbiosis with algae among the molluscs and no well-documented cases among such 'higher' invertebrate groups as the annelids, echinoderms and arthropods, or among the vertebrates.

(c) In the marine environment, dinoflagellates (members of the family Dinophyceae), especially *Symbiodinium microadriaticum*, are very common symbionts, whereas *Chlorella* is the dominant algal symbiont in freshwater hosts.

2.2 Freshwater associations between *Chlorella* and protists or animals

2.2.1 General introduction

Chlorella are unicellular green algae of the family Chlorophyceae. The cells are spherical or ellipsoidal, 2–10 μm in diameter and have a single parietal

Table 2.1 Survey of algal and cyanobacterial symbionts in protists and animals.

Host	Symbiont				
	Eukaryotes (algae)				
	Dinophyceae (dinoflagellates) Marine	Bacillariophyceae (diatoms) Marine	Haptophyceae Marine	Cryptophyceae Marine	Chrysophyceae Marine
			← ('zooxanthellae') →		
Protists	Several spp. in foraminifera and radiolaria	Several spp. in foraminifera	*Prymnesium*-like alga in radiolaria and acantharia	Unidentified sp. in ciliate protozoan *Mesodinium rubrum*	Unidentified sp. in colourless dinoflagellates e.g. *Peridinium balticum*
Animals (phylum)					
Porifera	*Symbiodinium microadriaticum* in clionid sponges				
Coelenterata	*Symbiodinium microadriaticum* in many spp.				
Platy-helminthes	*Amphidinium* in acoel turbellarian *Amphiscolops langerhansi*	*Licmophora* in acoel turbellarian *Convoluta convoluta*			
Mollusca	*Symbiodinium microadriaticum* in Tridacnidae and *Corculum cardissa*				
Echiura					
Chordata					

Symbiont

		Prokaryotes	
Prasinophyceae	Chlorophyceae	Prochlorophyta	Cyanobacteria
Marine	Freshwater and marine	Marine	Freshwater and marine
◄────	('zoochlorellae') ────────►		('cyanellae')
Pedinomonas in colourless dinoflagellate *Noctiluca miliaris*, *Pedinomonas* and *Tetraselmis* in radiolaria	*Chlorella* in various fresh-water ciliate protozoa, *Chlamydomonas* and *Chlorella* in foraminifera (marine)		Several spp. in amoeboid and flagellate protozoa (freshwater and marine) and diatoms (marine)
	Chlorella in several fresh-water sponges		*Aphanocapsa* and *Phormidium* in marine sponges
	Chlorella in freshwater hydra *Chlorella*-like alga in anemone *Anthopleura* (marine)		
Tetraselmis in acoel turbellarian *Convoluta roscoffensis*	*Chlorella* in various fresh-water neorhabdo-coel turbellarians e.g. *Phaenocora typhlops*		
	Chlorella in some freshwater bivalves, e.g. *Anodonta cygnea*		
			Unidentified sp. in *Ikedosoma gogoshimense* and *Bonellia fuliginosa*
		Prochloron with didemnid ascidian spp.	

Fig. 2.1 Examples of association between *Chlorella* and freshwater hosts, showing location of algal cells.

† The taxonomy of hydra is very confused. Hydra which contain *Chlorella* are considered by some authorities as a genus (*Chlorohydra*) distinct from all nonsymbiotic hydra species. Other taxonomists assign hydra which contain *Chlorella* to the genus *Hydra*, which includes a number of nonsymbiotic hydra species. The number of and relationship between hydra species which contain algae is unknown (two species have been distinguished by morphological criteria to date) and these hydra are often known simply as 'green hydra'.

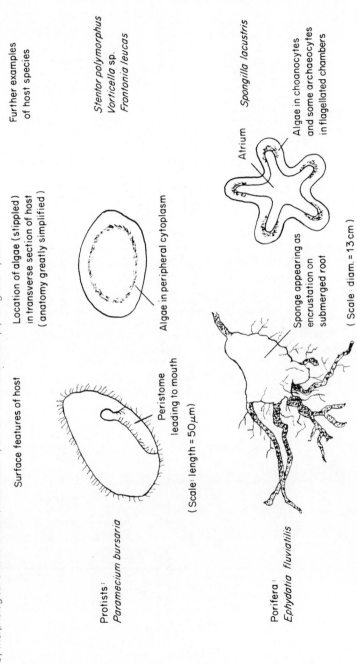

Surface features of host

Location of algae (stippled) in transverse section of host (anatomy greatly simplified)

Further examples of host species

Stentor polymorphus
Vorticella sp.
Frontonia leucas

Algae in peripheral cytoplasm

Peristome leading to mouth

(Scale: length = 50μm)

Protists:
Paramecium bursaria

Atrium   *Spongilla lacustris*

Algae in choanocytes and some archaeocytes in flagellated chambers

Sponge appearing as encrustation on submerged root

(Scale: diam. = 13 cm)

Porifera:
Ephydatia fluviatilis

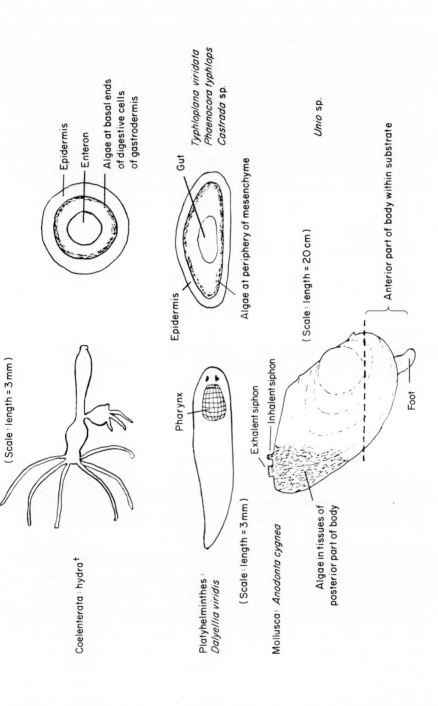

(Scale : length = 3 mm)

Coelenterata : hydra†

Epidermis

Enteron

Algae at basal ends
of digestive cells
of gastrodermis

Epidermis

Gut

Algae at periphery of mesenchyme

Typhloplana viridata
Phaenocora typhlops
Castrada sp.

Pharynx

Platyhelminthes :
Dalyellia viridis

(Scale : length = 3 mm)

Mollusca : *Anodonta cygnea*

Exhalent siphon

Inhalent siphon

Algae in tissues of
posterior part of body

Unio sp.

(Scale : length = 20 cm)

Anterior part of body within substrate

Foot

chloroplast and rigid cell wall. Neither motile nor sexual forms have been recorded and reproduction is by mitotic division, usually multiple fission into four or more (sometimes up to 64) autospores.

Chlorella species are very common and widespread algae in freshwater habitats, and they are also found in the marine environment and on certain terrestrial substrates, such as soil and rock. Symbiotic *Chlorella* have been reported in a variety of freshwater hosts, including ciliate protozoa, sponges, the coelenterate hydra, neorhabdocoel turbellarians and bivalve molluscs (Table 2.1, Fig. 2.1). The algae in different hosts vary in size, in ultra-structural features of the chloroplast and in characteristics of the cell wall. There have been few attempts to characterize symbiotic *Chlorella* to the level of species: *C. vulgaris* has been identified in some protozoa, hydra and turbellaria; *C. saccharophila* in foraminiferans; and *C. sorokiniana* in certain sponges (Douglas and Huss, 1986; Eaton and Young, 1975; Kessler, 1982).

2.2.1.1   Location of *Chlorella* in symbiosis

In hydra, sponges and protozoa, the *Chlorella* cells are intracellular, i.e. within host cells (Fig. 2.2a). Each algal cell is enclosed within an individual vacuole, known as the perialgal vacuole, and separated from the cytoplasm of the host cell by the host vacuole membrane (Fig. 2.2b). It is uncertain whether the location of *Chlorella* in turbellarians and molluscs is intercellular or intracellular. Whatever the cellular relationship between the host and symbiont, the algal cells in all hosts are restricted to a well-defined location, to which there is appreciable penetration of light (Fig. 2.1). They are asso-ciated with the tissues (particularly gills and mantle) of the posterior region of bivalve molluscs and are not found in the anterior part of the body which is embedded in the substrate. Hosts from other phyla are generally uniformly green in appearance, but the algal cells are confined to certain positions: the peripheral cytoplasm of protozoa; choanocytes and certain archaeocytes of sponges; digestive cells of the gastrodermis of hydra; and peripheral mesen-chyme of turbellaria. As a result, the algae are rarely more than a few milli-metres from the host surface. The surface layers of most hosts are not greatly pigmented and the shell of bivalve molluscs (which is opaque) bears many small translucent 'pits', probably caused by mechanical damage.

2.2.1.2   Persistence of the symbiosis from one host generation to the next

Direct transmission of *Chlorella* symbionts from one host generation to the next always occurs during asexual reproduction, as in binary fission of protozoa, budding and gemmule production of sponges and budding of hydra. In bivalves and neorhabdocoel turbellarians which reproduce exclu-sively sexually, the symbiosis is established when the adult bivalve or juvenile turbellarian acquires free-living *Chlorella* cells (Pardy, 1980; Eaton and Young, 1975). The mode of perpetuation of the symbiosis at sexual

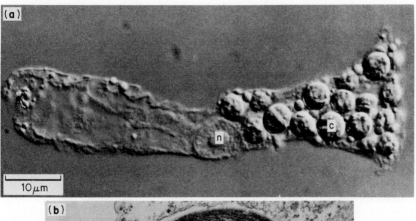

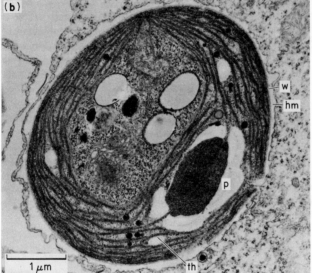

Fig. 2.2 *Chlorella* symbionts in digestive cells of green hydra. **(a)** Individual digestive cell with *Chlorella* symbionts (c) at base, n = host cell nucleus. *Photograph* P.J. McAuley. **(b)** Electron micrograph showing a *Chlorella* symbiont enclosed by a host vacuolar membrane (hm). Note wall of symbiont (w), thylakoids (th) and pyrenoid (p). *Photograph* C.R. Hawes.

reproduction in sponges is unclear, and there appears to be considerable variation in hydra (Muscatine and McAuley, 1982). Some newly hatched hydra are symbiont-free. Others contain symbionts which had either become associated with the external surface of the egg and so were well-placed to infect the hatching hydra, or alternatively had been incorporated into the egg cytoplasm prior to fertilization.

At the establishment of the symbiosis, the *Chlorella* cells invariably gain entry to the host by the normal feeding route. They are drawn into the various protozoa, sponges and bivalve molluscs with the feeding currents of water, and enter carnivorous or scavenging hosts (hydra and turbellarians) by virtue of their residence in or on prey organisms. For example, *Phaenocora typhlops* in nature becomes infected with *Chlorella* derived from the gut contents of tubificid worms on which it feeds (Eaton and Young, 1975), and in laboratory experiments, alga-free hydra can become infected when they feed on protozoa containing *Chlorella* (M.H. Christopher quoted by Douglas and Smith, 1984).

2.2.1.3   Survival of *Chlorella* and host in isolation from the symbiosis

In general, neither the *Chlorella* nor the hosts exhibit a high degree of dependence on the symbiosis. The *Chlorella* symbionts of most hosts can be isolated into culture by gentle homogenization and streaking of the homogenate onto simple nutrient agar. Despite the ease with which many symbiotic *Chlorella* can be isolated and maintained in culture, most have not been reported free-living in the natural habitat. One possible exception is the symbiont of the turbellarian *Phaenocora typhlops*, which may be derived from a free-living population of *Chlorella* (Eaton and Young, 1975). Symbiont-free individuals of most hosts of *Chlorella* are rarely found in nature but, in the case of hydra and several protozoa (e.g. *Paramecium bursaria*), they can be produced by a variety of treatments and maintained indefinitely under laboratory conditions.

2.2.1.4   Experimental studies of associations with *Chlorella*

Most experimental investigations of *Chlorella* symbiosis have been conducted on green hydra and *Paramecium bursaria*, principally because these organisms can readily be maintained under defined laboratory conditions. Other associations, notably that in *Phaenocora typhlops*, have also provided useful information. In the remainder of this chapter, the main lines of research will be described: namely, studies of nutritional interactions between the partners (2.2.2), regulation of the growth and division rate of the algal symbionts (2.2.3) and, thirdly, the specificity and mode of recognition in the establishment of the associations (2.2.4). The chapter will end with a general consideration of the benefit which both partners may derive from the symbiosis (2.2.5).

2.2.2   Nutritional interactions in *Chlorella* symbioses

2.2.2.1   Evidence for algal contribution to the nutrition of the host

All species which form an association with *Chlorella* need to feed for sustained growth and reproduction. Under routine laboratory conditions there is little or no difference between the growth rates of hosts with and without *Chlorella*, when food is abundant. Under conditions of low food

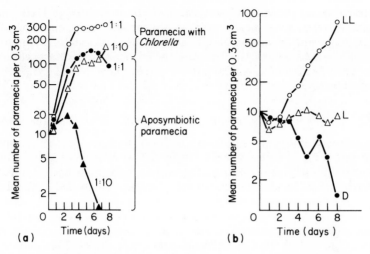

Fig. 2.3 Growth of *Paramecium bursaria* under various light and feeding conditions (after Karakashian, 1975). **(a)** Paramecia were maintained in medium containing a surplus of bacteria as food (1:1) or in a medium containing bacteria at one-tenth of this concentration (1:10). **(b)** Paramecia containing *Chlorella* were maintained in filtered culture medium in continuous darkness (D) or in 10 h light: 14 h dark regime with light intensity 2.3–3.3 klux (L) or 4.5–4.8 klux (LL).

availability, individuals with algae usually grow faster than aposymbionts and during starvation they display enhanced survival. This has been demonstrated experimentally in several associations, most notably *Paramecium bursaria* (Karakashian, 1975) (Fig. 2.3). When maintained in a culture medium containing the bacteria on which they feed, *P. bursaria* grow well at rates independent of light conditions. If the bacteria are reduced by dilution or removed by filtration of the culture medium, the growth of aposymbiotic individuals ceases and the paramecia die within a week. In continuous darkness, animals containing symbionts also die, but they survive under illumination and their initial division rate increases with light intensity, although sustained growth does not occur in the absence of food. This suggests that the initial division rate of the unfed host is determined by the rate of algal photosynthesis.

Comparable, although less comprehensive, results have been obtained for the hydra symbiosis (Douglas and Smith, 1984; Muscatine and Lenhoff, 1965). When starved under standard laboratory conditions, all hydra cease to grow, whether they contain *Chlorella* or not. Aposymbiotic animals die within two or three weeks but the hydra with *Chlorella* survive and remain green for at least three months, provided they are kept in the light. Similarly, when the turbellarian *Phaenocora typhlops* is starved under illuminated conditions, animals with *Chlorella* decline in length more slowly than aposymbionts (Young and Eaton, 1975).

These results all lead to the same conclusion, that *Chlorella* symbionts contribute to the growth and survival of their hosts through their photosynthetic activity. Since there is no evidence for substantial digestion of the algae under normal conditions, it is likely that the nutritional contribution of the algal cells is biotrophic (i.e. by release of nutrients from intact cells to the host). This deduction is supported by direct experimental evidence, as described below.

2.2.2.2 Supply of photosynthetic products from *Chlorella* to the host

The movement of organic photosynthetic products from alga to host is particularly amenable to experimental study by the use of the radioactive isotope ^{14}C, and has been investigated most thoroughly in the green hydra symbiosis. If green hydra are incubated in medium containing ^{14}C-labelled sodium bicarbonate with illumination, they incorporate radioactivity at a rate 10–20 times faster than in the dark or than aposymbiotic animals. After incubation with ^{14}C, the symbiosis is separated into 'host' and 'algal' fractions by the method shown in Fig. 2.4. A substantial proportion (about 30%) of the total radioactivity is recovered from the host fraction (Fig. 2.5a). This is an underestimate of the proportion of photosynthate received by the host because approximately 20% of the host tissue cannot be separated from the algal cells

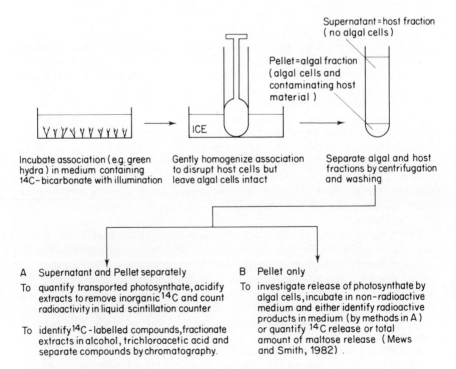

Supernatant = host fraction (no algal cells)

Pellet = algal fraction (algal cells and contaminating host material)

Incubate association (e.g. green hydra) in medium containing 14C–bicarbonate with illumination

Gently homogenize association to disrupt host cells but leave algal cells intact

Separate algal and host fractions by centrifugation and washing

A Supernatant and Pellet separately

To quantify transported photosynthate, acidify extracts to remove inorganic ^{14}C and count radioactivity in liquid scintillation counter

To identify ^{14}C-labelled compounds, fractionate extracts in alcohol, trichloroacetic acid and separate compounds by chromatography.

B Pellet only

To investigate release of photosynthate by algal cells, incubate in non-radioactive medium and either identify radioactive products in medium (by methods in A) or quantify ^{14}C release or total amount of maltose release (Mews and Smith, 1982) .

Fig. 2.4 Methods to investigate photosynthate release by symbiotic *Chlorella*.

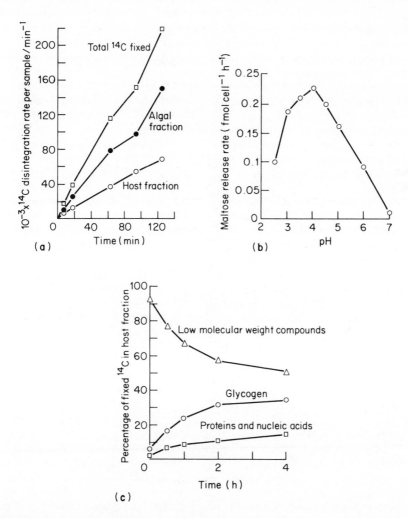

Fig. 2.5 Photosynthate release by the *Chlorella* symbionts of green hydra (Mews, 1980; A.E. Douglas, unpublished). **(a)** Rate of photosynthetic ^{14}C fixation and transfer to the host tissue. Intact hydra were incubated with ^{14}C-bicarbonate under illumination and the host and algal fractions were separated at intervals over 125 minutes. **(b)** The effect of pH on maltose release (see 2.2.2.2) by symbiotic algae. The algae were isolated from green hydra and incubated in 10 mM phosphate–citrate buffer, pH 2.5–7, for 1 hour under illumination and maltose release was assayed chemically. **(c)** Metabolism of fixed ^{14}C by the animal tissues of green hydra. Intact hydra were incubated with ^{14}C-bicarbonate under illumination for 20 minutes and then transferred to non-radioactive medium. At intervals, the host and algal fractions were separated and the labelled compounds in the host fraction indentified.

by this method and is counted as algal biomass (Douglas and Smith, 1983). Although methods to obtain substantially purer preparations of algal symbionts are available, reliable and accurate estimates of the percentage photosynthate transported to the host have not been obtained to date.

The algal cells continue to release photosynthetic products when isolated from the symbiosis and this release has two distinctive characteristics.

a) Although photosynthetically fixed ^{14}C accumulates in many compounds within algal cells, more than 90% of radioactivity released is in the form of one compound, the disaccharide maltose (Cernichiari *et al.*, 1969; Mews, 1980; Muscatine, 1965), accompanied by traces of a few other radioactively-labelled products, including alanine and glycolate. This suggests that there is a specific mechanism for the selective release of maltose.

b) Release is pH-dependent (Fig. 2.5b). The rate of release is maximal at pH 4 and declines with increasing pH to a very low level at pH 7. Low pH is the only factor known to induce photosynthate release by symbiotic *Chlorella*.

Maltose is probably synthesized near or at the cell surface from a hexose phosphate precursor (Cernichiari *et al.*, 1969). The findings that maltose release is pH dependent and that it is completely abolished by the metabolic inhibitor cyanide-n-chlorophenyl hydrazone (CCCP) which causes the collapse of the proton gradient across membranes, suggest that it is coupled to the electrochemical gradient of protons across an algal membrane. Maltose can be derived both from compounds containing newly-fixed carbon and from algal polysaccharide reserves (Mews, 1980). As a result, maltose release is not strictly photosynthesis-dependent and it can continue in darkness for several weeks (Douglas unpublished; Mews, 1980).

The maltose received by the hydra from its algal symbionts does not accumulate unchanged in the animal tissues. It is probably degraded to glucose by the action of the enzyme maltase (which has been identified in cell-free extracts of hydra (Mews, 1980)) and is subsequently metabolized to a range of products. Photosynthetically-fixed ^{14}C is ultimately recovered from the storage polysaccharide glycogen, proteins and nucleic acids in the host fraction (Fig. 2.5c).

The capacity to release a sugar, usually maltose, has been demonstrated in *Chlorella* from other hosts, including the protozoan *Paramecium bursaria*, the sponge *Spongilla lacustris*, the turbellarians *Dalyellia viridis* and *Typhloplana viridata*, and the bivalve *Anodonta cygnea*. Some, but not all, symbiotic *Chlorella* retain the capacity for maltose release at low pH after isolation into culture. This physiological feature is apparently unique to symbiotic *Chlorella*; strains of *Chlorella* which cannot form a symbiosis do not release maltose.

It is conceivable that algal cells release compounds which do not contain carbon derived from immediate photosynthesis, and therefore are not detected by the methods using the isotope ^{14}C, but this possibility has not been investigated experimentally.

2.2.2.3 Movement of nutrients from the host to the algal symbionts

In those associations where the algal symbionts are intracellular, all the nutrients received by the *Chlorella* are, of necessity, derived from or pass through the host cell. To demonstrate such movement, green hydra have been provided with food labelled with ^{3}H and ^{14}C, and these isotopes have subsequently been recovered from the algal fraction (Thorington and Margulis, 1981). The quantity and identity of the compounds which pass from the host to the algae are unknown.

Further evidence for the transport of nutrients from the hydra to algal cells comes from a study of the association maintained in continuous darkness with feeding. The algal symbionts continue to grow and divide, and the symbiosis persists for at least a year (Douglas and Smith, 1984). This indicates that the hydra provides all the organic and inorganic nutrients required by the *Chlorella*. Furthermore, the growth rate of the hydra declines to a rate significantly lower than that of aposymbiotic individuals under the same conditions (Table 2.2). These results have been interpreted as evidence that the nutritional requirements of the symbionts represent a cost to the host that is detectable as reduced growth rate (see 2.2.5.1).

Table 2.2 Growth rate of hydra maintained, with feeding, under 12 h light: 12 h dark regime or continuous darkness for 14 days. (The cultures were maintained under test conditions for 6 weeks prior to assay.) By analysis of variance and Scheffé's multiple range test, the growth rate of animals containing *Chlorella* in the dark is significantly lower than all other treatments and there is no significant difference between the growth rate of animals with and without algae in the light. Data from Douglas and Smith (1983).

	Specific growth constant (d^{-1})* mean ± s.e. (8 replicates)	
	12 h light: 12 h dark	24 h dark
Hydra containing algae	0.104 ± 0.004	0.067 ± 0.003
Alga-free hydra	0.094 ± 0.002	0.087 ± 0.003

* An index of the rate of increase in number of hydra (specifically, the slope of regression of $\log_e$ (number of hydra) on time).

2.2.3 Regulation of *Chlorella* symbionts

Symbiotic *Chlorella* grow and divide within their hosts and under normal conditions neither partner outgrows the other. Further, the proportion of alga to host rarely exceeds 1:10 by volume or by biomass for any *Chlorella* association, although there is some variation between different symbioses and with environmental conditions.

There is evidence that the size of the algal population in invertebrates is regulated by the direct intervention of the host. Several mechanisms are potentially available: digestion and/or expulsion of excess algae, and control of algal growth and division rates. In general, no conspicuous expulsion or digestion of *Chlorella* cells is observed under normal conditions, and since symbiotic *Chlorella* grow considerably faster in culture than they do in symbiosis (Jolley and Smith, 1978), the size of the algal population is probably controlled primarily by host repression of symbiont growth and division rates; the means by which this is achieved is known as 'regulation' (see 1.3.4).

The only association with *Chlorella* for which regulation has been investigated is that in green hydra and three mechanisms by which the growth and division rates of the algae may be controlled have been suggested.

a) A specific compound ('growth factor' or a metabolite essential for algal cell division) which controls algal proliferation is produced by the host. Early studies implicated hydra 'morphogens' (hypothetical compounds believed to control differentiation of hydra) diffusing down the body column from the head region (Pardy and Heacox, 1976) but more recent experiments of McAuley (1982) indicate that the results can be explained more persuasively in terms of a close link between host cell and algal division. This link might nevertheless be due to a metabolite produced in the host cell essential for algal division. For example, when hydra cells are stimulated to divide by feeding, the algal symbionts also divide (Fig. 2.6). If the nutritional value of the food is experimentally reduced, then algal cell division, but not host division, ceases (McAuley, 1985).

b) The supply of nutrients to the algal cells is restricted. Addition of sulphate and other inorganic ions to the culture medium of some hydra increases both the growth rate of algal symbionts and their number per digestive cell (Necklemann and Muscatine, 1983). Since sulphur is essential for *Chlorella* cell division, it was suggested that the host might regulate its symbionts by restricting the supply of essential inorganic nutrients. However, the availability of such minerals to algae in symbiosis is not known, other hydra

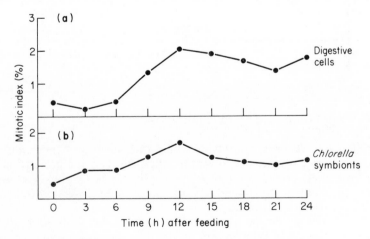

Fig. 2.6   Relationship between feeding and the division of host and algal cells in green hydra. The mitotic indices (per cent dividing cells) of hydra digestive cells **(a)** and algal symbionts **(b)** reach a maximum 12 hours after the hydra have been fed (McAuley, 1982).

strains showed only a transient or no response to the addition of minerals to the medium (Thorington and Smith, unpublished), and the effects of addition might have resulted from changes in ionic balance rather than increasing the supply of a limiting nutrient. More recently, Rees (1986) has produced persuasive evidence that the host might regulate *Chlorella* by restricting the supply of nitrogen to them. Thus, the activity of the primary enzyme of ammonia assimilation, glutamine synthetase, is over 50% higher in host tissues when symbionts are present. *Chlorella* in symbiosis have certain characteristics in common with nitrogen-deficient nonsymbiotic *Chlorella* in culture. It is not known whether the nitrogen supplied to symbionts is in the form of limited amounts of ammonia or amino acids.

c) The proportion of photosynthetic carbon allocated to algal cell growth, as opposed to maltose released to the host, controls the growth and division rates of the algal cells. The rate of maltose release by isolated algal symbionts is pH-dependent (Fig. 2.5b). In culture, symbiotic *Chlorella* do not grow at pH values where there is substantial maltose release, but with increasing pH, maltose release declines and algal growth and division is observed (Fig. 2.7).

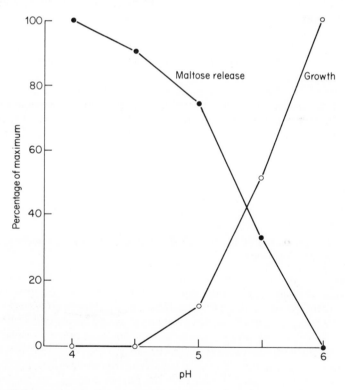

Fig. 2.7 Variation with pH of maltose release and growth of a *Chlorella* symbiont (strain 3N8) in culture. Growth expressed as a percentage of the rate at pH 6.0, maltose release as a percentage of the rate at pH 4.0. (Data of Douglas and Smith, 1984.)

Thus, small changes in the pH of the perialgal vacuole could have significant and controlling effects on symbiont division. This hypothesis has been developed to explain both the relationship between host and symbiont cell division and how the size of the algal population varies with environmental conditions (Douglas and Smith, 1984). Further supporting evidence for this proposed mechanism comes from studies of experimental associations between hydra and *Chlorella* strains derived from other hosts. All those strains which release amounts of maltose comparable to the native symbionts are constrained to grow at the same rate as the host, but the associations with *Chlorella* strains which release little maltose are regulated by the regular expulsion of algal cells (Douglas and Smith, 1984). The apparent inability of hydra to control the growth rate of the latter algae can be correlated with the relative insensitivity of growth of these strains to change in pH; however, there have been no direct measurements of the pH of the perialgal vacuole. Rees (1986) noted that this mechanism is compatible with his suggestion that regulation may occur by host restriction of ammonia availability (see (b) above), since a consequence of low levels of ammonia in the host would be to promote the maintenance of low pH in the perialgal vacuole. In hydra containing *Chlorella* releasing little maltose, host glutamine synthetase activity is reduced.

2.2.4 Recognition mechanisms in the establishment of the symbiosis

The usual method used to study specificity and recognition in symbiosis is to infect aposymbiotic hosts with the native symbionts, experimentally-altered symbionts or with other algae. These approaches provide information on the processes involved in the establishment of the symbiosis, the specificity of the association and the mechanisms involved in the discrimination between acceptable and unacceptable algae. The process of discrimination is termed *recognition* (see 1.3.6). The study of recognition in *Chlorella* symbioses has concentrated on green hydra.

2.2.4.1 Development of the association between hydra and acceptable algal symbionts

Experimental infection of hydra is most commonly achieved by injecting a suspension of algal cells into the enteron (digestive cavity) of aposymbiotic animals by means of a syringe fitted with a fine glass needle (Muscatine *et al.*, 1975). The development of a stable association can be divided into a sequence of stages (Fig. 2.8). At stage 1, most or all of the host digestive cells (which line the enteron), phagocytose algae and each algal cell becomes incorporated into an individual vacuole. The algal cells avoid digestive attack in the apical part of the host cell (stage 2) and, over the next 5–6 hours, the vacuole and enclosed alga is transported to the basal end of the digestive cell (stage 3). Transport is probably effected by host microtubules because inhibitors of

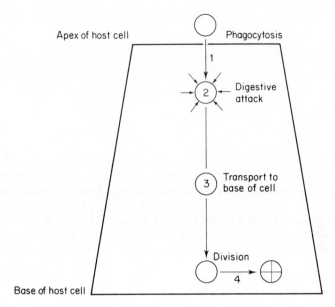

Fig. 2.8 Recognition stages of algal symbionts in the developing green hydra symbiosis (McAuley and Smith, 1982a). For explanation of the stages, see text (2.2.4.1).

microtubular assembly (e.g. colchicine) arrest the movement of algal cells. The algae subsequently divide and increase in number (stage 4) and the hydra become uniformly green in 3–4 weeks.

2.2.4.2 Discrimination against unacceptable algae in the development of the symbiosis in hydra

The fate of *Chlorella* cells which do not form a stable symbiosis with hydra varies with strain of both *Chlorella* and hydra (Jolley and Smith, 1980; McAuley and Smith, 1982a; Muscatine *et al.*, 1975). Cells of some strains of unacceptable *Chlorella* are phagocytosed only to a very small extent. Others enter the digestive cells but become aggregated together in a common vacuole, subjected to digestive attack and expelled. Cells of further ultimately unacceptable strains are transported in small numbers to the base of the host cell, but fail to grow and divide although they may persist for some weeks. The varying fates of different unacceptable algae indicate that each stage in the developing association involves a degree of recognition.

The selection which occurs on surface contact between algal and host cells (stage 1, Fig. 2.8) is particularly amenable to experimental investigation. Early studies concentrated on attempts to alter the surface characteristics of *Chlorella* in highly specific ways by proteases, lectins (which mask particular carbohydrate groups) and antibodies. No specific 'recognition' site or molecule on the surface of symbiotic algae has been identified by this approach; all

Table 2.3   Effect of surface charge of *Chlorella* on uptake by hydra digestive cells. Data from McNeil *et al.* (1981).

Alga	Electrophoretic mobility of algal cells at pH 7.2	Mean number of algal cells phagocytosed by digestive cells (as % of value for symbiotic *Chlorella*)
Symbiotic *Chlorella*	−2.03	100
Nonsymbiotic *Chlorella*	−1.73	26
Symbiotic *Chlorella* treated with poly-L-lysine	+1.49	36

reported effects of these treatments on phagocytosis can be interpreted in terms of a general deleterious effect on the algal or host cell or as a consequence of the substantial contamination of algal cells isolated from symbiosis with host material. However, one clearly established observation is that *Chlorella* which can form a symbiosis generally have a more negative net surface charge than nonsymbiotic *Chlorella* (Table 2.3). If the surface charge of symbiotic *Chlorella* cells is reduced or reversed by treatment with the polyanion poly-L-lysine, their uptake into the cell is much reduced (McNeil *et al.*, 1981).

The digestive attack of *Chlorella* in the apical region of digestive cells is achieved by fusion of host lysosomes with the membrane of the perialgal vacuole and the resultant exposure of the enclosed algal cell to a range of digestive enzymes (Hohman *et al.*, 1982). In *Chlorella* which avoid digestive attack, the vacuolar membrane surrounding the algal cells fails to fuse with the lysosomal membrane. Although differences between membranes of vacuoles containing different *Chlorella* are unknown in molecular terms, the ability to avoid lysosomal fusion is correlated with the capacity for maltose release. The stage in the development of the symbiosis at which algal cells start to release maltose is unknown. The contents of phagocytic vacuoles of some protozoa become acidic before fusion with lysosomes and, if this also occurs in the newly formed perialgal vacuoles of hydra, the algal cells may be stimulated to release maltose soon after phagocytosis. However, the factors which determine whether an alga is digested or not are undoubtedly complex. Thus, if algae capable of maltose release are introduced into hydra which already have their full complement of *Chlorella* symbionts, the incoming algae are nevertheless digested and expelled (McAuley and Smith, 1982b).

Transport to the base of the host cell is correlated with ability to release maltose. This was demonstrated in experiments using *Chlorella* strains releasing different amounts of maltose (Fig. 2.9). Cells which do not release maltose are transported in very small numbers.

The characteristics of algae and interactions with the host which determine whether the potential symbionts divide and establish a stable symbiosis once they reach the base of the cell (stage 4, Fig. 2.8) are not known. However,

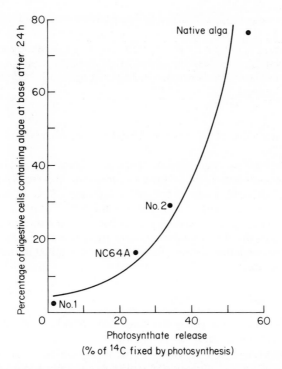

Fig. 2.9 Relationship between the proportion of photosynthate released by different strains of symbiotic *Chlorella* at pH 4 and the transport of the algae to the base of digestive cells when injected into aposymbiotic hydra (McAuley and Smith, 1982a). 'Native alga' = normal symbiont of green hydra; 'no. 1, NC64A, no. 2' = strains of symbiotic *Chlorella* isolated from *Paramecium bursaria*.

capacity for maltose production by the algae is probably not important, because different strains of algae, whose maltose release rates vary widely, attain similar population size in the stable symbiosis with hydra (Douglas and Smith, 1984).

It is clear from this account that there is no single stage in the establishment of the symbiosis at which recognition of symbionts occurs. Selection of algae occurs in stages, and on the basis of a number of different features, including surface charge and capacity for maltose release.

2.2.4.3 Establishment of the symbiosis in *Paramecium bursaria*

Recognition on surface contact and during early stages of infection of aposymbiotic *P. bursaria* with algae has not been studied and nothing is known of the mechanism by which symbionts reach the peripheral region of the protozoon (see Fig. 2.1). However, as in hydra (2.2.4.2), lysosomal fusion with vacuoles containing symbiotic *Chlorella* is inhibited in

P. bursaria (Karakashian, 1975) and in one study (Weis, 1979) the agglutinability of algae by the lectin concanavalin A was found to be correlated with the eventual establishment of the symbiosis. As in green hydra, maltose release by potential symbionts is likely to be an important characteristic, since permanent associations are not established with those *Chlorella* which cannot release maltose.

2.2.5   The benefit of symbiosis to *Chlorella* and its hosts

The benefit derived by each partner from an association is central to the concept of mutualism but, as pointed out in 1.3.9, this apparently simple criterion can be difficult to apply to real associations. This is partly because of the problems in the identification and quantification of benefit and partly because each partner derives costs as well as benefit from its association with a different organism. We can now consider the concept of benefit in more detail, using the particular group of associations described in this chapter to provide concrete examples.

2.2.5.1   The host

It is generally believed that the single most important benefit which the host derives from symbiotic *Chlorella* is nutritional. The host organism receives substantial amounts of maltose from the algal cells and this source of carbon and energy undoubtedly contributes to the enhanced survival of the host under conditions of limited food supply and starvation (see 2.2.2.1). However, the symbionts also make nutritional demands on the host. Such demands on green hydra in the dark have been suggested to cause a measurable reduction in growth rate of the host (see 2.2.2.3 and Table 2.2).

A number of authors have suggested that the hosts of symbiotic algae benefit from the provision of oxygen produced by photosynthesis but the significance of this source of oxygen to the host has been demonstrated only in the turbellarian *Phaenocora typhlops*, which lives in oxygen-deficient waters associated with pond sediments (Eaton and Young, 1975) (see also 3.3.2.2). Aposymbiotic hydra and *Paramecium bursaria* show no sign of oxygen deficiency in laboratory culture, but it is not known whether these associations encounter sufficiently oxygen-depleted conditions in nature for photosynthetic oxygen to be important. Oxygen is a potentially toxic element because, in oxidation reactions, it is converted to highly reactive products (superoxide and hydroxyl radicals and hydrogen peroxide). It is conceivable that in these symbioses, the oxygen produced by the *Chlorella* reaches a sufficiently high concentration in the host tissues that it represents a hazard or 'cost', requiring elevated levels of protective enzymes, such as superoxide dismutase. This situation has been demonstrated in the association between the marine coelenterate *Anthopleura elegantissima* the dinoflagellate *Symbiodinium microadriaticum* (see 3.2.3.3) but has not been investigated in freshwater associations with *Chlorella*.

There is some evidence that the presence of symbionts contributes to the avoidance of predation and parasitic attack in *Paramecium bursaria*. Gortz (1982) has found that aposymbiotic *P. bursaria* can be infected by bacteria of the genus *Pseudomonas* and the yeast *Rhodotorula rubra*, but although the pseudomonad and yeast were not overtly harmful to *P. bursaria*, symbiotic individuals containing *Chlorella* were resistant to these organisms. Further, the aposymbiotic animals lost the yeast or bacterial cells when they became infected with *Chlorella*. The presence of symbiotic *Chlorella* also renders *P. bursaria* distasteful to *Didinium nasutum*, a protozoan predator of paramecia (Berger, 1980). *D. nasutum* attacks symbiotic *P. bursaria* containing *Chlorella* less frequently, ingests it more slowly and is more likely to regurgitate it than aposymbiotic *P. bursaria* or nonsymbiotic species of *Paramecium*. It is not known whether other potential predators of *P. bursaria* are deterred by the presence of algae and whether *Chlorella* serve an anti-predator function in other invertebrate hosts.

2.2.5.2 The algal symbionts

Chlorella cells grow considerably more slowly in symbiosis than in culture (Jolley and Smith, 1978) and they lose a significant amount of their photo-synthetically-fixed carbon to their hosts. These are undoubtedly costs of the symbiotic habitat and they raise the question of whether the *Chlorella* can be said to benefit from the association. One could argue that the symbionts live in a 'habitat' (the host cell or tissues) which many *Chlorella* and other algal taxa are unable to colonize, and in which the symbionts attain a high population density. It has also been argued that symbionts derive the additional benefit of access to a better nutrient supply from the host than is available to nonsymbiotic algae but this would be difficult to demonstrate experimentally, and it is also possible that the host restricts nutrient supply as a means of keeping the growth rate of symbionts at a low level (2.2.3).

Chlorella may also benefit from the symbiosis by their acquisition of motility. This has been tested experimentally for the particular case of *Phaenocora typhlops* which lives in muddy ponds (Young and Eaton, 1975). *Chlorella* are uncommon in such habitats because they are not well-adapted to still water or unstable sediments. Thus, when *Chlorella* cells are added to a beaker of filtered pond water with a layer of sediment, they slowly sink into the sediment, where, in the absence of light for photosynthesis, they become pale yellow and moribund. Since *P. typhlops* maintains its position on the surface of the sediment, the symbiotic algal cells are assured of access to light and remain green and viable.

3
Algae in symbiosis II. With marine hosts (animals and protists)

3.1 Introduction

A great variety of algae occur in symbiosis with marine animals and protists (Table 2.1), but the most common algal symbiont is undoubtedly the dinoflagellate *Symbiodinium microadriaticum*. The most spectacular symbiosis with this alga is found in the stony corals (coelenterates of the order Scleractinia), which make a major contribution to the coral reefs of warm, shallow seas. These reefs represent an important marine habitat (covering 2×10^8 km^2 global surface area) for a range of other organisms; these include many 'lower' invertebrates which also contain algal symbionts. The very existence of the reef habitat is dependent on the metabolic activities of the coral symbionts, including photosynthesis, perhaps mineral recycling and, above all, enhancement of the synthesis of the coral's calcareous skeleton.

Several associations, particularly those between sea anemones and *S. microadriaticum* (3.2) and between the turbellarian *Convoluta roscoffensis* and the prasinophycean alga *Tetraselmis* (3.3) have proved particularly amenable to study and manipulation in the laboratory. This has made possible the experimental study of nutrient interactions, specificity and recognition. The results can be compared with those described for freshwater associations in Chapter 2 to see if the conclusions are generally applicable to associations between algae and invertebrates. The associations described in this chapter also raise further issues, for example, the effect symbiosis may have on the structural integrity of the symbiont (3.4.2) and the value of duration of the relationship as a criterion of symbiosis (3.5; see also 1.3.4).

3.2 Associations with dinoflagellate symbionts

3.2.1 The dinoflagellate symbionts

Dinoflagellates (class Dinophyceae) are unicellular, motile algae, usually brown in colour, with the unique feature of permanently condensed chromosomes. Typically, each cell has two flagella which emerge at the junction between a longitudinal and transverse furrow in the cell surface, and one flagellum extends along each furrow. In symbiosis, dinoflagellate cells retain

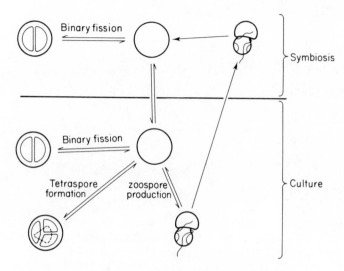

Fig. 3.1 Stages in the life cycle of *Symbiodinium microadriaticum*. In symbiosis, the coccoid, non-motile stage predominates; in culture, there is alternation between the motile zoospore and coccoid, non-motile stage (gamete production and sexual reproduction have been reported, but have never been demonstrated unambiguously).

the condensed form of the chromosomes but do not produce flagella (although flagellar bases are present) and are coccoid in shape. They can readily be isolated into culture, when it can be seen that the morphology and life cycle of cultured cells are comparable to those of nonsymbiotic dino-flagellates (Fig. 3.1). Structural features of the motile cell indicate they are closely related to the genus *Gymnodinium*. The isolates from different host species are generally considered as 'strains' of one species, *Symbiodinium microadriaticum* (= *Gymnodinium microadriaticum* = *Zooxanthella microadriatica*). However, strains may vary in morphology, biochemical characteristics and karyotype, and it has been argued that the differences between some strains may be too great for them all to be considered as members of a single species (Trench, 1986; Blank and Trench, 1985).

3.2.2 Associations between dinoflagellates and coelenterates

Dinoflagellates have been reported in members of all three extant classes of coelenterates: Hydrozoa (hydroids, siphonophores and stinging corals), Scyphozoa (the true jellyfishes) and Anthozoa (sea anemones, zoanthids, stony corals and octocorals). The most abundant coelenterates containing dinoflagellates are the stony corals (order Scleractinia), which, together with calcareous red algae and, in some cases, stinging corals (hydrozoans of the order Milleporina), produce coral reefs in shallow, tropical waters. Other coelenterates with dinoflagellates are often associated with coral reefs and

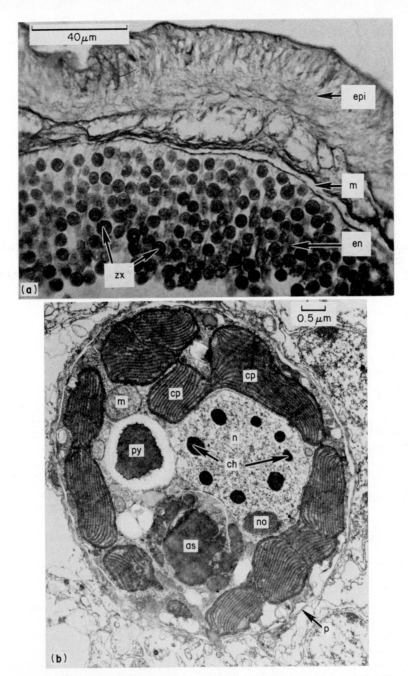

Fig. 3.2 *Symbiodinium microadriaticum* in symbiosis with the sea anemone *Anthopleura elegantissima* (from Trench, 1971). **(a)** Section of body wall of *A. elegantissima*, showing that *S. microadriaticum* (zx) is confined to the gastrodermis (en) and is not in the mesoglea (m) or epidermis (epi). **(b)** Electron micrograph of algal cell in *A. elegantissima*, showing nucleus (n) with permanently condensed chromosomes (ch), mitochondrion (m), chloroplast (cp), pyrenoid (py), assimilation product (as) and enclosing host membrane (p).

include octocorals, zoanthids, and rhizostome scyphozoans. Coelenterates that contain algae are relatively rare in temperate regions, although a few anemones, for example, *Anthopleura elegantissima* in North America and *Anemonia sulcata* in Europe, may be common or locally abundant.

Almost all dinoflagellate symbionts in coelenterates are intracellular and restricted to the gastrodermal layer of the host (Fig. 3.2a). They are separated from the host cytoplasm by an animal vacuolar membrane (Fig. 3.2b), which may sometimes be much-folded.

3.2.3 Nutritional interactions between coelenterates and their dinoflagellate symbionts

As for the freshwater associations described in chapter 2, nutritional interactions between *S. microadriaticum* and coelenterates are primarily biotrophic, and there is evidence for the movement of a variety of compounds between intact cells of symbiont and host.

3.2.3.1 Transport of photosynthate to the host

The movement of photosynthetically-fixed carbon from symbionts to the host was first demonstrated in the anemone *Anthopleura elegantissima* and corals *Manicina areolata* and *Montastrea annularis* in the following experiment (Muscatine, 1973). The intact association was incubated in sea water containing ^{14}C-labelled sodium bicarbonate (see 2.2.2.2) under illumination, then fixed, embedded and sectioned and the radioactivity in the tissues was located by its effect on photographic film. However, the full extent of photosynthate transport could not be deduced because soluble products (which form a large but variable proportion of the total) were lost during preparation of the material. Experiments using ^{14}C-tracer methods of the design depicted in Fig. 2.4 overcome this problem, and show that substantial movement of photosynthate occurs. In both corals and sea anemones, 35% or more of photosynthetically-fixed ^{14}C is recovered from the host tissue (principally as lipid and protein) and from mucus released from the association (Trench, 1971).

Algae freshly isolated from the symbiosis, and incubated with ^{14}C-bicarbonate, released ^{14}C-labelled glycerol, neutral amino acids (particularly alanine) and small quantities of glucose and organic acids (e.g. glycolate, fumarate) into the medium. The distribution of fixed ^{14}C amongst the released products differed from that within the algal cells (Fig. 3.3), suggesting that release is selective and not a consequence of cell damage during isolation. Translocation of fatty acids, intact neutral lipids and sterols to the host also occurs in corals (Trench, 1983). Thus, although photosynthate release is substantial and selective in dinoflagellate symbionts, a wider range of compounds is available for transport than in freshwater associations, whose *Chlorella* symbionts release only maltose with traces of alanine and glycolate (2.2.2.2).

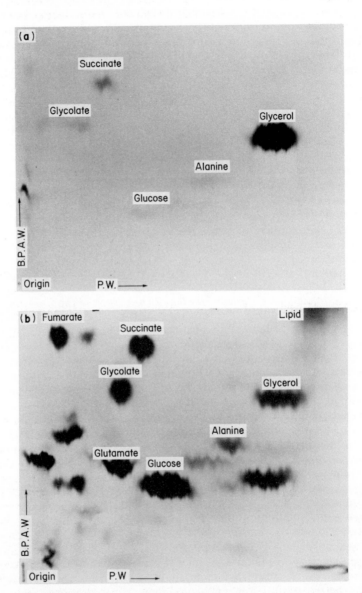

Fig. 3.3   Radiochromatograms showing distribution of photosynthetic products of symbionts isolated from *Anthopleura elegantissima* (from Trench, 1971). The isolated symbionts were incubated with ^{14}C-bicarbonate under illumination for 1 hour and radiochromatograms of the medium **(a)**, and of 80% ethanol-soluble intracellular products of the algae **(b)** were prepared.

The release of photosynthate by *S. microadriaticum* declines with time after isolation from the symbiosis and, unlike symbiotic *Chlorella*, cannot be stimulated by low pH (see Fig. 2.5b). However, when isolated symbionts are incubated with homogenized host tissue they release appreciable amounts of photosynthate for long periods (Table 3.1a). This has led to the suggestion that host tissue contains a 'factor' which stimulates photosynthate release (Hinde, 1983; Muscatine, 1967). In symbionts isolated from some hosts, e.g. *Anthopleura elegantissima*, the photosynthetic rate is also increased (Trench, 1971) (Table 3.1). The stimulation of photosynthate release ascribed to the putative 'host factor' is not present in extracts of animals freed of their symbionts (Table 3.1b) or in species which lack symbionts. However, the host factor is not species-specific. For example, homogenate of the coral *Pocillopora damicornis* induces photosynthate release by *S. microadriaticum* from tridacnid molluscs (see 3.2.8) and *vice versa* (see also 3.5.2.2).

The 'host factor' is thermolabile (Table 3.1b) and is possibly proteinaceous in nature, but has not been isolated or identified. It may be a single compound or a range of substances which affect the immediate environment of the algae so as to promote photosynthate release. The phenomenon of 'host factors' in symbioses with dinoflagellates requires much more investigation before its true significance can be decided; the possibility that they are artefacts caused by homogenizing host tissue cannot be excluded.

3.2.3.2 Movement of nitrogen and phosphorus compounds between the partners

It is frequently suggested that the algal symbionts of coelenterates take up host waste nitrogen and phosphorus compounds and metabolize them to a form which can be utilized by the host, thereby 'recycling' these elements within the symbiosis. Two lines of evidence are quoted to support this contention. First, coelenterates containing symbionts release less organic phosphorus and ammonia (the chief nitrogenous waste of coelenterates) than is released by aposymbiotic animals or species which lack symbionts (Table 3.2). This difference is widely believed to be due to the capacity of symbionts to assimilate ammonia and organic phosphorus. However, in the light of the demonstration that host tissues of the fresh water coelenterate, green hydra, can assimilate ammonia, and that this capacity varies according to the presence of symbionts (2.2.3), the evidence in Table 3.2 must be interpreted with caution until more is known of the assimilatory capabilities of marine coelenterates.

Secondly, *S. microadriaticum* in culture can utilize organic phosphorus (e.g. glycerophosphate) and nitrogen compounds (e.g. ammonia, urea) (Trench, 1986), although it is not known whether they can do so in symbiosis. The better studied *Chlorella* symbionts of green hydra can assimilate ammonia at pH 7.0, but not at the lower pH values at which the substantial maltose release characteristic of symbiosis occurs (Rees, 1986). Movement of nitrogen between the partners undoubtedly occurs. When *Anthopleura elegantissima* was fed on ^{15}N labelled protein, the isotope was recovered from

Table 3.1 Photosynthetic ^{14}C fixation and release by algal symbionts isolated from *Anthopleura elegantissima* (data of Trench, 1971).

(a) Variation with time since isolation from the host

At various times after isolation, the symbionts were incubated in sea water and ^{14}C-bicarbonate with or without homogenate of host tissue. The photosynthetic incorporation of radioactivity and release from symbionts into the surrounding medium over 10 hours were determined.

	Incubated in sea water			Incubated with host homogenate	
Time after isolation (h)	^{14}C fixed ($10^{-4} \times$ counts min^{-1} ml^{-1})	^{14}C released (% of total fixed)	Time after isolation (h)	^{14}C fixed ($10^{-4} \times$ counts min^{-1} ml^{-1})	^{14}C released (% of total fixed)
1	1.7	31	0	16.1	54
5	1.8	11	5	15.4	51
10	1.4	6	10	15.9	52

(b) Effect of different media

Freshly isolated symbionts were incubated for 1 hour in sea water and ^{14}C-bicarbonate containing various host homogenates. (Note that only unheated homogenates of hosts containing symbionts stimulate photosynthate release but all homogenates enhance photosynthesis.)

Treatment	^{14}C fixed ($10^{-4} \times$ counts min^{-1} ml^{-1})	^{14}C released (% of total fixed)
Sea water free of host homogenate	1.4	31
Host homogenate	14.1	58
Boiled host homogenate	4.5	30
Homogenate of aposymbionts	4.5	30
Homogenate from aposymbionts reinfected with algae	14.9	55

Table 3.2 Release of nitrogen and phosphorus by symbiotic coelenterates containing *Symbiodinium microadriaticum.*

(a) Exchange of ammonia by two coelenterates (from Cates and McLaughlin 1976). Groups of 10 animals were maintained for 5 hours in filtered sea water under illumination and net ammonia loss (+) or uptake (−) was measured.

	μg-atoms ammonia nitrogen per g wet weight	
Species	animals with symbionts	aposymbiotic animals*
Condylactis sp.	−0.05	+0.32
Cassiopeia sp.	+0.05	+0.36

(b) Exchange of phosphorus by corals (from Yonge and Nicholls 1931). Phosphorus exchange by 4 species of corals containing symbionts and the nonsymbiotic coral *D. nigrescens* incubated in filtered sea water for 24 hours was measured. Net phosphorus loss (+) or uptake (−) is expressed as percentage change of concentration in the medium.

Coral species		% change	
		untreated animals	animals with depleted complement of algae*
Favia sp.		−100	+276
Fungia danai		+117	+515
Psammocora gonagrea		+ 13	+688
Porites sp.		−100	+ 1
Dendrophyllia nigrescens:	sample 1	+856	
	sample 2	+624	
	sample 3	+284	

* These animals were obtained by prolonged dark treatment, which causes expulsion of algal symbionts (see 3.2.6).

the algal symbionts (Muscatine, 1980). A substance of low molecular weight which inhibits alanine uptake by freshly isolated symbionts has been reported in the host tissues of symbiotic *Cassiopeia xamachana* (Carroll and Blanquet, 1984) and it has been suggested that this 'factor' increases the net movement of alanine to the host in the intact association. Movement of phosphorus compounds has not been investigated.

3.2.3.3 Utilization of photosynthetic oxygen by the host

The net production of oxygen by coelenterates containing symbionts incubated in the light has been demonstrated on many occasions and this has led to the suggestion that the host tissues utilize photosynthetically-produced oxygen in respiration (see also 2.2.5.1. and 3.3.2.2). There is no direct evidence for or against this hypothesis. However, high oxygen levels have been recorded in the tissues of some of these coelenterates and there is evidence that the host may 'protect' itself from the potentially toxic effects of symbiont-derived oxygen by means of the enzyme superoxide dismutase. This enzyme functions in the removal of toxic oxygen radicals. When the sea anemone *Anthopleura elegantissima* is incubated for 14 days in 3-(3,4-dichlorophenyl)-1,1-dimethyl urea (DCMU), which inhibits photosynthetic oxygen evolution, the level of superoxide dismutase is reduced to 40% of that in animals maintained under photosynthetic conditions (Dykens and Shick, 1982).

3.2.4 The contribution of algal symbionts to host nutrition

Many investigators have considered the extent to which symbionts contribute to the nutritional and energy needs of the host. The experimental system of choice has usually been corals. This is not because corals are particularly amenable to studies of this type but because of the importance of these issues to the ecology of coral reefs. Reefs are renowned for their productivity in waters of low nutrient availability, and they are estimated to fix 4–6 g carbon $m^{-2} d^{-1}$ in comparison to 0.06–0.5 g $m^{-2} d^{-1}$ for the open ocean. A number of detailed studies have been carried out on corals in the natural situation and far more is now known about the contribution of dinoflagellate symbionts to coral nutrition than is the case for the otherwise better-studied *Chlorella* symbioses in freshwaters.

3.2.4.1 Alternative modes of nutrition available to coelenterate hosts (Muscatine, 1973)

A considerable amount of information about the mode of nutrition can be gleaned from the anatomy and behaviour of coelenterates. For example, dinoflagellate-bearing xeniids (a group of octocorals) are unresponsive to potential food items, lack nematocysts in their tentacles and have highly reduced digestive mesenteries. The implication, that xeniids do not exhibit holozoic feeding and largely depend on their symbionts for nutrition, is confirmed by their survival and growth under illumination in sea water which has been filtered to remove all particulate matter; they die in continuous darkness, whether maintained in filtered or unfiltered sea water. By contrast, sea anemones and stony corals are efficient carnivores which accept almost any particulate animal food. With their tentacles extended, some corals have a larger surface area available for prey capture per unit tissue bulk than any other group of animals. They also absorb organic compounds (e.g. sugars, amino acids) through the body wall from very low concentrations in the surrounding medium and feed on detritus.

Although most corals are highly adapted to the carnivorous mode of nutrition, the limited data available suggest there is insufficient zooplankton in the natural situation to support their energy needs. For example, from two independent studies of feeding in *Porites lobata* and *Montastrea cavernosa*, it was concluded that zooplankton provide only 10% of the associations' total energy needs (as estimated from respiration rates) (Muscatine and Porter, 1977). Indeed, as suggested by Johannes *et al.* (1970), the principal value of food material to corals may not be the supply of carbon and energy but the provision of vitamins, amino acids and other essential nutrients. However, these conclusions may not be applicable to all corals, and the importance of heterotrophy may vary with coral species, depth and type of reef.

3.2.4.2 Growth studies

The survival and growth of corals under various light and feeding conditions provides a useful guide to the contribution of the algal symbionts to host nutrition (see 2.2.2.1). Corals appear to be very versatile in their nutritional capabilities. Thus, Yonge demonstrated that *Fungia* and *Manicina* can be maintained for long periods in light or darkness if they are fed on zooplankton, whereas Franzisket observed the net growth of four Hawaiian coral species in the light without particulate food (Muscatine, 1973). Unfortunately, detailed interpretation of these studies is hampered by the lack of aposymbiotic animals as controls.

3.2.4.3 Direct estimates of the contribution of algal photosynthesis to the energy requirements of corals

Although ^{14}C methods (3.2.3.1) are invaluable in the study of photosynthate transport, they cannot be used to determine the gross amount of photosynthetically fixed carbon made available to the host. This is because the specific activity both of carbon dioxide at the site of fixation and of the compounds transported to the host are unknown. Therefore, alternative methods are needed to quantify the contribution of algal photosynthesis to host energy demands.

The ratio of photosynthetic oxygen release to respiratory oxygen uptake (P:R ratio) in corals is consistently greater than unity in the light. This was initially taken to indicate that corals are autotrophic. However, this conclusion is based on several untested assumptions, such as that all photosynthetically-fixed carbon is available to the host.

Muscatine and coworkers (Muscatine *et al.*, 1984) have developed a theoretical framework to quantify the fate of photosynthetically-fixed carbon. From estimates of the division rate of the algal symbionts, rates of photosynthetic oxygen evolution (which is related to the rate of carbon fixation), and respiratory oxygen utilization (a measure of host energy requirements) and the relative biomass of host and symbionts in the coral *Stylophora pistillata*, they calculated that less than 5% of net photosynthetically produced carbon is utilized by the algae for growth. The balance of net fixed carbon, more than 95% of the total, is therefore translocated to the host. This is sufficient to fuel host respiration and make a substantial contribution to host growth for colonies growing under high light intensity. However, for forms permanently growing in shade, the symbionts provide only 60% of the host basal respiratory requirements for carbon. In other words, *S. pistillata* is potentially entirely autotrophic with respect to energy and carbon in well-illuminated but not shady conditions.

3.2.4.4 Contribution of algal symbionts to the tolerance by the host of nutrient-poor conditions

A paradox of the coral reef ecosystem is its high productivity in waters that are notoriously poor in mineral nutrients, especially nitrogen and phosphorus. The proposed recycling and hence conservation of nitrogen and phosphorus within the coral-dinoflagellate symbiosis (3.2.3.2), if it could be demonstrated unambiguously, would make an important contribution to the high productivity of coral reefs. The *external* food-chain recycling loops which occur in the reef ecosystem have not been quantified and may be important in at least some reef environments. The availability of nitrogen may not be as limiting as has been believed since a substantial amount of nitrogenous compounds in the surface waters of reefs may also be produced by nitrogen fixation in a number of reef organisms, especially cyanobacteria.

3.2.5 The contribution of algal symbionts to calcification by corals (Goreau, 1959 and 1961)

All scleractinian corals produce exoskeletons of calcium carbonate laid down on a thin organic matrix external to the calicoblastic (i.e. skeleton-producing) epidermis. However, only those species which contain dinoflagellate symbionts have a sufficiently high calcification rate to maintain coral reefs against the constantly destructive forces of wave action or surf. The dependence of reef-building ('hermatypic') corals on their algal symbionts is the reason why the living parts of coral reefs are restricted to the photic zone of oceans (usually less than 40–50 m deep); ahermatypic species are common to a depth of 550 m.

The contribution of algal symbionts to calcification by corals was investigated by Goreau. For a range of species the radioactive isotope ^{45}Ca was incorporated into the skeleton three to 25 times faster in the light than in darkness or in the presence of the photosynthetic inhibitor 3-(3,4-dichlorophenyl)-1,1-dimethyl urea (DCMU). Also, the rate of ^{45}Ca incorporation by symbiotic corals was higher than in aposymbionts, especially in the light (Table 3.3).

Goreau proposed that the calcium component of the skeleton is derived directly from the sea water because the calcium:strontium ratio in the skeleton is similar to that of sea water. The ratio is higher in the animal tissues because most zooplankton on which corals feed exclude strontium from their bodies. In contrast to calcium, the carbonate of the skeleton is probably of metabolic origin because the ratios of the stable isotopes of both oxygen ($^{18}O:^{16}O$) and carbon ($^{13}C:^{12}C$) in the skeleton are comparable to the ratios in the coral tissues and lower than those in the ambient sea water. The ratios are low in the animal tissues because the isotopes ^{16}O and ^{12}C are utilized preferentially in metabolic reactions.

Goreau demonstrated that removal of carbonic acid is a crucial factor in

Table 3.3 Calcification rate of the coral *Manicina areolata* incubated with $^{45}CaCl_2$ for 80 hours (data from Goreau, 1959).

Incubation conditions	^{45}Ca incorporation (cpm per mg skeletal calcium) mean ± s.e.	
	Colonies containing algae	Alga-free colonies
Light	462 ± 63	28 ± 8
Darkness	72 ± 15	30 ± 6

the high calcification rate of hermatypic corals. The breakdown of carbonic acid (H_2CO_3) to bicarbonate (HCO_3^-) and carbon dioxide is catalyzed by the enzyme carbonic anhydrase, which is present in coral tissues. If the activity of carbonic anhydrase is inhibited by the compound 'diamox', calcification is substantially reduced. Combining these data with the dependence of calcification on algal photosynthesis (see above), Goreau concluded that the symbionts enhance calcium carbonate deposition by photosynthetic utilization of carbon dioxide (Fig. 3.4).

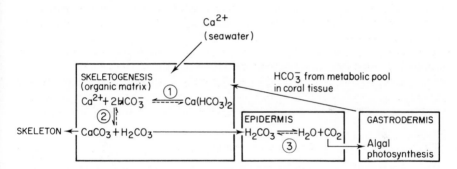

Fig. 3.4 Model devised by Goreau to show how calcification in hermatypic corals is enhanced by photosynthesis of the algal symbionts. It is proposed that fixation of carbon dioxide in algal photosynthesis shifts the equilibrium of reactions 1, 2, and 3 in the direction indicated, so enhancing calcium carbonate synthesis. Calcium carbonate is precipitated because the ambient seawater is supersaturated with respect to this compound (see 3.2.5. for full details).

There are two main difficulties with the model of Goreau. First, it cannot explain how the removal of carbon dioxide for algal photosynthesis does not also reduce the availability of bicarbonate for skeleton formation. Secondly, in some corals, for example *Acropora cervicornis*, the highest calcification rates are at the tips of coral branches where the density of symbionts is very low. Despite these problems, Goreau's model has gained widespread acceptance. This is partly due to the paucity of alternative theories (see Muscatine, 1973).

3.2.6   Regulation of the algal symbionts

The ratio of biomass of algae to host in coelenterates containing *S. microadriaticum*, as in *Chlorella* symbioses, lies in the range 1:10 to 1:100 (see 2.2.3), but it is not clear how the population of dinoflagellate symbionts is regulated.

Expulsion of symbionts from coelenterates under both normal conditions and conditions of stress has been observed. Small 'clouds' of *S. microadriaticum* above coral polyps have been reported and large-scale ejection from corals and sea anemones can be induced by natural disasters (such as hurricanes), low salinity, high temperature and prolonged incubation in darkness. The regular ejection of symbionts by some sea anemones, for example *Aiptasia tagetes*, *Anemonia sulcata* maintained under routine laboratory conditions, has been interpreted as the chief means by which the host regulates its algal symbionts (Steele, 1976), but Trench (1986) has argued that this is unlikely to be the sole regulatory mechanism.

An alternative approach has been to compare the division rate of the algae in symbiosis and in culture. In the hermatypic coral *Stylophora pistillata*, the temperate anemone *Anthopleura elegantissima* and the jellyfish *Mastigias* sp., the estimated algal specific growth rate is 0.01–0.1 d^{-1} (Muscatine *et al.*, 1984; Wilkerson *et al.*, 1983). This contrasts with specific growth rates of 0.3 d^{-1} or higher in cultured *S. microadriaticum* (Trench, 1986) and suggests that, as in the green hydra symbiosis with *Chlorella* (2.2.3), the host may control the algal growth and division rates.

3.2.7   Perpetuation of the symbiosis from one host generation to the next

3.2.7.1   Mode of transmission of symbionts

When coelenterates containing symbiotic dinoflagellates reproduce asexually by fission or budding, each offspring animal invariably receives its complement of algae. During sexual reproduction in some species, the algal cells are deposited in the egg cytoplasm prior to fertilization. In other species, the symbionts are acquired from the environment at each host generation. In the class Anthozoa, the modes of transmission can be correlated with neither the taxonomic position of the host nor the environment of the association (Table 3.4). The data for the other classes is limited but, of the relatively few examples studied, all Scyphozoa require reinfection at each generation but the Hydrozoa exhibit direct transmission.

The requirement of many species for establishment of the association at each sexual generation implies the presence of free-living *S. microadriaticum* in the environment. This alga has rarely been isolated from sea water samples and is generally thought not to lead a permanent free-living existence in nature. The main source of *S. microadriaticum* for infection is probably symbionts freshly released from their hosts. For example, packets of viable and often motile symbionts are extruded from some coelenterates (3.2.6) and

Table 3.4 Mode of acquisition of dinoflagellates by sexual progeny of coelenterate hosts (after Trench, 1986, and J. Turner, unpublished).

	Direct transmission	Acquisition of symbionts from environment
Class Anthozoa		
Scleractinia	*Pocillopora damicornis* *Stylophora pistillata* 4 spp. of *Porites*	*Pocillopora meandrina* *Favia doreyensis* (= *F. pallida*) *Acropora bruggemanni* and *A. formosa* *Fungia scutaria* *Goniastrea australiensis* *Astrangia danae* *Turbinaria mesenterina*
Actiniaria	*Anthopleura ballii* *Anemonia sulcata*	*Anthopleura elegantissima* and *A. xanthogrammica* *Aiptasia tagetes* and *A. pulchella*
Alcyonaria	*Eunicella stricta stricta*	*Eunicella stricta aphyta* *Briarium asbestinum* *Pseudopterogorgia elizabethae* and *P. bipinnata*
Class Scyphozoa		*Mastigias papua* *Cassiopeia andromeda* and *C. xamachana*
Class Hydrozoa	*Millepora* sp. *Myrionema amboinense* *Velella velella* *Aglaophenia pluma*	

when certain predators (e.g. the puffer fish *Arothron meleagris*) feed on coelenterates, the algal symbionts are not digested but pass intact through the digestive tract.

3.2.7.2 Specificity and the selection of symbionts

In general, an individual host contains a homogeneous population of *S. microadriaticum* and the symbionts in all members of one host species belong to the same strain (see 3.2.1). (One exception, *Palythoa mammilosa*, may contain one of two dissimilar strains, see Table 3.5.) The various host species in one geographical area may contain different strains of symbionts (Table 3.5).

Under laboratory conditions, strains of *S. microadriaticum* vary in their ability to infect different hosts. In one recent study, some strains completely failed to infect aposymbiotic *Aiptasia tagetes* (Table 3.5). The native strain grew fastest and attained the highest stable density in this host and there was a general trend of decreasing infectivity with increasing electrophoretic difference between the test strain and native strain. These results indicate a degree of specificity in coelenterate-dinoflagellate associations, which implies that the host is able to discriminate between different strains of

Table 3.5 Characteristics of *Symbiodinium microadriaticum* isolated from different coelenterate hosts (Schoenberg and Trench, 1980).

Strain of S. microadriaticum	Host species (Location)	Relationship to algae in *Aiptasia tagetes* S_J*	Infection of *Aiptasia tagetes* (number of algae per mm tentacle length 56 days after infection†)
A	*Aiptasia tagetes* (Bermuda, Florida)	1.0	24 791
A	*Pseudopterogorgia bipinnata* (Jamaica)	1.0	11 200
N	*Pseudopterogorgia americana* (Bermuda)	0.72	7950
Q	*Palythoa mammilosa* (Bermuda)	0.06	1421
D	*Condylactis gigantea* (Florida)	0.35	0
P	*Palythoa mammilosa* (Bermuda)	0.14	0
Z	*Zoanthus sociatus* (Bermuda)	0.06	0

* S_J – Similarity coefficient (based on isoenzyme pattern) to strain A, where 1.0 indicates identical pattern and zero indicates complete dissimilarity.
† Cultured cells of various strains of *S. microadriaticum* were pipetted onto the siphonoglyph of aposymbiotic *A. tagetes* and engulfed by the host.

S. microadriaticum. However, there has been little experimental investigation of the mechanisms by which the symbionts are recognized and selected (Trench, 1986).

3.2.8   Associations between dinoflagellates and tridacnid molluscs

The family Tridacnidae (giant clams) of bivalve molluscs comprises six species, all of which form symbiosis with *Symbiodinium microadriaticum*. The algal symbionts are extracellular, housed in the haemal sinuses of the siphonal tissue, which is greatly enlarged and extends along the entire dorsal surface of the animal (Fig. 3.5).

The algal symbionts make an appreciable nutritional contribution to the host. Experiments using ^{14}C-bicarbonate show that a substantial proportion of photosynthetically-fixed carbon is translocated to the animal tissues (Goreau *et al.*, 1973) and that the release of photosynthate by freshly isolated symbionts is stimulated by a homogenate of the host tissue (Hinde, 1983; Muscatine, 1967). Preliminary experiments of the design adopted by Muscatine and coworkers (1984) (see 3.2.4.3) indicate that the symbionts in

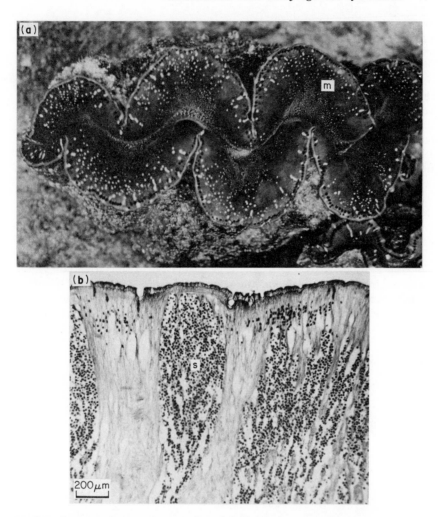

Fig. 3.5 Symbiosis between the giant clam *Tridacna gigas* and *Symbiodinium microadriaticum*. **(a)** View of living animal from above, showing fully expanded siphonal tissue (m) (courtesy of R.K. Trench). **(b)** Light microscope section through siphonal tissue, with haemal sinus (s) containing algal cells (from Trench *et al.*, 1981).

Tridacna maxima contribute 62–84% of the host's respiratory carbon needs (Trench *et al.*, 1981); the rest of the host's energy requirement is presumably supplied by holozoic feeding. Although algal cells in a disintegrating state have been observed in the siphonal tissue and gut, it is not known if they are undergoing autolysis or host digestive attack, and the consensus view is that the relationship between the partners is primarily biotrophic. The similarity of the nutritional interactions to those in symbioses between coelenterates and dinoflagellates indicates that neither the taxonomic identity of the host nor the structural relationship between host and symbiont (extracellular in tridacnids, intracellular in most coelenterates) has a major effect on the characteristics of photosynthate transport.

The symbiosis in tridacnids is established at each host generation when veliger larvae acquire *S. microadriaticum* through feeding. In one study of the developing symbiosis in *Tridacna squamosa*, no difference was found between the growth rate of hosts infected with *S. microadriaticum* isolated from tridacnids and those isolated from anthozoan or scyphozoan coelenterates, although aposymbiotic controls grew less well (Fitt and Trench, 1981). This suggests that the symbiosis in tridacnids may be of lower specificity than in coelenterates (see Table 3.5 and 3.2.7.2).

3.3   Symbiosis in *Convoluta roscoffensis*

3.3.1   Introduction

Convoluta roscoffensis is an acoel turbellarian ('flatworm') found on sandy beaches almost exclusively on the coast of France and nearby Channel Islands (Holligan and Gooday, 1975). It contains algal cells of the genus *Tetraselmis*, usually *Tetraselmis convolutae* (= *Platymonas convolutae*), which give the animal a deep green colour. Despite its restricted distribution,

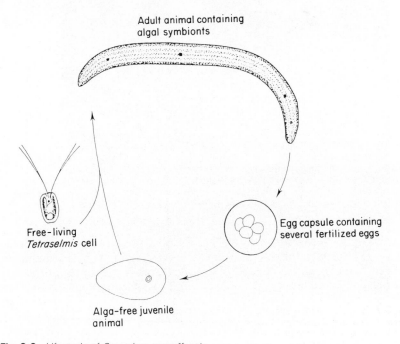

Adult animal containing algal symbionts

Free-living *Tetraselmis* cell

Egg capsule containing several fertilized eggs

Alga-free juvenile animal

Fig. 3.6   Life cycle of *Convoluta roscoffensis*.

C. roscoffensis has achieved some prominence in the experimental study of symbiosis, in large part due to the work of Keeble and Gamble at the beginning of this century (Keeble, 1912).

Adult *C. roscoffensis* always contain algal symbionts. They reproduce sexually and lay eggs free of any algae in a common gelatinous capsule (Fig. 3.6). The alga-free juveniles which hatch out become infected with algae by feeding on *Tetraselmis* which are usually associated with the egg capsules (see

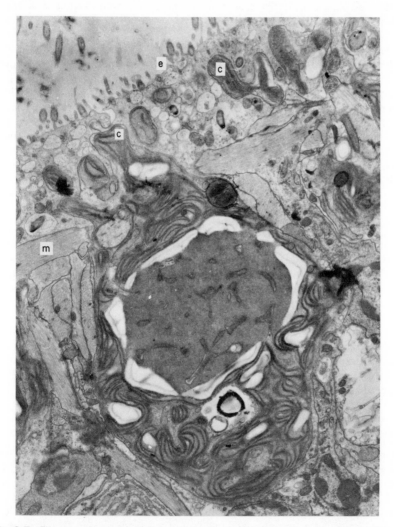

Fig. 3.7 Electron micrograph of *Tetraselmis convolutae* in *Convoluta roscoffensis*. The athecate algal cell is associated with the body wall musculature (m) of the animal. The algal cell, including parts of the chloroplast (c), project into the epidermal layer (e) of the host. (A.E. Douglas, unpublished micrograph.) Magnification × 7000.

3.3.3.3). Free-living cells of *Tetraselmis* have a pectinaceous cell wall (or 'theca'), an eyespot and four flagella, but these features are lost once the algae are in the animal. In the fully-established symbiosis, the algal cells are of irregular shape and situated just interior to the body wall musculature of the host (Fig. 3.7). Although they have been reported to be extracellular, more recent electron microscopic studies (McFarlane, 1982) demonstrate that they are enclosed in vacuoles within animal cells.

3.3.2   Nutritional interactions

The key role of algal symbionts in the nutrition of *C. roscoffensis* is indicated by the fact that aposymbiotic juvenile animals do not mature and eventually die if uninfected. Also adults which invariably contain *Tetraselmis* are unresponsive to any potential food items (Holligan and Gooday, 1975). However, experimental study of nutritional interactions is difficult because the symbionts have no cell wall and so are easily damaged by homogenization, part of the usual method to separate the partners of a symbiosis (see 2.2.2.2 and Fig. 2.4). No alternative method of separation has proved satisfactory. A further handicap to nutritional studies is the lack of aposymbiotic adult animals to act as controls.

3.3.2.1   Transport of photosynthate to the host (Muscatine *et al.*, 1974)

The importance of algal photosynthesis to the maintenance of *C. roscoffensis* is shown by the four-fold decline in length of animals incubated with the photosynthetic inhibitor DCMU for 28 days (Table 3.6). Radioactive amino acids and glucose are found in hydrolysates of eggs and mucus produced by animals previously incubated with ^{14}C-bicarbonate in the light, showing that photosynthate moves from symbiont to host, but there is no reliable estimate of the amount of this movement. The mobile products may be amino acids (freshly isolated symbionts release small amounts of alanine, serine, glutamine and fatty acids). There is no persuasive evidence that the release of photosynthate is stimulated by either host homogenate (see 3.2.3.1) or low pH (see 2.2.2.2).

3.3.2.2   Host utilization of photosynthetically produced oxygen

The association in *C. roscoffensis* is the only alga-invertebrate symbiosis for which there is direct evidence that the animal host utilizes photosynthetically produced oxygen for respiration (see 2.2.5.1 and 3.2.3.3). When *C. roscoffensis* is incubated with ^{14}C-bicarbonate under illumination and then transferred into the photosynthetic inhibitor DCMU, the tissues accumulate ^{14}C-labelled lactic acid, a common end product of anaerobic respiration in animal cells. Lactic acid production is abolished when DCMU is removed or oxygen bubbled into the medium (Boyle and Smith, 1975).

3.3.2.3 Synthesis of fatty acids and sterols by the algal symbionts (Meyer et al., 1979)

The fatty acids and sterols in *C. roscoffensis* are very similar to these classes of compounds in cultured cells of *Tetraselmis convolutae*. This suggests that the algal symbionts provide these compounds to the animal host.

To study fatty acid synthesis directly, *C. roscoffensis* were exposed to ^{14}C-acetate and the incorporation of ^{14}C into lipids was examined. In aposymbiotic juvenile animals, radioactivity was incorporated only into the carboxyl-terminal fragment of fatty acids, suggesting that 2-carbon units had been added to pre-existing long-chain fatty acids. Adult *C. roscoffensis* (which contain symbionts) incorporated radioactivity along the length of fatty acids in the light but, within 5 hours of incubation in darkness, the distribution of radioactivity was similar to that in juveniles. These results indicate that the algae exhibit photosynthesis-dependent synthesis and release of fatty acids, but that the animal is capable only of simple chain elongation reactions.

The transport of fatty acids and sterols from the algal symbionts to the host has not been demonstrated directly.

3.3.2.4 Recycling of nitrogen within the association

Boyle and Smith (1975) proposed that the algal symbionts recycle nitrogen within the symbiosis by utilizing uric acid, a nitrogenous waste product of the host, partly to produce amino acids which are released back to the host (Fig. 3.8). The movement of amino acids from algae to host has already been considered (3.3.2.1). The proposed utilization of uric acid by the symbionts is supported by several lines of evidence (Douglas 1983b).

a) *Tetraselmis convolutae* and related species in culture can utilize uric acid as sole nitrogen source for growth.

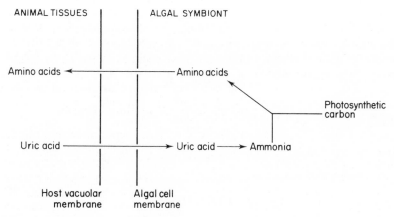

Fig. 3.8 Proposed recycling of nitrogen in *Convoluta roscoffensis* (after Boyle and Smith, 1975).

Table 3.6 Length and uric acid content of *Convoluta roscoffensis* containing algal symbionts. Data from Douglas (1983b).

	Length (mm) mean ± s.e.	nmol uric acid per µg protein mean ± s.e.
At start of experiment	2.09 ± 0.05	0.107 ± 0.009
After 28 d in media:		
Enriched sea water	3.74 ± 0.05	0.080 ± 0.011
Enriched sea water + 10^{-7} M DCMU	0.57 ± 0.02	0.304 ± 0.047
Unenriched sea water	1.54 ± 0.05	0.007 ± 0.002
Sea water with nitrogen-free enrichment	1.99 ± 0.05	<0.002

b) Uric acid accumulates in aposymbiotic juveniles but declines once the animals become infected with the appropriate alga.

c) Net utilization of uric acid in symbiotic *C. roscoffensis* is photosynthesis-dependent. When animals were maintained in the photosynthetic inhibitor DCMU, their uric acid content increased three-fold over 28 days (Table 3.6). This is not because algal utilization of uric acid is photosynthesis-dependent (in culture, *Tetraselmis* can grow with uric acid as sole nitrogen source in darkness) but probably because the enzyme which degrades uric acid, urate oxidase, has a stringent requirement for oxygen as electron acceptor. There is independent evidence that *C. roscoffensis* tissues are oxygen-deficient under non-photosynthesizing conditions (3.3.2.2).

d) The uric acid content of *C. roscoffensis* declined more than tenfold when animals were incubated in media without nitrogen supplement for 28 days (Table 3.6).

There is no direct evidence for the translocation of uric acid from the host to the algal symbionts or algal utilization of uric acid in the intact association.

The proposed recycling of nitrogen within the association is not sufficient to maintain *C. roscoffensis* in the absence of nitrogen supplement to the medium under laboratory conditions. When adult animals were maintained in media without nitrogen supplement, they declined in length by 5–25%, whereas those in nitrogen-enriched media grew to 1.8 times their original length (Table 3.6). This finding is of relevance to the natural situation because the environment of *C. roscoffensis* in the field is rich in organic nitrogen and nitrate (Holligan and Gooday, 1975).

3.3.3   Establishment of the association in juvenile *C. roscoffensis*

3.3.3.1   The origin of the algal symbionts

More is known about the origin of the algal symbionts under natural conditions in the *C. roscoffensis* association than in any other alga-invertebrate symbiosis which requires re-infection at each host generation (2.2.1.2, 3.2.7.1). Newly-hatched juveniles are very likely to encounter and ingest *Tetraselmis* cells in the discarded egg capsules (see Fig. 3.6 and 3.3.1). Some of these algal cells will have been released from the parent during egg laying and others, of free-living origin, will have settled and adhered to the capsule surface. Contrary to early reports, there is no experimental evidence that free-living cells exhibit chemotaxis towards egg capsules of *C. roscoffensis* (Douglas and Gooday, 1982). The free-living algae comprise a range of taxa and probably include *T. convolutae* and other *Tetraselmis* species which have been isolated from beaches inhabited by *C. roscoffensis*. Therefore, in the natural situation, juvenile *C. roscoffensis* recognizes and selects the appropriate alga from a range of alternative and closely-related taxa.

3.3.3.2   Recognition in the developing association (Douglas, 1983a; Provasoli *et al.*, 1968)

The development of the symbiosis is shown in Fig. 3.9. Experimental studies have identified several stages at which there is discrimination between acceptable and unacceptable potential symbionts. The characteristics of these stages bear remarkable similarities to those in *Chlorella* symbiosis with green hydra (Fig. 2.7).

The first stage of selection (or 'recognition', see 1.3.6) is at surface contact. All species of *Tetraselmis* but few other algal taxa are ingested. The pectinaceous theca of *Tetraselmis* is probably an important feature triggering

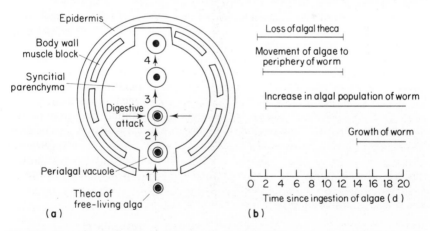

Fig. 3.9 Stages in the development of the symbiosis in *Convoluta roscoffensis* (from Douglas, 1983a). **(a)** The order of the stages identified from structural studies is as follows: 1, phagocytosis of algal cell; 2, subjection of alga to digestive attack; 3, loss of algal theca; 4, movement of alga to periphery of animal. For simplicity, the vacuole is depicted as surrounding a single alga at all stages (the number of algae per vacuole is unknown). **(b)** The temporal relationship between stages, where known. The extent of the lines indicates the duration of each stage.

Table 3.7 Length of juvenile *Convoluta roscoffensis* infected with different algae. The juveniles were infected with algae soon after hatching. (Provasoli *et al.*, 1968.)

Juvenile	Length of juveniles (mm)
On hatching	0.28
After 28 days Algal symbiont –	
*Tetraselmis convolutae**	1.54–1.65
Tetraselmis marinus	0.84–1.04
Tetraselmis verrucosa	1.26
Tetraselmis sp.	0.28–0.56

* The native symbiont

phagocytosis because athecate cells are not taken up. The surface characteristic has not been identified; uptake is unaffected by a variety of treatments designed to modify or alter surface glycoproteins. The capacity to photosynthesize or to release photosynthate may be necessary for the persistence, but not phagocytosis, of potential symbionts because under nonphotosynthesizing conditions *Tetraselmis* cells are readily ingested but are subsequently digested or expelled.

All *Tetraselmis* species so far tested form a viable association with *C. roscoffensis* under laboratory conditions, although there is some variation in the growth rate of juvenile animals containing different species (Table 3.7). The nature of selection at the later phases in the establishment of the symbiosis has been investigated by use of two algae, the native symbiont, *T. convolutae*, and an alternative symbiont, *T. marinus* (= *Prasinocladus marinus*) which supports relatively poor host growth (see Table 3.7). Juvenile animals containing *T. marinus* were maintained for 10–15 days, so that the algal cells were athecate and at the periphery of the animal, and then they were exposed to free-living *T. convolutae* cells. Invariably, *T. convolutae* displaced *T. marinus* from the animal within 6 days. Further experiments with other *Tetraselmis* species suggested that the alga which promotes greatest host growth is selected. It is not known how the difference between the algae is detected or how the inferior alga is lost. These experiments can explain, at least in principle, how adult *C. roscoffensis* in the natural situation contain only one species of algal symbiont; presumably, this is the alga which promotes greater host growth than all the alternative taxa which the juvenile animal ingests.

3.4 Symbiosis in protist hosts

3.4.1 The Foraminifera (Lee and McEnery, 1983)

Among the many symbiotic marine protists (Table 2.1), one group of protozoans, the Foraminifera, is of particular interest because of its long fossil record, abundance in warm, shallow seas, and unusual characteristics of large size (50 μm to 12 cm) and long life span (weeks to several years in nature). Foraminiferans secrete a shell, often of calcium carbonate, which is usually multi-chambered. Each chamber opens directly into another chamber and the entire shell is filled with protoplasm. There are many small perforations in each chamber and threadlike, branched pseudopodia which function in feeding project through these pores.

Symbiosis with algae is common to all the large benthic foraminiferans and is also found in some smaller planktonic species, for example, globigerinids. The algae are intracellular and enclosed in host membrane-bound vacuoles. A particularly intriguing aspect of these symbioses is the wide range of algae with which foraminiferans form associations. In different foraminiferan species, one may find dinoflagellates (*Symbiodinium microadriaticum, Amphidinium* species, *Gymnodinium vertebrales*), chlorophyceans (*Chlamydomonas* and *Chlorella* species), diatoms (a range of species, including members of the pennate genera *Fragilaria, Navicula, Nitzchia, Amphora*) and an unicellular rhodophyte, possibly *Porphyridium*. Furthermore, the associations in some foraminiferan species appear to be of relatively low specificity. Among certain species which harbour diatoms, some individuals contain more than one species of diatom and the identity of the symbiont(s) varies with time and place of collection. Other foraminiferans may contain algae of widely differing taxonomic affinity within a single host cell. For example, *Amphistegina* species may have *Chlorella* or diatoms in addition to the usual symbiont, *S. microadriaticum*. The factors which contribute to the low specificity of these associations are unknown.

There is little information on the nutritional relationships between the partners, although the importance of algal photosynthesis to the host is indicated by various morphological and behavioural adaptations of the foraminiferan hosts to maximize light capture, for example, large surface area per unit volume, reduction in thickness of the side walls of the shell, positive phototaxis and, among some planktonic species, the transport of symbionts into the extended pseudopodia during daylight and their withdrawal into the shell at night. However, it is not clear from preliminary growth studies whether algal photosynthesis contributes to host growth. The sustained growth of *Amphistegina lessonii* is light-dependent under conditions of feeding, but *Globigerinoides sacculifer* grows slowly and fails to reproduce when starved in the light. The role of algal photosynthesis in calcification of foraminiferan shells is better established. The rate of incorporation of ^{45}Ca into the shells can be stimulated up to fifty-fold by illumination. Further studies indicate that, as in the skeleton of hermatypic corals (3.2.5), the carbonate of the calcareous shell is largely of metabolic origin. These data on calcification have been obtained for a wide range of foraminiferan species, containing diatoms as well as dinoflagellates. This indicates that the enhancement of calcium carbonate deposition by symbiont photosynthesis is not restricted to coelenterate hosts or dinoflagellate symbionts.

3.4.2　Cryptic symbionts of protists (Taylor, 1979)

Most algal symbionts can be identified readily, even when they lack a cell wall and are in close contact with the surrounding host tissue (as in *Tetraselmis* symbionts of *C. roscoffensis*; Fig. 3.7). However, electron microscope studies have revealed that certain organisms, previously thought to be photosynthetic protists, are in fact associations between a non-photosynthetic host and algal symbionts. By detailed ultrastructural studies and analyses of photosynthetic pigments, it is now clear that the gymnostome ciliate *Mesodinium rubrum* contains a cryptic cryptomonad symbiont and the dinofla-

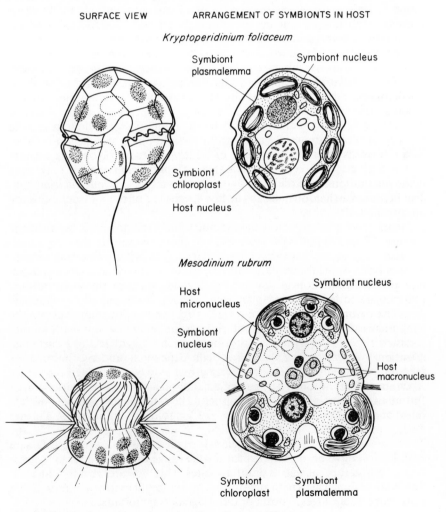

SURFACE VIEW　　ARRANGEMENT OF SYMBIONTS IN HOST

Kryptoperidinium foliaceum

Symbiont plasmalemma

Symbiont nucleus

Symbiont chloroplast

Host nucleus

Mesodinium rubrum

Host micronucleus

Symbiont nucleus

Symbiont nucleus

Host macronucleus

Symbiont chloroplast

Symbiont plasmalemma

Fig. 3.10　Cryptic symbionts in protists (from Taylor, 1979).

gellates *Peridinium balticum* and *Kryptoperidinium* (= *Glenodinium*) *folia-ceum* contain cryptic chrysomonads (Fig. 3.10). The true nature of these associations was not immediately apparent largely because the symbionts have no cell wall and are separated from the host cytoplasm by a single membrane (see 11.2), and because several structural features of the symbionts differ from related nonsymbiotic taxa of algae. In particular, the symbionts lack the characteristic shape of nonsymbiotic forms and the flagellar apparatus is entirely missing. In some samples of *M. rubrum*, the symbionts have lost their cellular integrity altogether. They are subdivided into many membrane-bound 'chloroplast-mitochondrial' complexes, each containing one or two chloroplasts and lacking a nucleus, and a separate membrane-bound structure containing a nucleus with cryptomonad characteristics. These findings are of particular interest to considerations of the evolution of eukaryotes (see 10.4).

The high degree of structural intimacy between symbiont and host in these cryptic symbioses has led to the view that the symbionts are transmitted directly at host reproduction and that the partners display considerable physiological interdependence. However, there are no experimental data to support these ideas.

3.5 Temporary retention of algae and plastids

In the associations described so far in this chapter, the relationship is permanent in the sense that, once established, it generally persists for the lifespan of the host and often through many host generations by direct transmission of the symbionts. However, some associations with algae are more transient because the algal cells fail to divide or only survive for short periods. There are also associations in which only the plastids of algal cells are retained; these plastids can function for only limited periods and cannot divide in the foreign environment because many of their structural components and enzymes are coded by genes in the algal nucleus and can only be obtained from the cytoplasm of the intact algal cell. It has been argued that such temporary associations are not symbioses (Hinde, 1980) because symbioses persist for long periods (see 1.3.4). However, the study of the temporary retention of foreign organisms or organelles can provide valuable insight into the evolution, persistence and nutritional interactions in true symbioses.

Temporary retention of algae and plastids appears to be particularly prevalent in two orders of opisthobranch molluscs, the Nudibranchia (true sea slugs) and slug-like Sacoglossa.

3.5.1 Temporary retention of dinoflagellates by Nudibranchia

The Nudibranchia are carnivorous and most species graze on sessile animals, such as sponges, coelenterates and bryozoans. Some species retain the dinoflagellate symbionts of their coelenterate prey within the gut. The dinoflagellates may be extracellular in the gut cavity or intracellular in cells lining the digestive diverticula (a pair of tubules which arise from the midgut and extend and branch within the body tissue, particularly to dorsal projections of the body wall called cerata).

Little is known about the nature of the relationship between dinoflagellates and their secondary nudibranch hosts. The dinoflagellates retained by *Pteraeolidia ianthina* can multiply, photosynthesize and release organic carbon sufficient to supply 80% of the animal's respiratory carbon demand in winter, and all of it in spring and summer (Hoegh-Guldberg and Hinde, 1986; Hoegh-Guldberg *et al*, 1986). This result is entirely consistent with the finding that nutritional interactions in true symbioses with dinoflagellates are biotrophic and are not affected substantially by the identity of the host (see 3.2.8). However, it is unlikely that these interactions occur in all nudibranchs that retain dinoflagellates (see below).

Despite the paucity of experimental data, much information can be gleaned from the general biology of nudibranchs which retain dinoflagellates. A particularly detailed study has been conducted on one genus of aeolid nudibranchs, *Phyllodesmium*, which feed on symbiotic octocorals (coelenterates of the class Anthozoa) (Rudman, 1981). In some species, for example *Phyllodesmium poindimieri*, the retention of dinoflagellates is minimal. Few algal cells are present in the gut and these are invariably associated with partially digested coelenterate tissue. The stomach and the ducts and cells of the digestive diverticula in other species, as in *P. hyalinum*, for example, are packed with dinoflagellates, some structurally intact and some in a disintegrating state. These nudibranchs rapidly become depleted of dinoflagellates if an appropriate food source is not available. By contrast, individuals of another species *P. longicirra* containing a rich complement of dinoflagellates are often found a long distance from octocorals or any other source of symbiotic dinoflagellates. This suggests that dinoflagellates may be retained for long periods in *P. longicirra*. Almost all the algal cells appear structurally intact. They reside within the cells of the digestive diverticula, which in this species form a particularly densely-branched and ramifying network of tubules throughout the body and especially into the cerata. The cerata are few in number compared to those of other *Phyllodesmium* species and are plate-like in structure, so increasing the surface area available for light capture by the enclosed dinoflagellates. It is very probable that these structural modifications of the digestive diverticula and cerata in *P. longicirra* have evolved in response to the retention of algal cells. This in turn suggests that the association has a long evolutionary history and that the dinoflagellate cells are of some significance to the mollusc. There is a real possibility that, as in *Pteraeolida ianthina* (see above), the dinoflagellates in *Phyllodesmium longicirra* are photosynthetically active and release photosynthetic products to the animal tissues.

Nudibranchs are not the only animals to feed on symbiotic coelenterates, but their retention of the dinoflagellate symbionts is most unusual. It is noteworthy that nudibranchs make secondary use of other items in their diet. For example, many aeolid species retain functional nematocysts derived from coelenterate food, presumably for their own defence.

3.5.2 Temporary retention of algal plastids by Sacoglossa

Most sacoglossan molluscs are herbivorous and feed by puncturing the cell wall of multicellular algae and withdrawing the cell contents by suction. A number of species, particularly of the family Elysiidae, retain the ingested plastids within cells of the digestive diverticula (Fig. 3.11). The plastids are structurally intact and are not associated with any other algal organelles. Some are enclosed in membrane-bound vacuoles and others lie free in the animal cytoplasm (Fig. 3.11c). Sacoglossans which retain algal plastids display various morphological features analogous to those in dinoflagellate-bearing nudibranchs (3.5.1) that increase light capture by the chloroplasts. Thus, in many species, the tubules of the digestive diverticula containing the plastids are much-branched and extend into well-developed dorsal papillae or flap-like 'parapodia'.

The plastids retained by sacoglossans are usually derived from siphonaceous green algae (predominantly of the order Caulerpales). There are two reasons for this: siphonaceous algae are a common food source for sacoglossans and their plastids are well-adapted to withstand the rigours of ingestion and incorporation into the animal environment. The siphonaceous algae are suitable for suctorial feeders because of their partially syncitial construction (Fig. 3.11b) (Clark and Busacca, 1978), while their chloroplasts are unusually resilient to osmotic and mechanical stress (Trench *et al*, 1973). However, less robust plastids of other algal taxa (e.g., xanthophytes, rhodophytes) are retained by some sacoglossans (Hinde, 1980).

3.5.2.1 Duration of retention of plastids

Several authors (Clark and Busacca, 1978; Hinde and Smith, 1974) have estimated the time that plastids are retained by sacoglossans from the rate of decline of chlorophyll content when the animals are isolated from food plants. These studies show that plastids are lost at widely differing rates in different sacoglossan species. However, this approach is not entirely satisfactory because the retention time in some species depends on the availability of fresh plastids from the food. For example, the turnover time of *Codium* chloroplasts in *Elysia viridis* is two weeks when animals are allowed to feed *ad libitum* on *Codium*, but considerably longer under the unnatural conditions of starvation (Gallop *et al.*, 1980). Using radiotracer methods to distinguish between plastids ingested by *E. viridis* at different times, it was further shown that the animal can distinguish between newly ingested and older plastids, preferentially rejecting the latter (Gallop *et al.*, 1980). Such selection of plastids is of obvious advantage to the mollusc because the photosynthetic activity of the plastids declines with time after separation from the plant (Hinde and Smith, 1975).

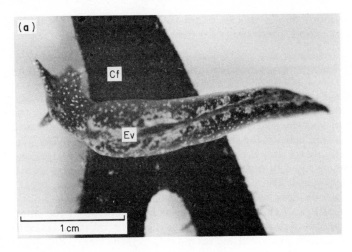

Fig. 3.11 Acquisition of plastids by *Elysia viridis*. **(a)** *E. viridis* (Ev) feeding on *Codium fragile* (Cf). **(b)** Plastids (cp) lining a siphonaceous filament of *C. fragile*. **(c)** (Right) Plastids (cp) of *C. fragile* containing starch grains (s) within digestive cells of *E. viridis*. (g) = glycogen granules in host cell.

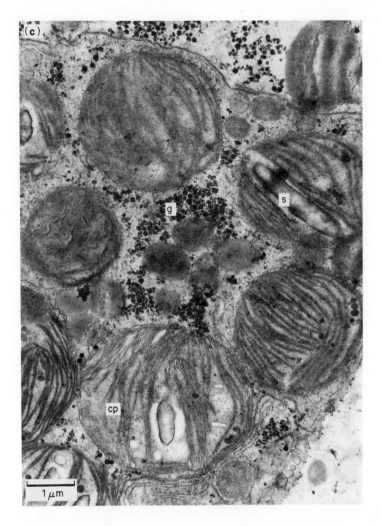

3.5.2.2 Contribution of plastids to the nutrition of sacoglossans

Most growth and physiological studies have been conducted on the temperate sacoglossan *Elysia viridis* (Fig. 3.11a) which can be maintained for long periods under laboratory conditions. Whether incubated in light or darkness and in the presence or absence of the food plant *Codium*, animals survive and remain green for several months, although they decline in weight (Hinde and Smith, 1975). Weight loss is greatest in animals cultured in darkness without food and least under conditions of feeding with illumination (Table 3.8). The

Table 3.8   Body weight of *Elysia viridis* maintained for 56 days under different light and feeding regimes: 12 hours light/12 hours dark ('light') or continuous darkness ('dark') with or without (i.e. fed and unfed) *Codium* food plants. (Hinde and Smith, 1975.)

| | Mean fresh weight of animals (as percentage of weight at start of experiment) | |
	Light	Dark
Fed	76	48
Unfed	69	32

importance of light to the maintenance of body weight indicates that photosynthetic activity of the plastids is of significance to the nutrition of *E. viridis*.

As in associations with algal cells, the nutritional interactions between sacoglossans and ingested plastids are primarily biotrophic. By use of the tracer ^{14}C-bicarbonate, it has been demonstrated that photosynthetic products of the plastids are translocated to the animal tissues, especially the mucous glands, and that photosynthetic carbon is incorporated into sugar moieties of mucus (Trench *et al.*, 1969). Unfortunately, the proportion of photosynthetically fixed carbon that is translocated to the animal cannot be estimated by the standard method (see Fig. 2.4) because of difficulties in separating the plastids from animal material (Gallop, 1974). An alternative approach, to determine the proportion of ^{14}C that is incorporated into an animal product, is feasible for the association in *E. viridis* because most of the mobile photosynthate is metabolized by the animals to galactose (Trench *et al.*, 1973). In intact *E. viridis*, 36% of the total fixed ^{14}C-bicarbonate is recovered from galactose. This represents a *minimal* estimate of the proportion of photosynthate released by *Codium* plastids to the animal (Trench *et al.*, 1973).

There is no direct information on the identity of the mobile product of photosynthesis. R.K. Trench and coworkers (Trench *et al.*, 1973) have suggested it is glucose. They showed that homogenates of *E. viridis*, in which the animal tissues but not chloroplasts are disrupted, fix ^{14}C-bicarbonate at a similar rate to intact *E. viridis* and that the principal product recovered from the supernatant (presumably released from the chloroplasts) was glucose. Alternatively, Hinde (1978) proposed that, as in higher plant chloroplasts, triose phosphates are the chief mobile photosynthetic products and they are rapidly metabolized to glucose by the animal tissues. Recent studies with isolated *Codium* chloroplasts show the existence of both a C_3 and a C_6 transport system for the export of products of photosynthesis (Rutter and Cobb, 1983).

The release of photosynthate by plastids in homogenates of *E. viridis* (see above) deserves further comment. About 40% of fixed ^{14}C is released under these conditions, whether the plastids have been ingested by *E. viridis* and incorporated into the animal tissues (Trench *et al.*, 1973) or isolated from *Codium* and resuspended with animal homogenate (Gallop, 1974). By contrast, only 2% of photosynthate is released by isolated plastids in a relatively pure preparation or maintained in a crude homogenate of *Codium* (Hinde, 1978). These data suggest that *E. viridis* tissue contains a 'factor' which stimulates photosynthate release. Analogous 'factors' have been postulated for associations between coelenterates and dinoflagellates (3.2.3.1). The relationship between the factors in *E. viridis* and in coelenterates is indicated further by the finding that homogenates of *E. viridis* stimulate photosynthate release by *Symbiodinium microadriaticum* isolated from the anemone *Anemonia sulcata* and homogenates of *A. sulcata* have a comparable effect on *Codium* plastids (Gallop, 1974).

3.5.3 Retention of plastids by protists

Subsequent to the discovery of intact plastids in sacoglossan molluscs, plastids have been reported in a range of marine protists, e.g. dinophycean and cryptophycean chloroplasts in ciliate protozoa of the genera *Prorodon* and *Strombidium* (Blackbourn *et al.*, 1973) and diatom chloroplasts in several foraminiferans (Lee and McEnery, 1983). It has been shown that the chloroplasts in the foraminiferans *Elphidium williamsoni* and *Nonian germanicum* are photosynthetically active and are retained for only short periods. Apart from this, experimental study of these associations is almost entirely lacking.

4
Symbiosis between nitrogen-fixing prokaryotes and plant roots

4.1 Introduction

Nitrogen fixation is the reduction of gaseous nitrogen to ammonia, and in the global nitrogen cycle (Fig. 4.1), it balances the continuous loss of nitrogen to the atmosphere through denitrification. About two thirds of the nitrogen fixed each year is by biological processes, and about one third by non-biological (mostly fertilizer manufacture). No eukaryote is known to fix nitrogen, but the property is widely distributed amongst prokaryotes (Table 4.1). Of these, the few which are symbiotic carry out more than half of all biological nitrogen fixation.

This chapter deals with the bacterial (*Rhizobium* and *Bradyrhizobium*, collectively known as rhizobia) and actinomycete (*Frankia*) symbionts both of which form nodules on plant roots and undoubtedly make the major con-

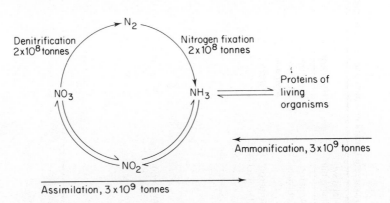

Fig. 4.1 The global nitrogen cycle, annual turnover (Postgate, 1978, 1982). N.B. Values for the total amounts of nitrogen passing through the cycle must be regarded as highly approximate since they are based on extrapolations from measurements of small areas to the whole globe. Approximate estimates for total global fixation published by the Agricultural and Food Research Council of the UK in 1985 give a total of 175 million tonnes N for biological fixation (agriculture = 90, non-agricultural = 85), and 95 million tonnes N for non-biological fixation (fertiliser manufacture = 50, combustion = 20, ozonization = 15, lightning = 10).

Table 4.1 Survey of prokaryote genera in which one or more species fix nitrogen (after Postgate, 1982).

	Habit when fixing nitrogen	Nonsymbiotic	Genera with symbiotic species fixing nitrogen
Heterotrophic	Anaerobic (obligate)	*Clostridium, Desulfovibrio, Desulfomaculum, Methanococcus*[3] (Belay et al., 1984) *Methanosarcina*[3] (Murray and Zinder, 1984)	–
	Anaerobic[1] (facultative)	*Klebsiella, Bacillus, Enterobacter, Citrobacter, Escherichia, Propionibacterium*	–
	Microaerobic[2]	*Xanthobacter, Thiobacillus, Aquaspirillum, Campylobacter, Arthrobacter, Methylocistus, Methylococcus, Methylomonas, Methylobacter, Azospirillum*	*Rhizobium, Bradyrhizobium Frankia (Azospirillum)*[4]
	Aerobic	*Azotobacter, Azotococcus, Azomonas, Beijerinkia, Derxia*	*(Azotobacter)*[4]
Phototrophic	Anaerobic (obligate)	*Chromatium, Chlorobium, Thiopedia, Ectothiospira*	–
	Anaerobic[1] (facultative)	*Rhodospirillum, Rhodopseudomonas*	–
	Microaerobic[2,5]	*Spirulina, Oscillatoria, Pseudoanabaena, Lyngbia, Plectonema, Phormidium, Synechococcus, Dermocarpa, Xenococcus, Myxosarcina, Chroococcidiopsis, Pleurocapsa*	–
	Aerobic[5]	*Cylindrosperma, Chlorogloeopsis, Fischerella, Gloeotheca*	*Anabaena, Nostoc, Scytonema, Stigonema, Calothrix, Dicothrix*

Notes: 1 Anaerobic (facultative) = can live aerobically, but only fixes nitrogen anaerobically. 2 Microaerobic = only fixes nitrogen at less than half atmospheric oxygen concentration. 3 Archaebacteria. 4 May be closely associated with plant roots, but do not form nodules. 5 Cyanobacteria (see Table 5.3).

tribution to symbiotic nitrogen fixation. Rhizobia are almost exclusively confined to legumes, while *Frankia* forms nodules on the roots of plants from a range of non-leguminous genera. Nitrogen-fixing bacteria closely associated with plant roots, but not forming nodules, will also be considered here. The next chapter deals with associations involving cyanobacteria (which may fix nitrogen, photosynthesise, or both) including those cycads which have cyanobacterial symbionts in specialized roots, sometimes known as 'nodules'.

The properties of the enzyme complex responsible for nitrogen fixation, nitrogenase, will be considered before describing the various symbioses.

4.1.1   Mode of action and properties of nitrogenase

Nitrogenase isolated from over thirty different symbiotic and nonsymbiotic prokaryotes has similar structure and properties. It is a complex of two enzymes and its mode of action is summarized in Fig. 4.2. The nitrogen fixation rate per unit enzyme is relatively low so that cells which fix nitrogen at high rates contain large amounts of the enzyme; in some organisms nitrogenase may comprise up to 20% of the cell protein.

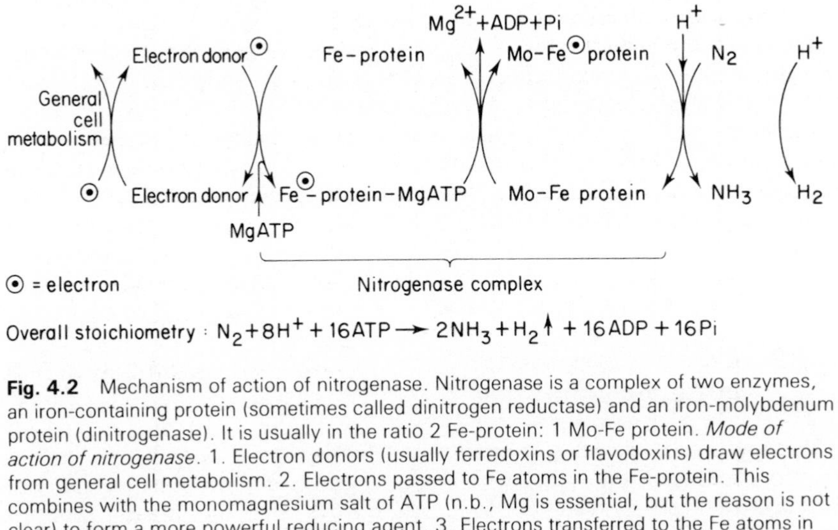

Overall stoichiometry : $N_2 + 8H^+ + 16ATP \longrightarrow 2NH_3 + H_2\uparrow + 16ADP + 16Pi$

Fig. 4.2 Mechanism of action of nitrogenase. Nitrogenase is a complex of two enzymes, an iron-containing protein (sometimes called dinitrogen reductase) and an iron-molybdenum protein (dinitrogenase). It is usually in the ratio 2 Fe-protein: 1 Mo-Fe protein. *Mode of action of nitrogenase*. 1. Electron donors (usually ferredoxins or flavodoxins) draw electrons from general cell metabolism. 2. Electrons passed to Fe atoms in the Fe-protein. This combines with the monomagnesium salt of ATP (n.b., Mg is essential, but the reason is not clear) to form a more powerful reducing agent. 3. Electrons transferred to the Fe atoms in the MoFe-protein. The oxidation state of the Mo atom is lowered, and it is able to bind N_2. 4. Further inputs of electrons result in the progressive reduction of the bound nitrogen until it is converted to ammonia and then released. 5. There are two binding sites for the Fe-protein on the MoFe-protein. Having donated an electron, an Fe-protein-MgATP complex dissociates, and another reduced Fe-protein-MgATP combines with the MoFe-protein. Thus, the reduction of the molecule of nitrogen requires several cycles of binding/dissociation by the Fe-protein-MgATP complex in order to deliver sufficient electrons. 6. Hydrogen evolution always occurs.

There are three distinctive features of this enzyme which are important to understanding the physiology of nitrogen fixation:-

(a) *Oxygen sensitivity*. Nitrogenase is irreversibly inactivated by oxygen. The site of nitrogen fixation within cells must always therefore be kept free of oxygen.

(b) *Energy requirement*. The energy requirements for nitrogen fixation are substantial. At maximum efficiency, nitrogenase needs 16 ATP molecules for each molecule of nitrogen fixed (Fig. 4.2). Generation of reductant probably requires about another 9 ATP molecules, making a total of at least 25 ATP molecules. These estimates exclude the energy required to produce carbon skeletons needed for ammonia assimilation.

(c) *Hydrogen evolution*. Hydrogen evolution is an intrinsic part of nitrogenase activity. About 25–30% of the energy used by nitrogenase is lost in the subsequent release of hydrogen.

There are several physiological strategies which prokaryotes can adopt to help overcome the problem that nitrogenase is highly oxygen-sensitive yet requires a great deal of energy. These include: obligate anaerobiosis (Table 4.1); facultative anaerobiosis (i.e., being tolerant of oxygen, but only fixing nitrogen under anaerobic conditions); and aerobiosis but with cellular mechanisms to protect the site of fixation (these can include high rates of respiration to 'scavenge' oxygen, changes in the molecular conformation of the enzyme to make the site of fixation inaccessible to oxygen – although this also temporarily inactivates nitrogen fixation).

However, the highest rates of nitrogen fixation are recorded for organisms in symbiosis with a plant root. The host provides an abundant source of energy from photosynthesis as well as carbon skeletons for ammonia assimilation, it can participate in excluding oxygen from the site of fixation. Thus, estimates for the rate of nitrogen fixation by nonsymbiotic bacteria in the soil are usually in the range of 1 to a few kg N ha^{-1} year^{-1}, while for pasture legumes they can be up to 300 kg N ha^{-1} year^{-1} and occasionally even higher.

4.1.2 Experimental methods in the study of nitrogen fixation and metabolism

The direct measurement of nitrogen fixation is more difficult than carbon fixation because there is no experimentally convenient radioactive isotope. The non-radioactive 'heavy' isotope, ^{15}N, is often used, but its assay requires that nitrogen in compounds is converted back to gas and the proportion of molecules containing ^{15}N measured by mass spectroscopy. This is less sensitive and more cumbersome, expensive and time-consuming than measuring radioisotopes. Also, techniques such as autoradiography of chromatograms and tissue sections cannot be used with ^{15}N.

Fortunately, a simple method of measuring biological nitrogen fixation is available, based on the unusually low substrate specificity of nitrogenase.

The enzyme catalyses the reduction of a variety of small molecules with triple bonds between carbon and/or nitrogen atoms. Amongst these is acetylene which nitrogenase reduces to ethylene, very small quantities of which can be easily assayed by gas chromatography. Acetylene reduction is the most widely used assay for nitrogen fixation, and has tenfold greater sensitivity than ^{15}N methods. However, care has to be exercised in quantitative interpretation of acetylene reduction data. The value used to convert acetylene reduction to nitrogen fixation may vary with factors such as the amount of hydrogen released. Furthermore, nitrogenase activity in some (but not all) legume species has been found to decrease when exposed to acetylene (Minchin *et al.*, 1983).

For long term studies, chemical assay of the increase in nitrogen content of the tissues can be informative, but like acetylene reduction, it gives no indication of the metabolic fate of fixed nitrogen.

Studies of the genetics of nitrogen fixation are developing rapidly, providing a wealth of information about nonsymbiotic bacteria, and increasingly about symbiotic systems (4.2.6).

4.2   Rhizobium nodules

4.2.1   The symbionts

Rhizobia are gram-negative motile rods, 0.5–0.9 μm wide and 1.2–3.0 μm long. They are defined as rhizobia solely by their ability to nodulate leguminous plants. The other genus in the family Rhizobiaceae is *Agrobacterium*, mainly pathogens which include the agent of crown gall disease of plants.

4.2.1.1   Classification of rhizobia

Not all rhizobia nodulate all legumes. It was originally observed that legumes nodulated by a particular rhizobium formed a group such that rhizobia isolated from any plant in the group could nodulate all other plants of that group. This formed the basis of classifying rhizobia according to their host range into 'cross-inoculation groups'. The bacteria constituting each group were given a specific name. Subsequently, as increasing numbers of rhizobial strains were isolated, examples accumulated of plants being infected by more than one rhizobium 'species', and of rhizobia infecting plants outside the host range of their 'species'. Some rhizobia with very broad host ranges were not given latin binomials and were simply referred to by names such as 'cowpea rhizobia'. There was therefore some confusion over the nomenclature of rhizobia.

Two quite separate groups of rhizobia can be distinguished on the basis of their cultural characteristics: 'fast-growers' and 'slow-growers' (Table 4.2). Some authors have considered the differences to be so distinct as to merit the groups being placed in the separate genera *Rhizobium* and *Bradyrhizobium*

Table 4.2 Classification of rhizobia (after Jordan (1984), in Bergey's Manual of Systematic Bacteriology, 9th Edition).

Genus	Popular name and cultural characteristics	Species and varieties	Examples of hosts
Rhizobium	'Fast-growing rhizobia'	R. leguminosarum var. viciae	Peas (Pisum)
		R. leguminosarum var. trifolii	Clovers (Trifolium)
	Cultural characteristics:	R. leguminosarum var. phaseoli	Beans (Phaseolus)
	Colonies usually grow to 2–4 mm diameter within 3–5 days after inoculation on to standard yeast-mannitol-mineral salts medium. Produce acid on standard medium	R. meliloti	Lucerne, alfalfa (Medicago)
		R. loti	Trefoil (Lotus)
		R. fredii	Some soyabeans (Glycine)
Bradyrhizobium	'Slow-growing rhizobia'	B. japonicum	Soyabeans (Glycine)
	Cultural characteristics:		
	Colonies do not exceed 1 mm diameter after 5–7 days on standard medium. Produce alkali		

n.b. Where there is doubt about the identity of a species, it is assigned to Rhizobium or Bradyrhizobium on the basis of its cultural characteristics, and then the host plant genus from which it was isolated is indicated in brackets.

(Graham, 1964; Vincent *et al.*, 1979). Although the two genera tend to have different host ranges (Table 4.3), there are a number of plants which can be nodulated by either, and even reports of both occurring within the same nodule (Trinick, 1982).

The 1984 edition of the standard text on bacterial classification, Bergey's Manual of Determinative Bacteriology, recognizes the separate genera of *Rhizobium* and *Bradyrhizobium* and proposes the classification shown in Table 4.2. Unfortunately, many authors do not yet follow this scheme. For example, the three varieties of *R. leguminosarum* are often still named as separate species, even though recent work shows that the difference in host range between them is due to only a small number of plasmid-borne genes (4.2.6), and that in other respects they are very similar, Likewise, *Bradyrhizobium japonicum* is still referred to as *Rhizobium japonicum* in most papers.

4.2.1.2 Nitrogen fixation by rhizobia in culture

Fast-growing rhizobia fix nitrogen only in the intact symbiosis; to date, they have not been induced to fix nitrogen in culture. Some slow-growing strains fix nitrogen in culture under microaerobic conditions (Table 4.1). They release nearly all the fixed nitrogen to the medium as ammonia, and therefore require combined nitrogen for growth. Rhizobia from *Sesbania* stem nodules are uniquely able to assimilate their fixed nitrogen and use it as the sole nitrogen source for growth in culture.

4.2.1.3 Free-living rhizobia in the soil away from the rhizosphere

Estimates of numbers of free-living rhizobia in the soil away from the rhizosphere have not been extensive and they have given conflicting results. Early reports (Nutman, 1963; Nutman and Ross, 1969) suggested that the soil population was substantially increased if appropriate host plants were present or had recently been grown in the soil. The population then declined to low levels in the continued absence of hosts. Using improved procedures but studying similar soils, Taylor and Beringer (1981) found that populations are relatively small away from the rhizosphere (in the range 10^2–10^4 rhizobia g^{-1} dry weight soil in fallow land that had not borne legumes for 20 years) but that the presence of a host did not always increase the density of rhizobia in the soil. They concluded that rhizobia are well adapted to life as free-living soil bacteria. However, rhizobia are not usually found in soils that have never borne legumes.

4.2.2 Plant hosts

Rhizobium nodules are almost entirely confined to members of the family Leguminoseae, but a strain of *Bradyrhizobium* has been reported in three species of *Parasponia* (= *Trema*) (Ulmaceae) (Trinick, 1973; Jordan, 1984),

Table 4.3 Comparisons between nodules of three major tribes of the sub-family Papilionoideae (partly based on Sprent, 1980).

Tribe and genera examined	Type of nodule	Type of rhizobia most often (but not invariably found)	Bacteroid morphology†	Transfer cells in nodules	Nitrogen compounds exported from nodules	Origin of tribe (and region where many species still occur)
Phaseoleae *Cajanus Calapogonium Glycine Macroptilium Phaseolus Psophocarpus Pueraria Vigna*	Determinate	Slow-growing	Swollen rods	−	Mostly ureides (allantoin and allantoic acid)	Tropical/sub-tropical
Vicieae *Lathyrus Lens Pisum Vicia*	Indeterminate	Fast-growing	Pleiomorphic	+	Mostly amides and amino acids (especially glutamine and asparagine)	Temperate
Trifolieae *Medicago Meliotus Ononis Trifolium Trigonella*	Indeterminate	Fast-growing	Pleiomorphic	+	Mostly amides and amino acids (especially glutamine and asparagine)	Temperate

This Table illustrates broad differences between genera of the three major tribes of the sub-family Papilionoideae which contain the majority of the economically important legumes. Although exceptions to these broad differences can occur (e.g. a few genera such as *Glycine* and *Phaseolus* can be infected by both fast and slow-growing rhizobia), they illustrate clear trends.

Notes. † 'Swollen rods' = no branching, and only some increase in size compared to bacteria; Pleiomorphic = bacteroids much swollen and often branched.

and there are unconfirmed reports of their occurrence in three genera of Zygophyllaceae.

The Leguminoseae, with about 600 genera and 18 000 species, are the third largest family of flowering plants. They have a great variety of habit, including trees, shrubs, herbs, water plants, climbers and xerophytes. They are particularly prominent in the tropics; the major dominant trees of the monsoon forests of the Far East include a large number of legumes.

There are three subfamilies. The Papilionoideae is the largest, with over two thirds of all species. Woody genera are more common in the tropics, and herbaceous in temperate regions. Nodules have been found in 95% of all the species so far examined. This subfamily contains virtually all the agriculturally important grain and pasture legumes. The proportion of species estimated to bear nodules in the other two subfamilies, both largely tropical, is less: 60–70% in the Mimosoideae and only 25–30% in the Caesalpinoideae.

Most information about the interactions between the partners of the legume symbiosis comes from the relatively few genera which are of agricultural importance.

4.2.3   Nodule structure

4.2.3.1   Nodule morphology

Legume nodules appear as globose or elongate swellings, varying from a few millimetres to a few centimetres in length. The symbionts occur within host cells in the central tissue of the nodule (Figs 4.3, 4.4).

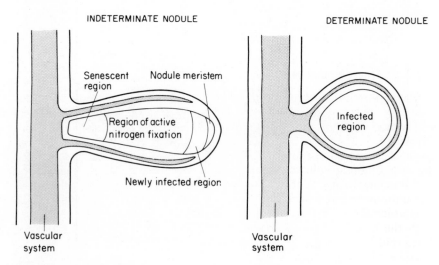

INDETERMINATE NODULE

DETERMINATE NODULE

Senescent region

Nodule meristem

Region of active nitrogen fixation

Infected region

Newly infected region

Vascular system

Vascular system

Fig. 4.3   Differences between indeterminate and determinate nodules (after Sprent, 1979, 1980).

The morphology of nodules is determined primarily by the host and not the symbiont. Two main types of nodule structure can be distinguished (Fig. 4.3). *Indeterminate* nodules are usually elongate and sometimes branched. The vascular system does not close over the apex, and the nodules have a meristem and are capable of a limited degree of continued growth. A sequence of developmental stages is apparent, with newly infected cells just behind the apex, then a region where the symbiosis is mature and the tissue is pink in colour (due to leghaemoglobin, see 4.2.4.3), and near the base is a senescing region which is greenish-brown due to the breakdown of the haemoglobin. Indeterminate nodules may persist from a few weeks to a season or longer.

Determinate nodules are usually spherical in shape. They lack a persistent meristem and the vascular system is closed over the apex of the nodule. In contrast to indeterminate nodules, each determinate nodule comprises a single developmental stage. The entire nodule passes through a sequence of stages, becoming first pink and later green or dark brown as the nodule senesces. Lenticels commonly occur on the surface of determinate but not indeterminate nodules. Determinate nodules do not usually persist for as long as indeterminate. There are a number of features of host and symbiont which are broadly correlated with the difference between determinate and indeterminate nodules, and these are summarized in Table 4.3.

The nodule morphology in a few legumes does not conform to this classification. In several species the nodule forms a collar around the root, and in *Sesbiana rostrata* and *Aeschynomene* species, the nodules are on the stem (with infection via the petioles).

Some nodules are 'ineffective' and never fix nitrogen. This may result from deficiencies in either host or symbiont, or from infection by rhizobia of a plant outside its host range. 'Effective' nodules are usually large and always pink in colour (due to the presence of leghaemoglobin, see 4.2.4.3). 'Ineffective' nodules are smaller and not pink.

4.2.3.2 Host-symbiont contact

In the mature, infected region of the nodule, virtually all the host cells contain large numbers of intracellular symbionts (Fig. 4.4b), enclosed either singly or in small groups, within membrane-bound vacuoles (Fig. 4.4c). The symbionts are termed *bacteroids* because they differ from bacteria outside the host cell in a number of ways. The bacteroids of fast-growing rhizobia are up to 40 times the volume of free-living rhizobial cells and may have one or two branches to give 'Y' or 'X' shapes. Bacteroids of slow-growing rhizobia are unbranched and increase in size to a lesser extent. The cell walls of bacteroids show increased invaginations, giving a greater area of exchange with the host, and their cell membranes also become highly permeable. Bacteroids of slow-growers sometimes lose their cell walls with age and become rounded protoplasts. All types of bacteroids contain substantial amounts of nitrogenase and may also show changes in DNA content and reduced numbers of ribosomes. Despite these changes, bacteroids are

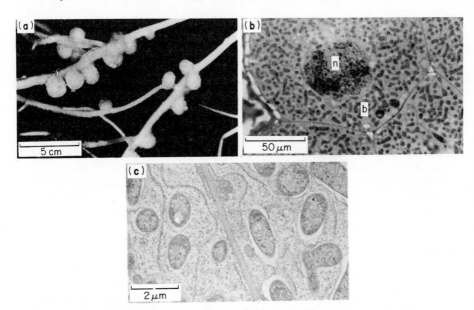

Fig. 4.4 (a) Pea root nodules containing *Rhizobium leguminosarum*. **(b)** Light micrograph of an infected plant cell from the nodule cortex, showing large numbers of *Rhizobium* bacteroids in the cytoplasm. n = nucleus, b = bacteroids. **(c)** Electron micrograph showing bacteroids enclosed by peribacteroid membranes. *Photographs* courtesy of N.J. Brewin.

capable of a limited degree of cell-division if they are placed *in vitro* in an osmotically protected medium.

4.2.4 Metabolic interactions between host and symbiont

4.2.4.1 Nitrogen fixation and release by symbionts

There is substantial indirect evidence that ammonia is the main product of nitrogen fixation released from bacteroids to the host cell. Isolated bacteroids release ammonia during nitrogen fixation (Bergerson, 1971), and cells of *Bradyrhizobium japonicum* in culture release 94% of the $^{15}N_2$ they fix into the medium (O'Gara and Shanmugam, 1976). Levels of the primary enzyme of ammonia assimilation, glutamine synthetase, are much lower in isolated bacteroids than in the host cells (Rawsthorne *et al.*, 1980); during development of the symbiosis, the amount of host cell glutamine synthetase rises in parallel with increases in nitrogenase activity and leghaemoglobin content. The mechanism of ammonia release has not been studied, but it is probably diffusion since isolated bacteroids are highly permeable. The amount of glutamine synthetase in host cells is in excess of that needed to assimilate the ammonia released, and this may help to promote diffusion out of the bacteroids.

4.2.4.2 The supply of carbon to the nodule and to the bacteroids

A high rate of nitrogen fixation in nodules depends on photosynthesis by the host (Rawsthorne *et al.*, 1980). When soyabean shoots are darkened or defoliated, nitrogenase activity in the nodules declines. In intact plants, rates of nitrogen fixation are higher in daylight than during the night. The amount of nitrogen fixed by excised cowpea roots is positively correlated with the amount of sucrose supplied to them. Various experiments have shown that ^{14}C fixed by photosynthesis in the leaves is translocated to nodules where it is rapidly metabolized (e.g., Gordon *et al.*, 1985). If the carbon dioxide concentration of the atmosphere is increased, the rates of both photosynthesis and nitrogen fixation may show dramatic increases (Fig. 4.5).

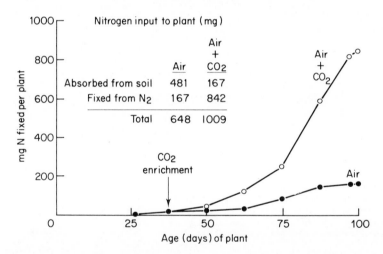

Fig. 4.5 Effect on nitrogen fixation by soyabeans of enriching air with CO_2 (800–1200 p.p.m.). Note that uptake of combined nitrogen from the soil is reduced as fixation is increased in plants growing in enriched air.

Photosynthate reaching the nodules has two main functions, firstly to supply energy and reducing power, and secondly to provide carbon skeletons for the assimilation of ammonia into nitrogen compounds. Nodules on young pea plants consumed 32% of the net carbon fixed in photosynthesis over a 9 day period (Fig. 4.6). In general, estimates for a variety of legumes show that 13–28% of total photosynthate is consumed by the nodules during the period of vegetative growth of the host (Minchin *et al.*, 1981). Approximately half of the carbon supplied to nodules is returned to the shoot

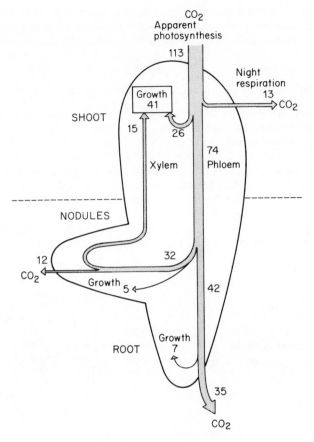

Fig. 4.6   Flow sheet for carbon in effectively nodulated plants of *Pisum sativum* (cv. 'Meteor'), relying solely on the atmosphere for their nitrogen. The study period covered is 21–30 days after sowing, a time when the roots and nodules are still growing actively. Data are expressed on the basis of a net gain by the shoot of 100 units of carbon from the atmosphere (from Minchin and Pate, 1973).

in the form of organic nitrogen compounds, about 40% is consumed in nodule respiration, and the remainder is used in nodule maintenance and growth.

The energy requirements of nitrogen fixation are substantial. Estimates by various investigators show that the fixation of 1 g nitrogen requires the respiration of 5–7 g carbon (Minchin *et al.*, 1981). If the associated costs of ammonia assimilation are included, then the value rises to about 11–13 g carbon per g nitrogen (Witty *et al.*, 1983; Ryle *et al.*, 1984). Nodulated clover plants using N_2 as sole nitrogen source fixed 810 mg CO_2 for the synthesis of 1 g dry weight of host tissue, while non-nodulated plants using nitrate fixed only 510 mg (Silsbury, 1977).

Although there are many experimental observations on the interaction of nodules with the rest of the plant, far less is known about the interaction of bacteroids with host cells. The identity of the carbon compounds supplied to the bacteroids is not known. Photosynthate is usually translocated to the nodule as sucrose, but isolated bacteroids cannot metabolize this sugar; instead, they utilize organic acids such as succinate and malate. Bacteroids contain substantial amounts of poly-β-hydroxybutyric acid (sometimes up to 50% of their dry weight) but its function is not known; it may provide a source of energy and carbon skeletons to allow nitrogen fixation to proceed in darkness, albeit at a reduced rate (Rawsthorne *et al.*, 1980). Glycogen is another storage compound in bacteroids, but the relationship of its synthesis and breakdown to changes in the supply of carbon from the host cell has not been elucidated. Nodules are often very active in dark fixation of carbon dioxide, and levels of enzymes such as PEP carboxylase are much higher than in the rest of the root system. This could be another supplementary source of organic acids for bacteroids to carry out nitrogen fixation in the dark, but this possibility has not been fully investigated.

4.2.4.3   Leghaemoglobin and the effect of oxygen on nodules

Leghaemoglobin is invariably present in effective nodules where it is confined to the bacteroid-containing cells. It is present in sufficient quantities for nodules to appear pink, and it comprises 8–12% of the soluble protein in lupin and up to 20% in soyabean nodules. Ineffective nodules are white,

Table 4.4   Measurements of bacteroid-containing host cells from 30-day old soyabean nodules (after Bergerson, 1980).

	Measurement
Host cell volume	12×10^{-8} cm^3
Envelopes/cell	9.5×10^3
Envelope diameter	2.9×10^{-4} cm
Bacteroids/envelope	3.0
Percentage of host cell cytoplasmic volume* occupied by:	
Cytoplasm	15–17
Bacteroids	46
Envelopes + bacteroids	83–85
Envelope space	37–39
Leghaemoglobin concentration, host cell volume* basis	0.70 mM

* This volume includes envelopes and contents, ground cytoplasm, mitochondria and amyloplasts, but excludes the host nucleus, which clearly contains no leghaemoglobin.

suggesting leghaemoglobin is absent or present in only very small amounts. The synthesis of leghaemoglobin involves both partners of the symbiosis. The apoprotein is coded by the host genome, and haem synthesis by the symbiont genome.

Leghaemoglobin is essential to nitrogen fixation in the nodule presumably because, analogous to the role of haemoglobin in mammalian blood, it functions to bind and carry oxygen. The rate of flux of oxygen bound to leghaemoglobin through a liquid is over 10 000 times greater than that of free dissolved oxygen. Direct measurements with microelectrodes confirm that the concentration of free oxygen within nodule tissue is very low. Bacteroids occur in large numbers in host cells (Table 4.4), and they have a high demand for oxygen for respiration. The terminal oxidases of bacteroids have a high affinity for oxygen, and they have high rates of oxygen consumption at low concentrations of free oxygen (Bergerson, 1980). Initial attempts to establish the precise intracellular location of leghaemoglobin gave conflicting results, but it is now established that leghaemoglobin is in the host cytoplasm and not within the vacuoles containing the bacteroids (Bergerson, 1980; Robertson *et al.*, 1984).

A rapid increase in external oxygen concentration results in damage to nitrogenase in the nodules of some, but not all, legumes (Witty *et al.*, 1984; Minchin *et al.*, 1985). Protection is not mediated by leghaemoglobin but probably through a rapid increase in the diffusion resistance of the nodule tissues to oxygen (Sheehy *et al.*, 1985).

4.2.4.4   Uptake hydrogenase and its role in reducing the effects of hydrogen loss

Although hydrogen evolution always occurs during the action of nitrogenase (4.1.1. and Fig. 4.2), some nonsymbiotic nitrogen-fixing bacteria, such as *Azotobacter*, do not release hydrogen because they possess an enzyme, uptake hydrogenase, which oxidizes hydrogen to water with the concomitant production of ATP (Fig. 4.7). These organisms thereby recover some of the

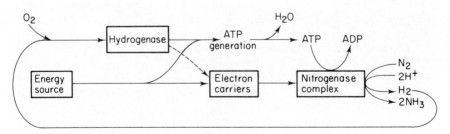

Fig. 4.7 A schematic representation of nitrogen-hydrogenase relationships in H_2-uptake positive (Hup$^+$) bacteroids from legume nodules. It has been demonstrated that H_2 oxidation will protect bacteroid nitrogenase from O_2 damage and support both ATP synthesis and nitrogenase activity (Evans *et al.*, 1980).

energy lost in hydrogen evolution, and the utilization of oxygen affords additional protection to nitrogenase.

The bacteroids of many rhizobial strains lack an uptake hydrogenase, and up to a quarter of the energy flux through nitrogenase is consequently dissipated in hydrogen evolution (Evans *et al.*, 1980). However, active uptake hydrogenase has now been identified in some strains of both *Bradyrhizobium* and *Rhizobium* and there is evidence that legume yields may be increased when inoculated with such rhizobia.

4.2.4.5 Ammonia assimilation by the host

There are two principal pathways of ammonia assimilation in plants: (a) glutamic dehydrogenase (GDH), which catalyses the reaction:

$$\text{2-oxoglutaric acid} + \text{NH}_4 + \text{NAD(P)H} \rightarrow \text{glutamic acid} + \text{NAD(P)} + \text{H}_2\text{O}$$

and (b), a two step process involving the enzymes glutamine synthetase (GS) and glutamate synthase (GOGAT), and known as the GS/GOGAT pathway,

(i) glutamate + NH_4 + ATP $\rightarrow$ glutamine + ADP + Pi + H (GS)
(ii) glutamine + 2-oxoglutarate + NAD(P) + H $\rightarrow$ 2 glutamate + NAD(P)H (GOGAT).

Both systems are widely distributed in plants, but the GS/GOGAT pathway is the principal pathway in host cells of nodules. Although the GS/GOGAT pathway consumes 1 molecule of ATP per molecule of ammonia assimilated, it has the advantage that ammonia can be assimilated from low concentrations. The Michaelis constant for GS is 20 μM, while that for GDH is 14 mM in plants. As a result, nitrogenase can operate without significant inhibition by its end product, and damage to plant cells from ammonia toxicity is avoided.

Although glutamine is rapidly transported in plant vascular systems, it is frequently converted before export from the nodule to other compounds: asparagine is particularly common in temperate legumes with indeterminate nodules; and the ureides allantoin and allantoic acid in tropical legumes with determinate nodules (Table 4.3). Such conversions may economize in the use of carbon skeletons since the ratio of N:C in glutamine is 2:5, in asparagine 2:4, and in ureides 4:4. Ureides are much less soluble in water than asparagine (which may leave nodules at near saturating concentrations) so that large-scale export of ureides requires a substantial flux of water through the nodule; determinate nodules offer less resistance to water flow than is offered by indeterminate nodules (Sprent, 1980).

4.2.4.6 Host regulation of nodulation

The host appears to regulate the degree to which its roots are nodulated. If previously formed nodules are excised, nodulation of the rest of the root system is increased, suggesting that the presence of existing nodules inhibits formation of additional nodules. In *Vicia*, the rate of infection thread formation (see 4.2.5.1) decreases abruptly at the time when the first nodules develop to visible size. Given the high energy costs of nitrogen fixation, it might be important to the competitive ability of the host to limit the number of nodules to no more than is needed for its nitrogen nutrition.

4.2.4.7   Effect of environmental factors on nodulation

The degree of nodulation is affected by a variety of environmental factors, but there are four which are of particular importance: pH, nitrogen status of the soil, availability of phosphate, and moisture levels.

Nodulation is inhibited in acid soils, and does not occur at all below about pH 4; .there are therefore significant areas of vegetation in which this symbiosis is absent, even though some host plants can still grow. In pure culture, the lowest pH at which rhizobia will grow varies from pH 4 to 6; slow growing rhizobia are somewhat more tolerant of acid conditions than fast-growing. Rhizobia also do not grow above about pH 9–10, but such values are rarely encountered in natural soils.

When appreciable quantities of nitrogen fertilizer are added to leguminous crops, nodulation is inhibited and the host becomes much less susceptible to infection.

Phosphate deficiency also severely limits nodulation – nodules are rich in phosphate, and there is a high ATP requirement for nitrogen fixation. On phosphate-poor soils, nodulation of legumes is markedly stimulated by mycorrhizal infection (7.8), which probably improves the phosphate nutrition of the host.

Reduced water supply limits symbiotic nitrogen fixation in many regions of the world, and this is manifested not only by reduced nodule function but also by inhibition of nodule formation or even loss of existing nodules. At the other extreme, many legumes fail to develop nodules in waterlogged soil, possibly because of poor aeration.

4.2.4.8   Does symbiotic nitrogen fixation meet the needs of the host plant?

There is nearly always some combined nitrogen available in the soil, so that fixation is rarely the sole source for the host plant in nature. The relative importance of atmospheric and combined nitrogen has been explored for various crop plants. When plants are grown without combined nitrogen, it may not be until about 4 weeks after germination before they begin to receive substantial supplies from symbiotic fixation. This may explain why addition of small amounts of combined nitrogen frequently stimulates nodulation in seedlings, presumably tiding the plant over the initial period of nitrogen shortage. As the season progresses, plants often show increasing dependence on fixation, and in soyabean, there is a heavy reliance on fixation during seed development (perhaps reflecting the unusually high protein content of legume seeds).

4.2.4.9　The effect of symbiosis on the population of free-living rhizobia in the immediate rhizosphere

The soil population of free-living rhizobia away from the rhizosphere is low (4.2.1.3) but it increases in the vicinity of host roots (4.2.5.1). It is not clear why this occurs. The extent to which viable bacteria are released to the soil when nodules decay has not been rigorously studied. Although bacteroids have some capability for division, many are lysed in the senescent regions of the nodule. Viable bacteria remain within the infection thread, but they may not number more than about 10^6–10^7 per nodule (Beringer *et al.*, 1979). Further, nodules persist for weeks or even a whole season before senescing, so they decay at far too slow a rate to account for the observed build up of rhizobia near the roots. The most likely hypothesis is that after infection of the roots, rhizosphere conditions become particularly suitable for the growth of free-living rhizobia.

4.2.5　Establishment of the symbiosis

4.2.5.1　Initiation and development of a nodule

Amongst temperate legumes, nodulation has been studied in greatest detail in those of agricultural importance such as clover. Initially, the soil population of rhizobia increases rapidly when roots of potential hosts enter their vicinity. Rhizobia probably multiply in response to some of the variety of compounds released by actively growing plant roots, known collectively as 'root exudate'. This might contain specific attractants for rhizobia, but it has not yet been proven. Rhizobia are normally motile and they can migrate through the soil at rates up to 2 cm day^{-1}. In an experiment with alfalfa (lucerne), when motile and non-motile strains were mixed together (even in a ratio of 1:1000), nodulation was almost always achieved by the motile strain (Ames and Bergman, 1981). This may not necessarily have been due to chemotaxis, since motility in itself greatly increases the chance of encountering a root.

Infection begins with the adhesion of rhizobia to the surface of a root hair (Fig. 4.8). A very characteristic phenomenon is that the infected root hair then curls (Fig. 4.9a), often like a shepherd's crook. The cause of curling is not known. In soyabeans, the root hair cells become infected before the root hair is produced, but when the root hair subsequently emerges, it curls over the site of infection.

Next, an *infection thread* is formed. This is a narrow tubular ingrowth whose walls are formed by the host and which carries rhizobia from the root hair surface into the cortex; cell membrane encloses the wall of the thread. The mechanism by which the infection thread is formed and grows inwards

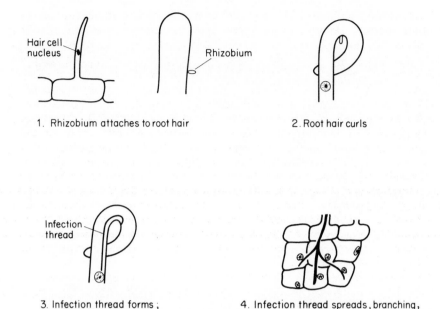

1. Rhizobium attaches to root hair

2. Root hair curls

3. Infection thread forms ;
   appears to be directed by
   hair nucleus

4. Infection thread spreads, branching,
   through cortex, passing close to
   host cell nuclei

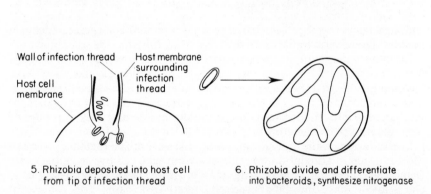

5. Rhizobia deposited into host cell
   from tip of infection thread

6. Rhizobia divide and differentiate
   into bacteroids, synthesize nitrogenase

Fig. 4.8   Stages in the infection of host by rhizobia in clover (after Sprent, 1979).

is a matter of controversy. Some authors believe that the thread is formed by an invagination of the root hair wall, which then continuously grows to extend the thread inwards. Others believe that rhizobia initially penetrate through the root hair wall by enzymic action, and the thread is then initiated by host synthesis of wall material. As the thread grows inwards, it often branches extensively. Initially its growth appears as if being directed by the root hair cell nucleus. The nucleus is often found near the site of infection, and it remains close to the tip as it moves towards the base of the cell. If the nucleus moves away from the thread, growth of the thread often stops. As the thread enters the cortex, it may pass through existing cells, and again it appears to associate closely with host cell nuclei. As the thread grows inwards, bacterial cell division continues. The bacteria are embedded in a mucopolysaccharide matrix and they become aligned along the thread, often as a single row. Not all threads develop successfully and many frequently abort.

Subsequently, indeterminate and determinate nodules develop somewhat differently. In indeterminate nodules, mitotic activity is initiated in a small group of cells directly ahead of the thread, after the thread has penentrated 3–6 cell layers of the cortex. A meristematic area is thus formed and it is entered by the thread. Penetrated cells and those adjacent to them cease to divide and have enlarged nuclei. Further mitotic activity is initiated in cortical cells, and a meristem which is not infected forms towards the apex of the nodule. The infection thread eventually begins to extend backwards towards the epidermis, continually branching and invading more cells. Vascular strands develop and become connected to those of the young root. In the nodule pericycle and xylem are 'transfer cells' (cells in which the inner surface of the wall is ridged with outgrowths, so increasing the surface area of the cell membrane which lines it; such cells occur in regions where there are high rates of solute transfer).

In determinate nodules, mitotic activity begins in all cell layers of the cortex while the infection thread is still in the root hair cell or penetrating its basal wall. A spherical mass of cells is produced, into which the thread enters and penetrates cells, eventually developing into the typically spherical nodules. No transfer cells are found.

In both types of nodule, bacteria are released into host cells in the same way. The thread penetrates into the host cell, and the thread wall disintegrates at the tip and sides. The host membrane which had enclosed the thread remains and buds off vesicles containing rhizobia in their mucopolysaccharide matrix (Fig. 4.9c). The peribacteroid membrane is thus derived from the host plant membrane.

In the few tropical legumes which have been investigated, no infection threads occur and the initiation of nodules follows a rather different course. Detailed studies have been carried out with *Arachis hypogaea* (groundnut), and also the tropical forage legume *Stylosanthes* (Chandler *et al.*, 1982). Root hairs develop only where lateral roots emerge. In the initial infection in *Arachis*, bacteria enter the root in the space between the root hair cell and the adjoining epidermal and cortical cells. Host cells in the infected area separate from each other at the middle lamella, and strands of rhizobia in a mucopolysaccharide matrix form in the resulting intercellular spaces. Adjacent host cells have increased numbers of mitochondria and amounts of endoplasmic reticulum, suggesting increased metabolic activity. The nodules develop from infected cortical cells of the lateral root which emerges near the root hairs. Invasion of cells by rhizobia is preceded by structural changes in the host cell wall, which then forms protrusions inwards. Its cellulose structure appears to breakdown in the region of invasion, and membrane-bound rhizobia are released into the cytoplasm. These rhizobia then multiply rapidly, and are distributed by repeated division of infected host cells.

The early stages of infection in *Stylosanthes* (Chandler *et al.*, 1982) differ from *Arachis* mainly in that infected cells collapse and rhizobia penetrate the

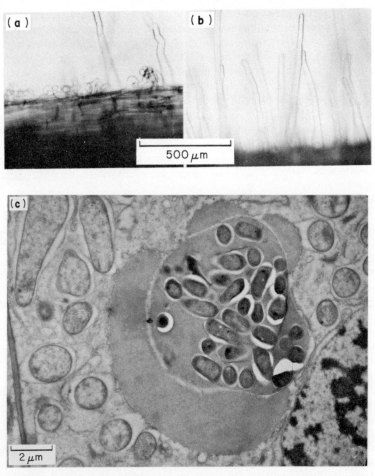

Fig. 4.9   Infection of roots by rhizobia. **(a)** Roots of *Vicia sativa* grown in the presence of infective rhizobia showing root hair curling. *Photograph* J.A. Downie **(b)** Similar roots in the presence of a non-infective strain show no curling. *Photograph* J.A. Downie **(c)** Electron micrograph illustrating two stages in the infection of host cells by rhizobia. In the centre of the micrograph rhizobia are embedded in matrix material derived from the infection thread. Subsequently, individual bacteria are engulfed by endocytosis, and then differentiate into the enlarged nitrogen-fixing bacteroids seen in the plant cytoplasm around the borders of the micrograph. *Photograph* E.A. Wood.

cortex by the progressive collapse of infected cells. This host response resembles the defence mechanism of some plants to invasion by pathogenic organisms. However, uninfected host cells expand in a way which propels infected cells deeper into the cortex.

In legumes generally, the mode of infection and the type of nodule which develops is under the control of the host plant and not the rhizobium. The same rhizobium strain will infect by an infection thread in soyabean, and without a thread in some tropical legumes. Fast-growing and slow-growing rhizobia form the same type of nodule on the same host, while the same rhizobium strain forms determinate nodules on one host, but indeterminate on another.

4.2.5.2 The role of lectins and their contribution to determining specificity

The preceding sections have shown that the formation of an effective nodule involves a series of stages: attachment of rhizobia to a root hair, curling of the hair, initiation of an infection thread, growth of the infection thread, deposition of membrane-enclosed bacteria into host cells, transformation of bacteria into bacteroids, synthesis of leghaemoglobin, and synthesis of nitrogenase. Failure to form an effective nodule can occur at any of these stages. In total, they constitute a sequence of recognition events, none of which is the sole determinant of specificity (Dazzo and Truchet, 1984).

Nevertheless, considerable attention has been paid to the role of lectins in determining specificity of the initial stage of adhesion of rhizobia to root hairs. Lectins are proteins or glycoproteins which bind with high specificity to sugars or sugar residues in polysaccharides, glycoproteins or glycolipids. There are four main reasons for the interest in lectins in this symbiosis: (i) initial adhesion is the easiest stage to study experimentally; (ii) in some (but not all) legume/rhizobium associations, a high degree of specificity is expressed at this stage; and (iii) lectins are of central importance in some kinds of host/pathogen interactions and in cell agglutination phenomena (hence they are sometimes called phytohaemagglutinins).

An experiment which originally drew widespread attention to the possible importance of lectins in attachment of rhizobia to root hairs was that of Bohlool and Schmidt (1974). They showed that a lectin isolated from soyabean seeds bound to 22 of 25 rhizobium strains which could nodulate soyabean, but not to any of 23 other strains which did not nodulate. Some subsequent experiments with various legume/rhizobium combinations gave similar results (including demonstrations that the specific sugar which binds to a lectin could prevent adhesion of rhizobia to root hairs). However, other experiments gave a less clear correlation between lectin binding and specificity of adhesion. For example, Dazzo and Hubbel (1975) found that concanavalin A bound to all 19 rhizobium strains they tested, only two of which could nodulate the legume from which this lectin was isolated (jackbean). Other investigators showed that some soyabean lines which lack detectable lectin could nevertheless nodulate satisfactorily. More recent experiments show that the lectin-binding properties of rhizobia vary with culture age and conditions, and this may partly explain some of the conflicting results which have been obtained. No experimental studies have examined the development of the symbiosis beyond the attachment state, so there is no direct correlation of lectin-binding with formation of an ultimately effective nodule. Furthermore, nearly all experiments use lectins isolated from seeds, and only rarely have there been direct demonstrations of the occurrence of lectins at the site of infection. Most experiments have been concerned with temperate legumes, and there are few studies of associations where specificity between host and symbiont is low (including, for example, reported cases of two rhizobium 'species' existing in the same nodule). Thus, despite much investigation, the general hypothesis relating lectin-binding to specificity in legumes is still a matter for debate (Etzler, 1985).

However, recent experiments indicate that in a few associations, lectin-mediated attachment of the bacterium to the root hair is an important stage in the infection process. In particular, the experiments of Dazzo and his coworkers on the *Trifolium* (clover)/*Rhizobium trifolii* (= *R. leguminosarum* var. *trifolii*) association can be described (Dazzo and Truchet, 1984). Using a variety of techniques including immunofluorescence, a lectin, trifoliin A, was conclusively shown to occur on the surface of clover root hairs, especially at the tips which are the common sites of infection. Trifoliin A binds specifically to *R. leguminosarum* var. *trifolii* and not *R. meliloti*. It also binds specifically to the sugar 2-deoxyglucose (and not, for example, to N-acetylglucosamine which specifically binds to the soyabean lectin). 2-deoxyglucose inhibits binding of var. *trifolii* to the root hairs, and it also displaces trifoliin A from the root hair surface so that trifoliin A is washed off. The lectin can be found normally in root extracts. Trifoliin A has multiple binding sites, and the theory has been advanced that there are receptor sites for the lectin on the surfaces of both root hair and bacterium, and that trifoliin A can be released from the root hair and act as a bridging molecule between host and symbiont. Further experiments show that the roots also release enzymes which act on the lectin receptors of the bacterial capsule so that they only bind trifoliin at one pole, and the bacteria then adhere end-on to the root hair surface. The initial adhesion is between fibrils from the capsule and globular aggregates on the surface of the root hair wall. After this initial anchorage, further fibrillar material of unknown origin and composition is formed between bacterium and root hair surface as if to make the anchorage firmer. When nodulation is progressively inhibited by incubating roots in increasing concentrations of nitrate, there is a striking correlation between reduction in bacterial adhesion to roots and reduction in the amount of trifoliin A on root hair surfaces (Fig. 4.10). The genetic determinants of trifoliin A binding can be transferred to the nonsymbiotic bacterium *Azotobacter vinelandii*, and such transformed bacteria can bind (but not infect) root hairs. However, it is also found that some non-nodulating strains of rhizobia will bind to clover root hairs, but to a much smaller extent than var. *trifolii*.

4.2.6 Genetics of nitrogen fixation and of the symbiosis (Postgate, 1982; Long, 1984; Evans *et al.*, 1985)

The genetics of nitrogen fixation in nonsymbiotic bacteria, especially *Klebsiella*, has been studied intensively. The array of techniques available to molecular biologists, including gene transfer and complementation, has shown that nitrogenase is specified by a linked cluster of 17 genes, collectively known as the *nif* genes, arranged in 7 subclusters (operons) which are transcribed separately; each operon includes both structural and regulatory genes. The *nif* genes are expressed after transfer to *Escherichia coli* and other bacteria which did not previously fix nitrogen. When transferred to *Agrobacterium*, no nitrogenase activity is detectable, but this is not due to impairment of the *nif* genes because they functioned again when transferred out of *Agrobacterium* and into *E. coli*. Regulator genes act in response to accumulation of ammonia, switching off the nitrogenase genes.

The organisation of the structural *nif* genes in rhizobium shows striking similarities to *Klebsiella*, and some individual genes cloned from *Klebsiella* have been used in the mapping of the rhizobium genome. However, there may be some differences in regulatory genes since ammonia and other fixed nitrogen products repress nitrogenase synthesis in *Klebsiella* but not in rhizobium.

It is difficult to study the genetics of nitrogen fixation in rhizobia for three main reasons: (a) fast-growing rhizobia do not exhibit nitrogenase activity in culture, i.e. *nif* is only expressed when the bacteria are in symbiosis; (b) although slow-growing rhizobia fix nitrogen in culture, it is under microaerobic and other conditions which are too stringent for convenient handling in the kinds of genetic experiments needed; and (c) manifestation of nitrogen fixation in symbiosis depends not only on symbiont but also on host plant genes. Despite these difficulties, more is known of the genetics of the legume/rhizobium association than any other symbiosis. In addition to the *nif* genes, there are about 18–20 further 'nodulation' (*nod*) genes in rhizobium associated with the development of an effective nodule. They have not all been identified, but are known to include a few genes which specify host range. For example, the ability of some *R. leguminosarum* strains to nodulate a wider range of hosts than others is due to a single gene. Three genes are known to be concerned with root hair curling, and these are regulated by a fourth which interacts with compounds in the root exudate. Some other genes are involved in leghaemoglobin synthesis.

In most and possibly all *Rhizobium* species, the genes concerned with symbiotic interactions are carried on a large plasmid. They include both the *nif* and *nod* genes and also uptake hydrogenase genes where these occur. The analogy with the tumour-inducing plasmids of *Agrobacterium* has attracted a number of investigators. Some homologous regions in the plasmids of these two bacteria have been discovered and they may be derived from a common ancestor (Prakash and Schilperoort, 1982). A key difference from *Agrobacterium* is that plasmid DNA of *Rhizobium* has never been found incorporated into host DNA.

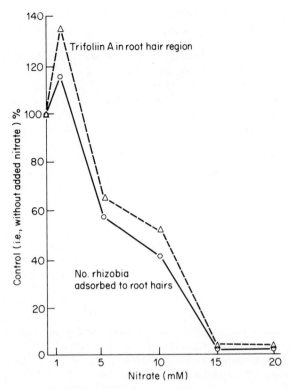

Fig. 4.10   The effect of nitrate on adsorption of *R. leguminosarum* var *trifolii* 0403 to root hairs (solid line) and on immunologically detectable trifoliin A (dotted line) in the root hair region of clover seedlings (Dazzo and Brill 1978).

Plasmids from the different varieties of *Rhizobium leguminosarum* have been transferred into a non-nodulating strain (Johnston *et al.*, 1978). There is little overall genetic difference between the varieties apart from the genes specifying host range.

Less is known of the host genes. About 18–20 polypeptides occur in nodules which are not found in either bacteroids, cultured rhizobia or uninfected roots (Legocki and Verma, 1980). It has been suggested that they are the products of host genes involved in nodulation, and they presumably include those involved in leghaemoglobin synthesis.

Thus, about 30–40 symbiont genes and perhaps at least 20 or so host genes are involved in nodulation. Many are inactive in the free-living partners, but are switched on during the establishment of the symbiosis; some others such as xanthine oxidase are present in the symbiont-free host but increase in quantity in the nodule. The development of an effective nodule appears to depend upon the coordinated sequential expression of sets of genes in each partner.

4.3 Actinorhizas

Actinorhizas is the term recently given to nodules housing symbionts of the actinomycete genus *Frankia*. They occur on the roots of a variety of woody angiosperms, all non-leguminous. Rates of nitrogen fixation in the field are broadly comparable to the middle range of those recorded for legumes bearing rhizobium nodules.

4.3.1 *Frankia* symbionts

Frankia symbionts were first unequivocally isolated into culture in 1978 (Callaham *et al.*, 1978), and there have been some hundreds of isolates subsequently. Much less is known about *Frankia* than rhizobia. In culture, *Frankia* is slow-growing, filamentous and septate; it produces sporangium-like structures in which spores are formed. Early indications suggested *Frankia* could be classified into cross-inoculation groups like rhizobia, but this soon proved unsatisfactory, and there is still no generally accepted classification. Serological criteria suggest that there may be two main groups of isolates (Wheeler, 1984).

All isolates tested fix nitrogen in culture, and are unlike rhizobia in achieving optimum fixation rates at oxygen concentrations close to atmospheric. Many, but not all, have uptake hydrogenase.

There is very little information about free-living *Frankia* symbionts in the soil (Akkermans and van Dijk, 1981). They undoubtedly occur, since plants become nodulated in soils which have not previously borne hosts for a number of years. However, as with rhizobia, nodulation will not occur if soils have never previously borne hosts. There is only fragmentary evidence as to the length of time for which free-living populations can persist, and this has to be interpreted with care since the extent to which *Frankia* can be transported in wind-blown soil particles is not known. Nodulation of *Ceanothus velutinus* occurred in soils which had not borne this plant for 100 years, but there was a sharp decline after a further 50 years.

4.3.2 Host plants

Actinorhizas have been reported from over 140 species of host plants, distributed amongst 17 genera and eight families (Table 4.5). Although they are less numerous than nodule-bearing legumes, some are nevertheless of ecological importance. Unlike legumes, they are prominent in certain pioneer habitats, and some can grow on acid soils. *Casuarina* is one of the most important tree genera of the semi-arid areas of the world. For example, it colonizes the very infertile coral sand of a large number of coral islands in the tropics. *C. equisetifolia* was important in the recolonization of Krakatoa after the island was virtually sterilized by the volcanic explosion of 1883. Shrubs such as *Hippophae rhamnoides* occur widely on sand dunes in W.

Table 4.5   Plants known to bear actinorhizas (Akkermans and van Dijk, 1981).

Order	Family	Genus (and number of species with actinorhizal nodules)
Casuarinales	Casuarinaceae	*Casuarina* (18)
Coriariales	Coriariaceae	*Coriaria* (13)
Fagales	Betulaceae	*Alnus* (33)
Cucurbitales	Datiscaceae	*Datisca* (2)
Myricales	Myricaceae	*Myrica* (20) *Comptonia* (1)
Rosales	Rosaceae	*Rubus* (1) *Dryas* (3) *Purshia* (2) *Cercocarpus* (3)
Rhamnales	Eleagnaceae	*Eleagnus* (14) *Hippophae* (1) *Shepherdia* (2)
	Rhamnaceae	*Ceanothus* (31) *Trevoa* (1) *Discaria* (5) *Colletia* (3)

Europe and make significant inputs to the nitrogen content of the soil; *Myrica pennsylvanica* has a similar habitat in the USA. Actinorhizal plants were probably of particular importance in the recolonization of land surfaces of Europe after the last ice-age. The pollen record shows that genera such as *Alnus, Dryas, Myrica* and *Hippophae* were widely distributed in this period.

4.3.3   The structure of actinorhizas

Actinorhizas are perennial coralloid structures, rather larger than legume nodules, sometimes being several centimetres across and up to 0.5 kg fresh weight. They are essentially infected lateral roots which branch profusely but with very restricted apical growth. Unlike legume nodules, infected tissue is external to the vascular tissue (Fig. 4.11). There are air-spaces in the nodule which may amount to 3–10% of total volume. Actinorhizas often persist for 3–4 years, and a maximum age of 8 years has been recorded in *Alnus*.

A progressive sequence of developmental stages can be seen in a typical actinorhiza (Fig. 4.11). The apical meristem is uninfected. Non-dividing cells basal to the meristem are entered by symbiont filaments which first curl around the host nucleus. Host cells then become filled with tight bundles of branching filaments, and in the next stage, the tips of the filaments swell to form spherical or club-shaped vesicles; because the filaments are much branched, they appear as clusters of vesicles. In *Alnus*, there is one cluster occupying most of the volume of each cell. Vesicles are the site of nitrogen

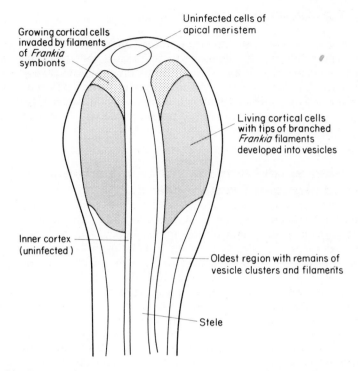

Growing cortical cells invaded by filaments of *Frankia* symbionts

Uninfected cells of apical meristem

Living cortical cells with tips of branched *Frankia* filaments developed into vesicles

Inner cortex (uninfected)

Oldest region with remains of vesicle clusters and filaments

Stele

Fig. 4.11 Diagram of a lobe of an actinorhiza of *Alnus* (after van Dijk and Merkus, 1976).

fixation. In the next stage, vesicle clusters appear to disintegrate in the senescent region of the nodule.

Although all *Frankia* strains form spores in culture, only some form spores in symbiosis. The spores appear as highly packed, thick-walled cells of irregular shape, 0.5–1.0 μm in diameter, and, in symbiosis, they are abundant in the regions where vesicles are formed and where they are disintegrating.

4.3.4 Metabolic interactions between host and symbiont

Much less is known about host/symbiont interactions in actinorhizas than in rhizobium nodules. Vesicle clusters isolated from actinorhizal homogenates fix nitrogen and they have two particular similarities to rhizobium bacteroids: GS and GDH levels (4.2.4.5) are very low, implying that ammonia is probably released to the host; and malate and fumarate but not glucose can sustain nitrogenase activity. Nodulation and nitrogenase activity is inhibited by combined nitrogen. There are some reports of the presence of haemoglobin. The main transport compound away from the nodules is citrulline.

4.3.5　Establishment of the symbiosis

The initial stages of infection have been studied mainly in *Alnus*. As in many legumes, the symbiont first makes contact with a root hair, and this is followed by curling of the hair. Filaments of the symbiont then grow and develop within the root hair cell. The cortical cells beneath it then divide and become infected by symbiont filaments. A lateral root is induced, close to the site of infection, and as it grows out, it becomes infected. Nothing is known of recognition mechanisms.

4.4　Other associations between plant roots and nitrogen-fixing bacteria

Nitrogen-fixing bacteria may occur in the rhizosphere, in varying degrees of intimacy with the root system. For example, *Azotobacter paspali* is found only in association with the roots of the tropical grass *Paspalum notatum*. The bacteria may be firmly attached to the root surface by mucigel, or penetrate between the cells of the outer cortical layers of the root. Nitrogen fixation occurs, but at lower rates than for legume nodules. Nitrogen-fixing species of *Azospirillum* also associate with the roots of a number of tropical grasses, including maize, and may invade the surface of the root.

　In aquatic habitats, nitrogen-fixing bacteria occur in the rhizosphere of marine angiosperms such as *Zostera* and *Thalassia* and freshwater species such as *Potamogeton*.

5

Cyanobacteria (including prochlorophytes) in symbiosis

5.1 Introduction

The cyanobacteria represent a large, ancient and diverse group of prokaryotes characterized by the possession of chlorophyll a and oxygen-evolving photosynthesis. They have a characteristic colour, which accounts for their earlier name, 'blue-green algae'. Some are unicellular but many are simple or branched filaments. Many cyanobacteria can combine oxygenic photosynthesis with the capacity for nitrogen fixation, an oxygen-intolerant reaction (4.1.1). In filamentous forms, the two processes are separated spatially: photosynthesis in vegetative cells and nitrogen fixation in specialized cells called heterocysts (Fig. 5.1). Heterocysts also contain uptake hydrogenase (see 4.2.4.4).

Recently, another group of prokaryotes with chlorophyll a and oxygenic photosynthesis has been recognized, the prochlorophytes, comprising a single formally described genus *Prochloron*. Although both prochlorophytes and cyanobacteria are allied to Gram-negative bacteria, they differ in certain respects (Table 5.1) and their exact relationship is unclear (Doolittle, 1982). The prochlorophytes have attracted particular interest because they are the only prokaryotes known to possess chlorophyll b and so may be related to the putative ancestor of plastids in green algae and plants (10.4.4).

5.2 Cyanobacteria as hosts (Paerl, 1982)

Many filamentous cyanobacteria bear non-photosynthetic bacteria on their surface. The bacteria are frequently embedded in the mucilaginous sheath of the cyanobacterium. In many cases, they are concentrated around heterocysts or the junctions between heterocysts and vegetative cells. The bacteria are predominantly Gram-negative in aquatic habitats and Gram-positive in terrestrial environments.

Although certain bacteria are antagonists of cyanobacteria, there is growing evidence that at least some of the associations are mutually advantageous to the partners, primarily through the exchange of metabolites. Several lines of evidence indicate that the bacteria utilize organic carbon compounds derived from the cyanobacterium: when *Anabaena* fixes $^{14}CO_2$ by photo-

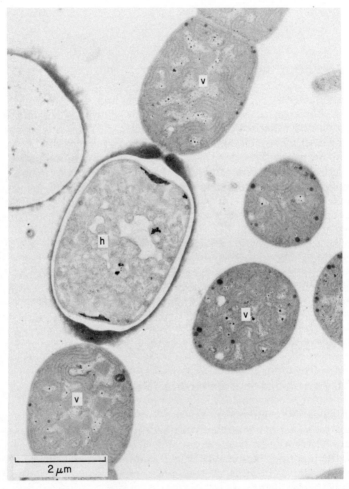

Fig. 5.1   Part of filament of the free-living cyanobacterial symbiont *Anabaena azollae*. A heterocyst (h) is the site of nitrogen fixation and it is larger and paler than the vegetative cells (v). *Photograph* courtesy of Professor D.O. Hall and Dr. D.J. Shi. Heterocysts lack the capacity for photosynthetic oxygen evolution and so nitrogenase does not require protection from internally-produced oxygen. Protection from exogenous oxygen is probably afforded by oxygen-binding glycolipids in the heterocyst cell wall and the high respiratory rate of these cells.

Table 5.1 Characteristics by which cyanobacteria and prochlorophytes differ. Some taxonomists consider cyanobacteria and prochlorophytes as separate phyla, but others view prochlorophytes as aberrant cyanobacteria.

Cyanobacteria	Prochlorophyta
Thylakoids single	Thylakoids stacked
Accessory pigments (phycobilins) concentrated in structures (phycobilisomes) associated with outer surface of thylakoids	Lack phycobilins and phycobilisomes
Lack chlorophyll *b*	Possess chlorophyll *b*
Unicellular, colonial and branched or unbranched filamentous forms; some exhibit gliding motility	Unicellular or filamentous and nonmotile
Nonsymbiotic forms in variety of habitats and particularly abundant in nitrogen-poor habitats and hot springs	Only one nonsymbiotic form isolated to date (Burger-Wiersma *et al.*, 1986)
In symbioses with other prokaryotes, protists, fungi, plants and animals. Many can be cultured	In symbiosis with didemnid ascidians. Cannot be maintained indefinitely in culture
Many genera capable of nitrogen fixation	One report of nitrogenase activity in a prochloron/ascidian association (Paerl, 1984)

synthesis, radioactivity is subsequently recovered from the symbionts. The symbionts can assimilate a range of amino acids and sugars, and the net release of photosynthate from axenic cyanobacteria into the medium is considerably greater than from those with ectosymbiotic bacteria. The released products have not been identified. Further experiments indicate that the metabolism of the cyanobacteria is promoted by the respiratory activity of its symbionts. Bacterial oxygen consumption enhances nitrogen fixation possibly by reducing the oxygen tension in the immediate vicinity of the heterocysts, while carbon dioxide release from the bacteria increases the concentration of carbon dioxide (both directly and by depression of the pH of the medium) available for cyanobacterial photosynthesis. Some cyanobacteria grow better in association with their bacterial symbionts than in axenic culture. Thus, a bacteria-free culture of *Nostoc sphaericum* did not form macroscopic colonies on agar unless it was inoculated with bacteria from a colony of *N. sphaericum* (Schwabe and Mollenhauer, 1967); inoculation with bacteria from a related cyanobacterial species *N. pruniforme* led to limited colony formation.

By contrast to the very common occurrence of ectosymbioses in cyanobacteria, intracellular symbionts are rarely observed. One example concerns rod-shaped bacteria identified in a small proportion of the cells of the cyanobacterium *Pleurocapsa minor* (Wujek, 1979). The infected cells are structurally intact, suggesting that the symbionts are not pathogenic, but there has been no experimental study of this association.

5.3   Cyanobacteria as symbionts

5.3.1   Introduction

A variety of both unicellular and filamentous cyanobacteria enter into symbiosis with hosts from a very broad range of eukaryote groups (Table 5.2).

In symbiosis, some cyanobacteria fix both carbon dioxide (photosynthetically) and nitrogen, while others may show only one of these properties. In general, if the host is photosynthetic, then cyanobacterial symbionts have high rates of nitrogen fixation (with a corresponding increase in heterocyst frequency) and low or undetectable rates of photosynthesis. With non-photosynthetic hosts, cyanobacterial symbionts photosynthesize at appreciable rates, but the extent of nitrogen fixation has not been studied thoroughly except in some lichens where rates are comparable to related non-symbiotic cyanobacteria.

5.3.2   Associations in animals

5.3.2.1   Marine sponges (see also 9.8)

Associations with cyanobacteria occur in representatives of 38 genera of marine sponges from the classes Calcarea and Desmospongia (Wilkinson, 1983a). They have a wide geographical range and are particularly common in shallow tropical waters and on coral reefs; for example, 9 of the 10 most common sponges on the fore-reef slope of the Great Barrier Reef contain cyanobacteria (Wilkinson, 1983b). They are absent below the photic zone. Two genera of symbionts have been identified: the unicellular *Aphanocapsa* and the filamentous *Phormidium*. Both genera of symbionts may be intercellular or intracellular (see Fig. 9.5) and positioned either throughout the sponge tissue or lying in the superficial tissue only.

Experimental investigations have only recently been initiated into these widespread symbioses. The cyanobacterial symbionts are photosynthetically active and 7 of the 9 common associations on the Great Barrier Reef display net evolution of oxygen under natural conditions (Wilkinson, 1983b). From studies using $^{14}CO_2$ (methodology as in Fig. 2.4), Wilkinson (1983b) estimated that 5–12% of photosynthetically fixed carbon is translocated to the host, possibly as glycerol. The nutritional significance of photosynthate release to the host is indicated by the faster growth rate of *Verongia aerophoba* in the light than in darkness (Wilkinson and Vacelet, 1979). It has also been suggested that the symbionts in surface tissues protect the host from high light intensity (Sara, 1971). Low levels of nitrogen fixation have been demonstrated in two sponges, *Theonella swinhoei*, in which the cyanobacteria are intercellular, and *Siphonochalina tabernacula*, which has intracellular populations of cyanobacteria and non-photosynthetic bacteria (see 9.8). Wilkinson and Fay (1979) have proposed that the cyanobacteria fix nitrogen and the bacterial symbionts (where present) enhance the fixation

Table 5.2 Survey of associations involving cyanobacteria and prochlorophytes as symbionts

		Hosts	Symbionts — Taxonomic identity	Growth form	Location	N₂ fixation
Protists	Non-photosynthetic	Paulinella chromatophora	?	u	i	o
		Cryptella cyanophora	?	u	i	o
		Peliaia cyanea	'Synechococcus-like'	u	i	o
		Glaucocystis nostochinearum	?	u	i	o
		Gloeochaete wittrockiana	?	u	i	o
		Cyanophora paradoxa	Cyanocyta	u	i	–
	Photosynthetic (diatoms)	Rhizosolenia styliformis	Richelia intracellularis	f	i	+
		Rhopalodia gibba	?	u	i	?+
Animals	Sponges	About 38 genera	Aphanocapsa spp.	u	e/i/i + e	?+
			Phormidium	f	e/i	o
	Echiuroid worms	Ikedosoma gogoshimense	?		e	o
		Bonnellia fuliginosa	?		e	o
	Ascidians	Didemnid ascidians	Prochloron sp.	u	e	?
Fungi	Ascomycotina (lichens)	Approximately 40 genera	Chroococcus, Gloeocapsa	u	e	o
			Calothrix, Dicothrix	f		
			Nostoc, Scytonema, Stigonema	f		(including 'unicellular'
			Anacystis, Hyphomorpha, Hyella	f		+ Scytonema see 5.3.3)
	Basidiomycotina (lichens)	Cora sp.	Scytonema	f	e	+
		Dictyonema sp.		f	e	o
Plants	Liverworts	Anthoceros, Blasia, Cavicularia, Pellia, Dipolaenia, Riccardia, Riccia	Nostoc	f	e	+
	Mosses	Sphagnum	Nostoc	f	i	o
			?Anabaena	f	i	
	Pteridophytes	Azolla	Anabaena azollae	f	e	+
	Gymnosperms	Cycadales	Nostoc	f	e(i)	+
			Anabaena	f	e(i)	+
	Angiosperms	Gunnera	Nostoc	f	i	+

u = unicellular i = intracellular – = no fixation + = proven
f = filamentous e = extracellular o = no texted

rate by their respiratory utilization of oxygen (see 5.2), but this requires confirmation.

Little is known about the mechanisms by which these associations persist. Structurally intact cyanobacteria have been identified in the oocytes and nurse cells of several sponges (Fell, 1983), suggesting that symbionts are transmitted directly in these associations.

5.3.2.2   Echiuroid worms (Kawaguti, 1971)

Large numbers of both cyanobacteria and non-photosynthetic bacteria occur in cells of the subepidermal connective tissue of two species: *Ikedosoma gogoshimense*, which lives in muddy sand near the low tide mark, and *Bonellia fuliginosa*, on coral reefs. No experimental data are available on these associations, but photosynthetic activity of the cyanobacteria is not likely to be significant since the symbionts are exposed only in darness or dim light, when the proboscis of the host is expanded.

5.3.3   Associations with fungi – lichens

Most lichens are associations between ascomycete or basidomycete fungi and algae but about 8% of species have cyanobacterial symbionts. The general features of lichens are described in chapter 6 but aspects of particular relevance of cyanobacteria are considered here.

Table 5.3 Heterocyst frequency in cyanobacterial symbionts of lichens. Data from Kershaw (1985).

Genus	Cyanobacteria as sole symbionts		Cyanobacteria restricted to cephalodia	
	Species	Heterocyst frequency	Species	Heterocyst frequency
Lobaria	*scrobiculata*	3.9	*amplissima*	21.6
			laetevirens	30.4
			pulmonaria	35.6
Nephroma	*laetevirens*	4.1	*arcticum*	14.1
	parile	4.9		
Peltigera	*canina*	4.9	*aphthosa*	21.1
	evansiana	4.7		
	polydactyla	5.8		
	praetextata	4.4		
	venosa	7.8		
Solorina			*crocea*	17.8
			saccata	14.7
Sticta	*fuliginosa*	6.0		
	limbata	4.9		

Most cyanobacterial symbionts of lichens are filamentous and belong to the common heterocystous genera *Nostoc* and *Scytonema*, (Table 5.2). The symbionts are extracellular. In homoiomerous lichens (see 6.2.2), the structure of the symbionts is similar to that in culture. By contrast, in heteromerous lichens, the filaments of the symbionts are often contorted, appearing as packets of cells and in the lichen *Heppia*, the *Scytonema* symbiont becomes unicellular and lacks heterocysts (Marton and Galun, 1976). About half of the lichens with cyanobacterial symbionts also have algal symbionts; the algae occupy the 'symbiont layer' (Fig. 6.2a) and the cyanobacteria are restricted to cephalodia (Fig. 6.2d).

All lichens containing cyanobacteria so far examined – over 70 species, (Millbank, 1984) – both fix nitrogen and are photosynthetic (Galun and Bubrick, 1984). Where cyanobacteria are the sole symbionts, the heterocyst frequency and both photosynthetic and nitrogen fixation rates are comparable to values for nonsymbiotic cyanobacteria. By contrast, when algal symbionts are present and cyanobacteria are restricted to cephalodia, heterocyst frequencies (Table 5.3) and nitrogen fixation rates are higher, but rates of photosynthesis are reduced.

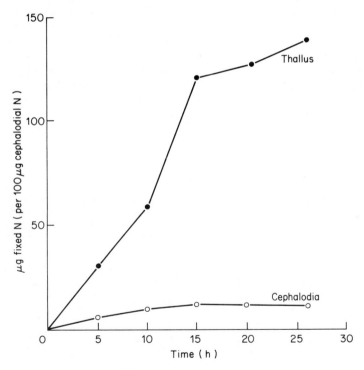

Fig. 5.2 Incorporation of fixed ^{15}N into cephalodia of lichens and subsequent transport to the rest of the thallus (after Millbank and Kershaw, 1969).

Table 5.4   Release of fixed ^{15}N from *Peltigera canina* (Rai *et al.*, 1983). Lichen thalli were incubated in 0.01% (w:v) digitonin for 18 hours to disrupt the fungal membranes, and then exposed to $^{15}N_2$ with digitonin. After 6 hours, the distribution of label in thallus and extracellular products was determined.

	% Fixed ^{15}N
Retained within thallus	44.5
Released to medium:	
Ammonia	53.7
Organic N	1.8

Where cyanobacteria are restricted to cephalodia, 90% or more of the fixed nitrogen is released to the rest of the thallus (Fig. 5.2); where cyanobacteria are the sole symbionts, about 55% is translocated, as for example, in *P. polydactyla* and *P. canina* (Rai *et al.*, 1983). The fixed nitrogen is translocated principally as ammonia. This was demonstrated in studies using the detergent digitonin which disrupts the fungal (eukaryotic) but not cyanobacterial (prokaryotic) membranes (see 6.4.1.2). When discs of *P. canina* are incubated with digitonin, products of cyanobacterial nitrogen fixation, which are normally translocated to the fungus, accumulate in the medium instead. Ninety-seven percent of the released ^{15}N-nitrogen is ammonia, with traces of organic nitrogenous compounds (Table 5.4).

The substantial net production of ammonia by the symbionts results from the suppression of synthesis of the cyanobacterial enzymes for its assimilation (glutamine synthetase, GS, and glutamate synthetase, GOGAT) (Stewart *et al.* 1983). When the symbionts are brought into culture, these enzymes are synthesized (Table 5.5) and ammonia is rapidly assimilated. Stewart *et al.* (1983) have speculated that within the lichen, a fungal product specifically represses the transcription of the genes for the enzymes

Table 5.5   The distribution of the primary enzymes of ammonia assimilation in host, symbionts and intact thallus of the lichen *Peltigera aphthosa* (which has the algal symbiont, *Coccomyxa* in the thallus and the cyanobacterial symbiont, *Nostoc* in cephalodia). (Rai *et al.*, 1981.)

| | Enzyme activity (nmol product min^{-1} (mg protein)$^{-1}$) ||
	Glutamine synthetase	Glutamate dehydrogenase (NADPH-dependent)
Intact thallus	28	90
Thallus with cephalodia removed	18	35
Cephalodia	2	398
Medulla of thallus (solely fungal tissue)	0	24
Nostoc symbiont in culture	60	2
Coccomyxa symbiont in culture	37	22

responsible for ammonia assimilation in the cyanobacteria. The effect is specific to the cyanobacteria for, in the cephalodiate lichen *P. aphthosa*, the GS and GOGAT activities of the algal symbiont, *Coccomyxa*, are not repressed (Table 5.5).

The lichen fungus assimilates the ammonia it receives into glutamate via the enzyme glutamate dehydrogenase (GDH); GS and GOGAT are not detectable. Carbon skeletons for ammonia assimilation are provided both by photosynthate from the symbionts and by substantial dark carbon fixation in the fungal tissues. Pulse-chase experiments on the cephalodiate lichen *P. aphthosa* using ^{15}N [Rai *et al.*, 1981] suggest that glutamate may be metabolized to alanine by aminotransferase activity within the cephalodia and that alanine is the principal form of combined nitrogen transported within the fungus to the main part of the thallus.

5.3.4 Associations with plants

5.3.4.1 Introduction

The distribution of symbioses with cyanobacteria among plants illustrates the general point that these associations involve relatively few host species from various different phyla (see 5.3.1). The symbionts are invariably members of the family Nostocaceae, which are filamentous and heterocystous and in general, they can readily be cultured *in vitro*. There follows a general description of the characteristics of the symbiosis in different plants.

Liverworts

Symbiosis with *Nostoc* (probably *N. sphaericum*) has been demonstrated in several genera of liverworts, of which *Anthoceros* and *Blasia* have been studied in greatest detail (Rodgers and Stewart, 1977). The association is restricted to the gametophyte generation of the host, represented by a leaf-like thallus; the sporophyte generation is symbiont-free. The symbionts occur in mucilage-filled cavities, which open by a ventral pore and appear as dark-green spots on the undersurface of the thallus.

Mosses (Granhall and Hofsten, 1976)

Associations between cyanobacteria and mosses are widespread in the sub-arctic mires of northern Scandinavia. Although the cyanobacteria are usually separate from or associated with the external surface of the mosses, intracellular *Nostoc* has been reported in the water-filled non-photosynthetic 'hyaline' cells of *Sphagnum lindbergii* and *S. riparium* (but not in several other *Sphagnum* species). In Britain, a *Sphagnum* sp. also occasionally contains the cyanobacterium *Haplosiphon*.

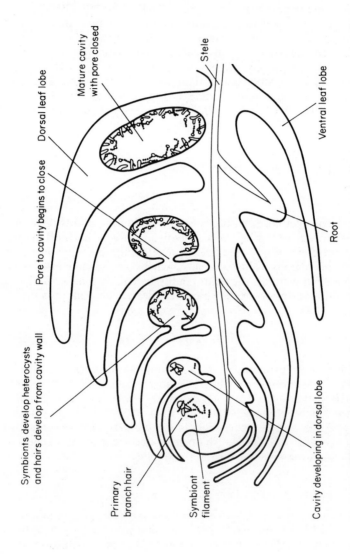

Fig. 5.3 Section along a branch of *Azolla* illustrating the formation and development in the dorsal leaf lobes of the cavities which house the symbionts. At the apex, a specialized epidermal cell (the primary branched hair) which originated in the axil of the leaf primordium, becomes detached as the leaf develops. The primary branched hair appears to carry some of the symbiont filaments from the apical colony into the cavity as it is forming. Subsequently, other hairs (both simple and branched) develop from the wall of the cavity, making extensive contact with the symbiont filaments. The filaments at the apex lack heterocysts, but these develop rapidly after colonization of cavities, eventually comprising 15–20% of the cells. (Derived from Peters and Calvert, 1983.)

Labels in figure:
- Symbionts develop heterocysts and hairs develop from cavity wall
- Pore to cavity begins to close
- Dorsal leaf lobe
- Mature cavity with pore closed
- Stele
- Ventral leaf lobe
- Root
- Primary branch hair
- Symbiont filament
- Cavity developing in dorsal lobe

Azolla

Azolla, comprising six species, is a genus of free-floating water ferns. In the dominant sporophyte generation, the branching stems bear two rows of leaves, each of which has a thin, ventral, submerged lobe and a thicker, dorsal, floating lobe. The symbionts, known as *Anabaena azollae*, occur within a closed mucilage-lined cavity on the ventral side of each dorsal lobe (Figs 5.3, 5.4). These symbionts are derived from a colony at the stem apex, from which they become dissociated as each leaf and its cavity develops (Peters and Calvert, 1983). In contrast to liverworts, the association persists through the life cycle of *Azolla*. In the gametophyte generation, the symbionts are located under the caps of the megasporocarps (Lumpkin and Plucknett, 1980).

Cycads

The cycads are a family of nine genera with about 90 species, of which approximately 30 species contain cyanobacteria in specialized and highly branched lateral roots called coralloid roots. The symbionts, variously referred to as *Anabaena* and *Nostoc*, are restricted to a discrete zone in the outer part of the root cortex, where they occupy mucilage-filled intercellular cavities lined by elongated cortical cells (Obukowicz *et al.*, 1981). Occasionally, intracellular symbionts are seen. Although the coralloid roots are negatively geotropic, they frequently do not emerge above the soil surface and so the symbionts are usually in permanent darkness.

Gunnera

The genus *Gunnera* comprises about 40 species, all of which contain symbionts identified as *Nostoc punctiforme*. In the fully established association, the symbionts are intracellular, located in meristematic cells of glands at the base of host leaves. The symbiosis is initiated in young seedlings when two glands below the site of cotyledon attachment become infected with *Nostoc*. As each true leaf develops, its gland is invaded by symbionts derived from the population at the shoot apex (Silvester and McNamara, 1976).

5.3.4.2 Nutritional interactions

The symbionts of all plant-cyanobacterial associations exhibit high levels of nitrogen fixation and the intact associations grow well under low nitrogen conditions (Granhall and Hofsten, 1976; Halliday and Pate, 1976; Hill, 1977; Silvester and Smith, 1969; Stewart and Rodgers, 1977). Correlated with this, the heterocyst frequency is high: 30–43% in liverworts (Rodgers and Stewart, 1977), up to 30–40% in *Azolla* (Hill, 1977), 20–30% in cycads (Grilli Caiola, 1980) and 60% in *Gunnera* (Silvester, 1976) (see also below).

In several associations, the rate of nitrogen fixation and heterocyst frequency varies markedly with the age of the association. These changes have

Table 5.6   Variation in heterocyst frequency and nitrogen fixation rates of symbionts with distance from stem apex in *Gunnera* (Silvester, 1976).

	G. albocarpa	
Distance from apex (cm)	heterocysts* (%)	nitrogen fixation† (%)
0	23(0)	32
5	32(0)	100
10	41(0)	75
15	63(5)	7
20	65(15)	4

* Percentage of total number of cells (with percentage of heterocysts in a disintegrating state shown in parentheses).
† Percentage of maximum value.

been examined in *Gunnera* in which each gland represents a discrete infection, the age of which increases with distance from the apical meristem (see 5.3.4.1). There is an initial increase in nitrogen fixation rate and heterocyst frequency with age but in the oldest glands, the fixation rate declines dramatically and, although the heterocyst frequency remains high, the cyanobacteria are in a disintegrating state (Table 5.6). The symbiosis may undergo a comparable developmental sequence in cycads (Grilli Caiola, 1980; Obukowicz *et al.*, 1981) and *Azolla* (Hill, 1977).

The movement of a substantial proportion of fixed nitrogen from symbiont to the host plant has been demonstrated in liverworts (Stewart and Rodgers, 1977), *Azolla* (Kaplan and Peters, 1981) and the cycad *Macrozamia communis* (Bergerson *et al.*, 1965). In their detailed study of the liverwort *Anthoceros punctatus*, Stewart and Rodgers (1977) utilized the fact that the sporophyte generation is attached to the gametophyte but contains no symbionts (see 5.3.4.1). The sporophyte incorporated substantial amounts of ^{15}N-nitrogen when attached to the symbiont-bearing gametophyte but no detectable ^{15}N when it was dissected free from the symbiont-bearing gametophyte. The absence of nitrogen fixation in experimentally-produced aposymbiotic gametophytes confirmed that the nitrogen was fixed by the cyanobacteria. As in lichens (5.3.3.1), the fixed nitrogen is probably translocated to the liverwort host as ammonia, because 98% of the total nitrogen released to the medium by symbionts freshly isolated from *Blasia pusilla* was ammonia.

There is preliminary evidence that, as in lichens (5.3.3.1), the release of ammonia from the symbionts results from low levels of the enzymes for ammonia assimilation, GS and GOGAT. The GS activity of symbionts freshly isolated from *Anthoceros* sp. is 25% of that in cultured symbionts (Stewart *et al.*, 1983) and the absolute level of GS in *Azolla* symbionts is 5-10% of that of nonsymbiotic cyanobacteria (Haselkorn *et al.*, 1980). Unlike lichens, the principle enzyme of ammonia assimilation in host tissues of liverworts and *Azolla* is GS and not GDH (Peters and Calvert, 1983; Stewart *et al.*, 1983). Further, the symbiont of *Azolla* contains appreciable levels of GDH (Ray *et al.*, 1978), which has considerably lower affinity for ammonia than GS. Possibly, symbiont GDH serves a regulatory function by its assimilation of excess ammonia if the intracavity concentration becomes too high (Ray *et al.*, 1978).

In all associations, the symbionts exhibit low or undetectable levels of photosynthesis, as measured by light-dependent carbon dioxide fixation and oxygen evolution (Peters and Calvert, 1983; Rodgers and Stewart, 1977; Silvester, 1976; Stewart *et al.*, 1983) and they are presumably dependent on the host plant for their carbon and energy requirements. The movement of host photosynthate to the symbionts has been investigated only in liverworts (Stewart and Rodgers, 1977). *Blasia pusilla* was incubated in ^{14}C-sodium bicarbonate, with part of the thallus in light and part in darkness. The symbionts in the dark portion of the thallus accumulated photosynthetically fixed ^{14}C, demonstrating the transfer of host photosynthate to the symbionts (control experiments showed that dark fixation by the association was negligible). In experiments of similar design with the liverwort *Anthoceros punctatus*, ^{14}C fixed by the illuminated sporophyte (which is symbiont-free) was subsequently recovered from symbionts in the darkened gametophyte. The mobile compound may be sucrose, for thalli of *B. pusilla*, from which the symbionts have been excised, selectively release this sugar into the medium. Further, cultured symbionts grow in darkness with sucrose as sole carbon source (Stewart and Rodgers, 1977). There is also circumstantial evidence that photosynthetically-produced sucrose is translocated from *Azolla* to its symbionts (Peters and Calvert, 1983).

In those associations where the symbionts are predominantly or exclusively extracellular (i.e. liverworts, *Azolla*, cycads), contact between the partners is substantially increased by simple or branched epidermal hairs (Fig. 5.4a, b) projecting from the surrounding host cavity wall (Duckett *et al.*, 1977; Obukowicz *et al.*, 1981; Peters *et al.*, 1978). In both *Azolla* and the liverwort *Blasia*, the cells of the hairs have a highly elaborated cell wall and dense cytoplasm with many mitochondria and abundant endoplasmic reticulum (Duckett *et al.*, 1975 and 1977). These features are characteristic of 'transfer cells', which are found in a variety of anatomical situations in plants and are implicated in the transfer of solutes. The projecting cells are produced only in infected cavities of liverworts but are present in aposymbiotic *Azolla*.

5.3.4.3 Specificity of the associations

Incidence of symbionts other than cyanobacteria

Cyanobacteria are the principal or sole symbionts in all associations except *Sphagnum*, the hyaline cells of which may also contain green algae, non-photosynthetic bacteria and fungi (Granhall and Hofsten, 1976). The symbionts of *Azolla* share the cavity with small numbers of bacteria, identified as *Pseudomonas* and *Azotobacter* (Lumpkin and Plucknett, 1980). These bacteria are not capable of nitrogen fixation but may enhance fixation by the cyanobacteria through their utilization of oxygen (see 5.2). Micro-organisms other than cyanobacteria are totally absent from the cortical

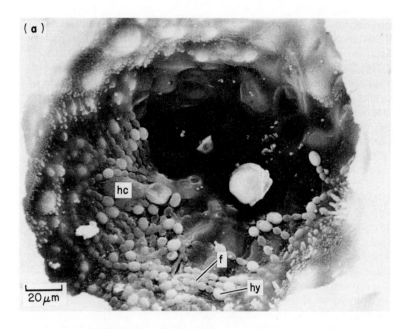

Fig. 5.4   *Anabaena/Azolla* symbiosis. **(a)** Scanning electron micrograph of a cavity in *Azolla filiculoides*, showing filaments (f) of *Anabaena azollae* lining the cavity. Note the two-celled epidermal hair (hc), and the frequent heterocysts (hy). (*Photograph* R.J. Robins and R.J. Turner, courtesy of FEMS Microbiology Letters.) **(b)** (Right) Scanning electron micrograph showing association of *Anabaena* filaments (f) with hair cells (hc) in *A. filiculoides*. (*Photograph* courtesy of D.O. Hall and D.J. Shi.)

cavities of cycad roots (Grilli Caiola, 1980; Obukowicz *et al.*, 1981) and this has been attributed to the antimicrobial effect of phenolic compounds, which are concentrated in the cells lining the cyanobacterial zone (Obukowicz *et al.*, 1981).

Specificity of the associations with cyanobacteria

In most cases only one genus of symbiont has been identified in a given host genus (Table 5.2) and it is unclear whether the few exceptions (notably in cycads) are real or due to misidentification of the symbionts (Stewart *et al.*, 1983).

Experimental studies to determine the range of cyanobacteria which can enter into symbiosis have been conducted on *Gunnera* and liverworts (Bonnett and Silvester, 1981; Enderlin and Meeks, 1983; Rodgers and

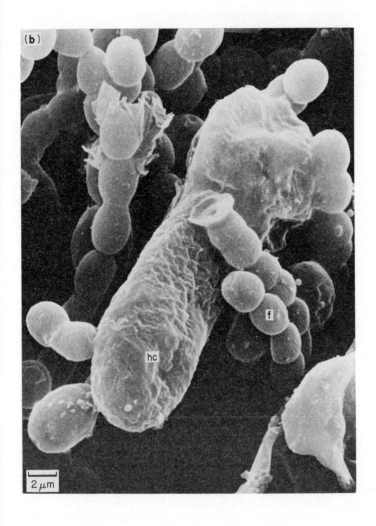

Stewart, 1977). These hosts can establish viable associations with most *Nostoc* strains isolated from symbioses with plants or lichens, as measured by infection of the plant tissues (Table 5.7), high nitrogen fixation rates and growth of the associations. The data in Table 5.7 also indicate that at least some nonsymbiotic *Nostoc* can form an association and the results on the interaction between *Anthoceros* sp. and *Nostoc* strain ATCC 27904 demonstrate that the capacity for nitrogen fixation is not a sufficient characteristic for infectivity.

5.3.5   Associations in protists

5.3.5.1   Cryptic symbioses in non-photosynthetic protists

A number of protists contain photosynthetic cyanobacterium-like structures known as cyanelles. (The term 'cyanelle' or 'cyanella' was originally devised to describe any cyanobacterial symbiont but, as considered in 2.1, this meaning of the term is no longer in general use.) Except for the thecate amoeba *Paulinella chromatophora* (Fig. 5.5b), none of the hosts can be assigned to a known protist taxon and some biologists group these organisms together as members of a new, but probably artificial phylum, Glaucophyta (Reisser, 1984). The cyanelles are invariably unicellular and have a very thin cell wall, surrounded by a membrane, presumably of host origin. Some bear a distinct resemblance to the plastids of red algae and, since no cyanelles have ever been cultured, it is not easy to distinguish them from organelles.

Many studies of these associations have concentrated on the question as to whether the cyanelles should be considered as symbionts (i.e. organisms) or incipient organelles. A wide range of structural and biochemical data summarized in Jaynes and Vernon (1982), particularly on *Cyanophora paradoxa* (Fig. 5.5a), demonstrate their cyanobacterial origin but they also exhibit several features more characteristic of organelles. Thus, the DNA content of cyanelles in *C. paradoxa*, at 1.2×10^8 daltons, is only 10% of that of nonsymbiotic cyanobacteria and comparable to that of plastids (Herdman and Stanier, 1977). However, the cyanelles in *C. paradoxa* differ from plastids of green algae and higher plants in that they contain the genes for both the large and small subunits of the enzyme of photosynthetic carbon dioxide fixation, ribulose bisphosphate carboxylase (Heinhorst and Shively, 1983); in green algae and higher plants, the large subunits are coded by the plastid genome and the small subunits by the nucleus. Thus, the cyanelles could be considered to 'represent a bridge between cyanobacteria and chloroplasts' (Aitken and Stanier, 1979).

Little is known about the physiology of the associations. All cyanelles so far examined (in *C. paradoxa, Glaucocystis* and *Gloeochaete*) exhibit high levels of photosynthesis and in *C. paradoxa* about 15% of fixed carbon is translocated to the host, primarily as glucose (Trench *et al.*, 1978). The only association which has been tested for a capacity to fix nitrogen (*C. paradoxa*) has no detectable nitrogenase activity (Floener *et al.*, 1982).

Persistence of the associations depends on the balanced growth and division rates of the protists and cyanelles, both of which reproduce by binary fission. In *C. paradoxa*, the division rates of the partners are sometimes not quite equal and, as a result, the number of cyanelles per host cell varies between 1 and 8, depending on growth conditions (Trench *et al.*, 1978). By contrast, division of the host cell and its two cyanelles in *Paulinella chromatophora* is closely coupled. At host cell division, one cyanelle enters each of the two daughter cells, and then immediately divides to restore the number per cell.

Table 5.7 Specificity of cyanobacteria–plant symbioses. (Data from Bonnett and Silvester, 1981; Enderlin and Meeks, 1983.)

Cyanobacterium	Source	Infectivity # Anthoceros sp.*	Gunnera manicata†
(a) Isolated from symbiosis			
Nostoc sp.	Anthoceros (New Zealand)	+	+
	Anthoceros (California)	+	n.d.
	Anthoceros (Scotland)	n.d.	+
	Gunnera (New Zealand)	+	+
	Cycas (New Zealand)	+	+
	Macrozamia sp. ''	+	n.d.
	Macrozamia lucida	n.d.	–
	Encephalartos (S. Africa)	n.d.	–
	Peltigera polydactyla (New Zealand)	n.d.	+
	Peltigera aphthosa (Oregon)	+	–
Anabaena azollae	Azolla caroliniana (U.S.A.)	–	–
(b) Nonsymbiotic cyanobacteria			
Nostoc commune	CCC1453/3	n.d.	+
N. muscorum	ATCC 29150	+	n.d.
N. muscorum	ATCC 27904 (not N-fixing)	–	n.d.
N. muscorum	N-fixing revertant of ATCC 27904	–	n.d.
Anabaena oscillaroides	Waikato River, New Zealand	n.d.	–
A. flos-aquae	Waikato River, New Zealand	n.d.	–
A. cylindrica	ATCC 29414	–	n.d.
A. variabilis	ATCC 29413	–	n.d.

Infective (+); noninfective (–); not determined (n.d.). Cyanobacteria were designated infective if they invaded the cavities of Anthoceros and glands of Gunnera.

* Pieces of aposymbiotic gametophyte thallus were incubated with suspensions of cyanobacteria in nitrogen-free medium for 2–3 weeks.

† Suspensions of cyanobacteria were applied to the cotyledons of aposymbiotic seedlings, which were maintained under low nitrogen conditions prior to assay.

ATCC – American Type Culture Collection; CCC – Cambridge Culture Centre.

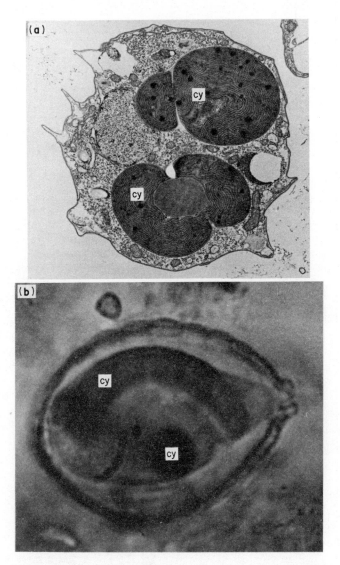

Fig. 5.5   Cyanelles. **(a)** Transmission electron micrograph of *Cyanophora paradoxa* with cyanelles (cy). *Photogaph* R.K. Trench. **(b)** Photomicrograph of *Paulinella chromatophora* with two sausage-shaped cyanelles (cy).

5.3.5.2 Diatoms

The filamentous cyanobacterium *Richelia intracellularis* occurs in the diatom *Rhizosolenia styliformis* (Fig. 5.6), which is often abundant in the photic zone of the North Pacific. The short filaments of *R. intracellularis* each bear a terminal heterocyst and fix nitrogen at high rates. They are also capable of photosynthesis, and autoradiographic studies (Mague *et al.*, 1974) suggest they are responsible for most of ^{14}C-carbon dioxide fixation in the association. *R. intracellularis* filaments have also been observed in the diatom *Hemiaulus membranaceus*, but they are not believed to persist in cells of this species for more than a few days.

The diatom *Rhopalodia gibba* contains unicellular cyanobacteria with thin cell walls. These symbionts are reminiscent of the cyanelles in various non-photosynthetic protists (5.3.5.1). They are capable of nitrogen fixation at low rates (Floener and Bothe, 1980).

5.4 Prochlorophytes as symbionts

Prochloron sp. has been reported in about 20 species of colonial ascidians, predominantly of the family Didemnidae, but also in members of the families Polychlinidae, Polycitoridae and Styelidae (Kott, 1980; Kott *et al.*, 1984). The *Prochloron* cells are invariably extracellular and either embedded in the tunica (the coat which envelops the colony) or in the common exhalent tubes of the colony.

Ascidians which contain *Prochloron* are found in warm shallow seas, particularly in positions of high light intensity on coral reef flats (Kott, 1980). By contrast, symbiont-free species occupy less well-illuminated habitats, such as caves and crevices on the slopes of reefs. This habitat preference of the

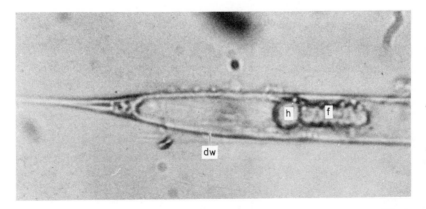

Fig. 5.6 The diatom *Rhizosolenia styliformis*, which contains the cyanobacterium *Richelia styliformis*. Diatom wall (dw), filament of *Richelia* (f), terminal heterocyst (h).

ascidians and the light requirement for growth of *Prochloron*-bearing colonies of *Tridemnum cyanophorum* suggest that the photosynthetic activity of *Prochloron* is significant to the nutrition of the host. The translocation of photosynthetic carbon to the host in the intact association has not been investigated but *Prochloron*, freshly isolated from the symbiosis, release very little photosynthetically-fixed carbon (Fisher and Trench, 1980).

To date, there has only been one report of a nonsymbiotic prochlorophyte (Burger-Wiersma *et al.*, 1986) and it has so far proved impossible to maintain isolates from didemnids indefinitely in culture. The symbiont of *Diplosoma similis* requires the amino acid tryptophan for cell division *in vitro* (Patterson and Withers, 1982), but even under the most favourable culture conditions, growth ceases after 4–5 cycles of division. The symbiosis with ascidians persists by direct transmission, by the carriage of *Prochloron* cells on the surface of the tadpole-like larva of the host. The *Prochloron* is distributed generally over the trunk of the larvae in many *Tridemnum* species, restricted to small pockets at the posterior of the trunk of *T. paracyclops* and *Lissoclinum* species and carried in a layer of hair-like projections, called a rostrum, at the posterior end of the trunk of *Diplosoma* species (Kott, 1980). This variation has led Kott to suggest that the symbiosis with *Prochloron* has evolved independently on several occasions in different genera and species of ascidians. Four distinct types of *Prochloron* have been identified (Kott *et al.*, 1984), but only one species, *P. didemni*, has been described formally. Three of the types (including *P. didemni*) occur in a variety of ascidian genera and the fourth is found exclusively in *Didemnum molle* (Kott *et al.*, 1984).

6
Fungi in symbiosis I. As hosts: lichens

6.1 Introduction

Lichens (associations between fungi as hosts and algae or cyanobacteria as symbionts) are one of the most widespread examples of symbiosis; about 8% of the earth's land surface bears lichen-dominated vegetation (Larson, 1987). The appearance of the lichen plant (or 'thallus') is usually quite unlike either of its components grown in isolated culture. Indeed, it was not realized that lichens were symbioses until 1867 (Schwendener, 1867); before that time they were regarded as a class of plants distinct from either fungi or algae (and the lichen symbionts were believed to be reproductive bodies). Lichens are classified into families, genera, and species, and their taxonomy is based exclusively on fungal characteristics.

There are approximately 13 500 species of lichen-forming fungi (Hawksworth and Hill, 1984), and they represent about 20% of the known species of fungi. All lichen fungi are members of the Ascomycotina, except for about 20 species which are members of the Basidiomycotina. Lichen Ascomycotina are diverse, including both perithecia- and apothecia-bearing (Fig. 6.2b) forms, and are distributed amongst 16 orders (five of which are entirely of lichen-forming fungi, eight predominantly so, and three predominantly of non-lichen-forming fungi). The lichen symbiosis has therefore presumably evolved on a number of different occasions. Only a very few lichen fungi have been found in a free-living condition.

Over 30 genera of unicellular or simple filamentous algae and cyanobacteria have been recorded as lichen symbionts (Table 6.1). Normally, only one species of symbiont is found in association with each species of lichen fungus; the main exceptions are about 520 lichen species which normally contain both an algal and a cyanobacterial symbiont, the latter being confined to distinct structures termed cephalodia (see 5.3.3 and Fig. 6.2d). The commonest symbionts, occurring in over 70% of lichen species are unicellular chlorophyte algae of the genera *Trebouxia* (Fig. 6.2a) and *Pseudotrebouxia* (some lichenologists do not regard these as distinct genera, and assign all 'trebouxioid' algae into the single genus *Trebouxia*). The extent to which lichen symbionts can exist free-living is uncertain, partly because of the poor state of their taxonomy (see footnote to Table 6.1) and partly because of inadequate field observations. Although *Trebouxia* and *Pseudo-*

Table 6.1 Survey of autotrophic symbionts in lichens.

Algae		
Chlorophyceae – Chlorococcales	Unicells	Asterochloris, Chlorococcum, Chlorella, Coccomyxa*, Gloeocystis, Hyalococcus, Myrmecia*, Pseudochlorella, Pseudotrebouxia**, Trebouxia**, Trochischia
Chlorophyceae – Ulotrichales	Simple filaments, sometimes reduced to unicells in lichen, but not in culture	Cephaleuros, Chlorosarcina, Coccobotrys, Dilabifilium, Leptosira, Phycopeltis, Physolinum, Pleurococcum*, Pseudopleurococcum, Stichococcum, Trentepohlia**
Xanthophyceae	Simple filaments	Heterococcus
Phaeophyceae	Simple filaments	Petroderma
Cyanobacteria		
Chroococcales	Unicellular or colonial, no heterocysts	Aphanocapsa, Chroococcus, Gloeocapsa
Pleurocapsales	Filamentous or nearly so, no heterocysts	Hyella
Nostocales	Filamentous, no true branching, heterocysts	Anabaena, Calothrix, Dicothrix, Nostoc**, Scytonema*
Stigonematales	Filamentous, true branching, usually with heterocysts	Fischerella, Hyphomorpha, Stigonema

** = very common, occurring in a wide range of lichen families.
* = moderately common, found in at least 8 genera of lichens.

Note No two authors of textbooks or review articles on lichens agree completely on the names and numbers of genera of symbionts recorded for lichens, although all agree on the 'very common' and 'moderately common' genera. This reflects both the confused state of the taxonomy of these kinds of organisms, and the need to isolate symbionts into pure culture before they can be identified with certainty. Trebouxia and Pseudotrebouxia symbionts are often characterized down to the species level; some Trentepohlia symbionts are characterized to species level, but species of Nostoc symbionts are not usually recognized.

trebouxia are abundant throughout the world in lichens, there have been very few reports of free-living colonies of trebouxioid algae (Tschermak-Woess, 1978) and some of these are near lichens which contain them as symbionts (Galun, 1987; Slocum *et al.*, 1980). It seems very unlikely that they can sustain a free-living existence indefinitely.

Lichens are widely distributed in terrestrial habitats, occurring from the equator to higher latitudes than any plants, and from sea-level to over 9000 m altitude. Many species are found in barren environments, and they often constitute the dominant vegetation in large areas of tundra, and arctic-alpine habitats in montane regions. However, lichens can also be abundant in relatively nutrient-rich habitats such as temperate and tropical forests, and the upper part of the intertidal zone of rocky seashores. The widespread distribution of lichens is largely due their ability to colonize almost any stable, solid substrate exposed to adequate light intensity; over a hundred species have been identified on the long-lived leaves of certain tropical trees, and there are a number of reports of lichens colonizing glass windows. Lichens are not found on unstable substrates (e.g., disturbed soil, rapidly eroding rock surfaces), and very few species occur in permanently submerged habitats. They are exceptionally sensitive to atmospheric pollution, especially sulphur dioxide, so they are virtually absent from city centres and only poorly represented in nearby rural areas. Because different species vary in their sensitivity to pollution, the species composition and growth forms on substrates such as tree bark can be used as accurate indicators of the level of air pollution (Hawksworth and Rose, 1976).

The experimental study of interactions in the lichen symbiosis has provided a particularly useful insight into photosynthate translocation from autotrophic symbionts to their hosts. Lichens were the first symbiosis in which such translocation was directly demonstrated, and the extracellular location of the symbionts has enabled experimental manipulations additional to those available for intracellular symbionts (Chapters 2 and 3). By contrast with most other symbioses, the experimental synthesis of a lichen from its isolated components has proved difficult. Only recently have reliable techniques become available (Ahmadjian and Jacobs, 1981; Ahmadjian 1987).

An understanding of the interactions in the lichen symbiosis is dependent upon a basic knowlege of the structure, biology and physiology of the intact lichen. The substantial information on these topics is briefly summarized in Sections 6.2 and 6.3, and the reader is referred to the comprehensive account of the biology of lichens published in this series (Hale, 1983), and also to other recent texts (Lawrey, 1984; Hawksworth and Hill, 1984; Brown, 1986; Peveling, 1987).

6.2 The structure of lichens

6.2.1 Gross morphology (Fig. 6.1)

Most lichens occur as crusts on the surface of (Fig. 6.1a), or sometimes within, the substratum. Some are foliose but adhere tightly to the substratum (Fig. 6.1b). A minority of species are more loosely attached, and have a leafy (Fig. 6.1c, d), filamentous (Fig. 6.1e) or shrubby appearance (Fig. 6.1f); those consisting of small, often overlapping leafy scales ('squamules') are termed squamulose. For convenience, almost all experimental investigations have been carried out with loosely attached lichens (see Fig. 6.1d), but there is no reason to believe that they differ in any important way from crustose forms.

6.2.2 Structural organisation (Fig. 6.2)

The symbionts are always extracellular, and in the great majority of lichens they are confined to a layer just beneath the upper surface (Fig. 6.2a, b). In most lichens, the symbionts comprise about 5–10% of the mass or volume of a lichen. Above the symbiont layer is an often thin but dense upper cortex of compacted fungal hyphae which are metabolically active. The upper cortex is usually opaque when dry but transparent when wet; this is why many lichens change colour when moistened, and why it has been suggested that the upper cortex in dry lichens protects symbionts from damage by bright sunlight. Below the symbiont layer is a relatively thick medulla of loosely arranged thick-walled hyphae between which are numerous air spaces (Fig. 6.2b). In many lichens, abundant crystalline deposits of secondary metabolites occur on the exposed surfaces of symbionts and fungal hyphae (Fig. 6.2e); the crystals are hydrophobic and are believed to prevent waterlogging of the air-spaces in saturated lichens (see 6.3.4). In many species, the fungus forms other structures such as a lower cortex or rhizoids. In the lichen *Xanthoria parietina* Collins and Farrar (1978) apportioned the volume of the thallus as follows: fungal host 47%, *Pseudotrebouxia* symbiont 7%, airspaces 18%, and 'extracellular matrix' 28%. 'Extracellular matrix' is usually fibrillar in structure and probably fungal in origin (Bednar and Juniper, 1965). It occurs between the fungal hyphae in the cortex and sometimes other regions. ·

In a few of the lichens containing cyanobacteria, the symbionts are not confined to a discrete layer but are distributed throughout the thallus. Such a structural organisation is called *homiomerous* (in contrast to *heteromerous* lichens which have a distinct symbiont layer). Homiomerous lichens have received little experimental investigation, and although no precise estimates are available, the mass of the symbiont may equal that of the host.

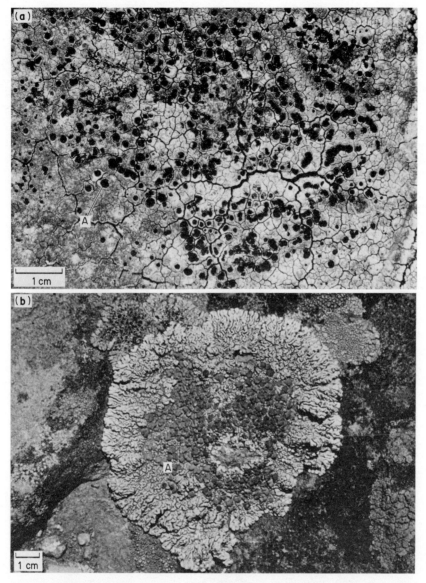

Fig. 6.1 Gross morphology of lichens. **(a)** *Lecidea dicksonii*, a crustose lichen which grows closely appressed to the rock surface. There are numerous dark-coloured fungal fruit bodies (A) (apothecia, see Fig. 6.2b) on the surface. **(b)** *Lecanora muralis* a foliose lichen growing on the surface of limestone rock. The numerous small discs (A) on the surface of thallus are fungal fruit bodies (apothecia, see Fig. 6.2b).

Fig. 6.1(c)   *Peltigera canina*, a foliose lichen only loosely attached to the substratum.
(d) *Peltigera polydactyla*, a foliose lichen extensively used in experiments on the physiology
of the symbiosis together with a sample of discs cut from thalli (see Section 6.4).

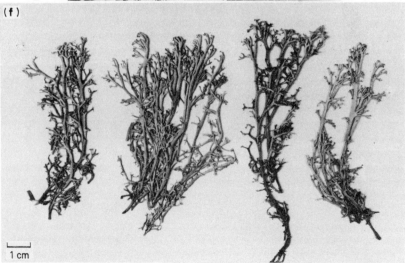

Fig. 6.1(e) *Ramalina reticulata*, a filamentous lichen growing on trees in the locally humid climate on the Californian coast. **(f)** *Cladonia rangiferina* (Reindeer Moss), a fruticose lichen that carpets large areas of tundra.

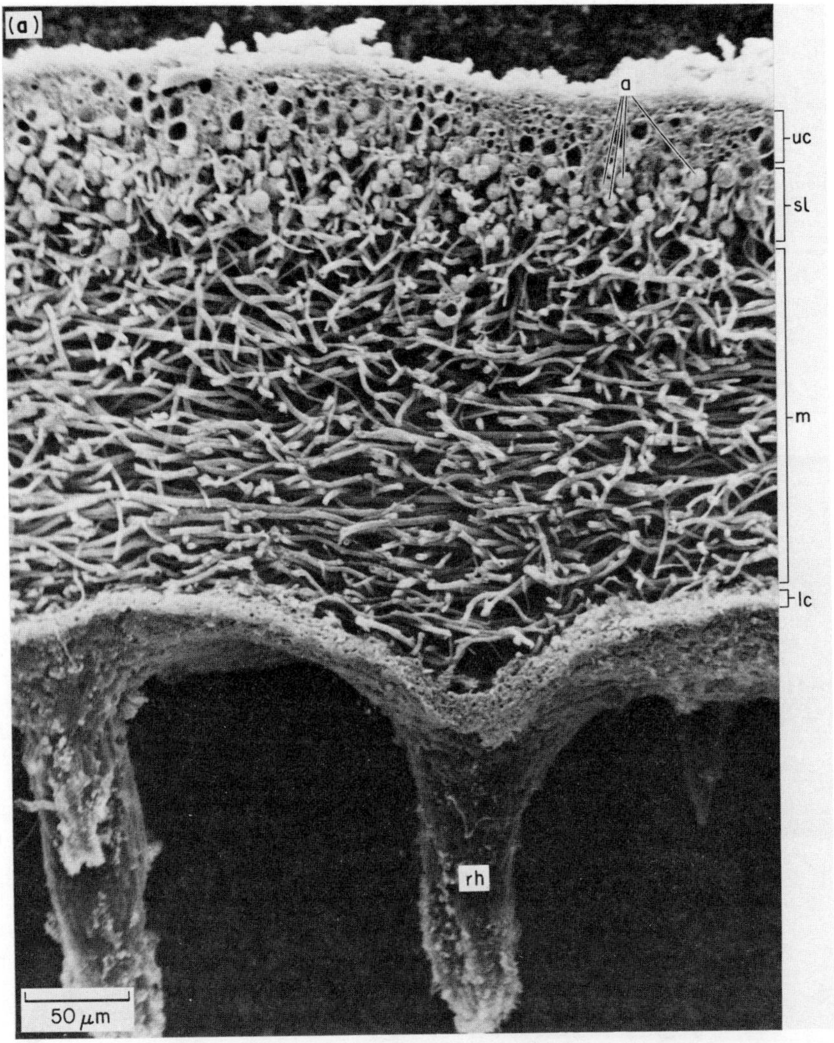

Fig. 6.2 Structure and organisation of lichens. **(a)** Scanning electron micrograph of a transverse section through *Parmelia borreri*, a foliose lichen with *Trebouxia* symbionts. uc = upper cortex, sl = symbiont layer, a = alga, m = medulla, lc = lower cortex, rh = rhizoid. Crustose lichens growing on rock lack a lower cortex, but would have hyphae penetrating the substratum; the margin of the thallus is often free of algae. (Scanning electron micrograph of Catherine Lines). **(b)** Schematic section through a typical foliose lichen thallus bearing an apothecium with asci and ascospores. a = ascus with spores. Other abbreviations as in (a). After Ahmadjian (1963). **(c)** Soredia – vegetative propagules comprising symbiont cells with attached fungal hyphae being released from the surface of a thallus. After Ahmadjian (1963.) **(d)** Cephalodia – structures containing cyanobacterial symbionts (cy) in those lichens which also have algal symbionts. Cephalodia may be external, as here (schematically shown for the lichen *Peltigera aphthosa*) or internal (A.L. Smith, 1927).

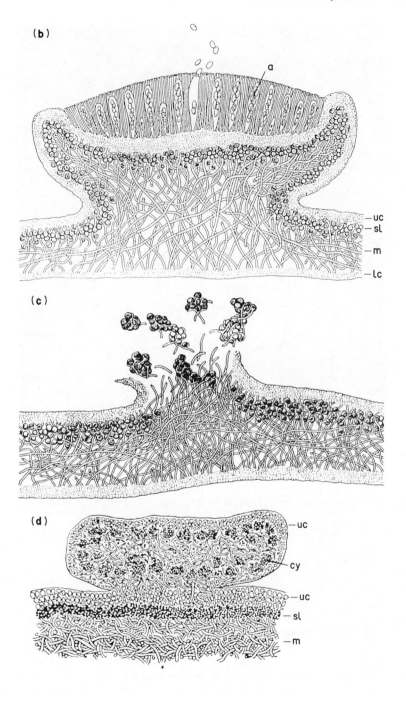

(b)

(c)

(d)

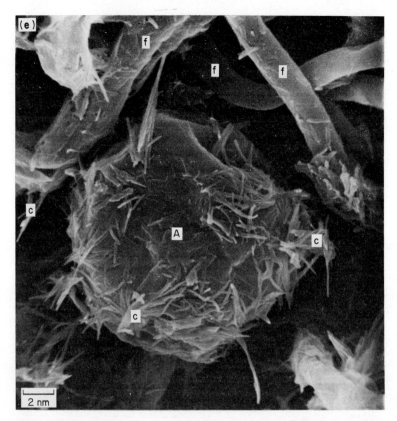

Fig. 6.2(e)   Crystalline deposits of secondary lichen products on the surface of a symbiont in the lichen *Xanthoria parietina* A = algal symbiont, c = crystalline deposits, f = fungal hyphae. (scanning electron micrograph by Catherine Lines).

6.2.3   Morphological contact between host and symbiont

The nature of the contact between host and symbiont varies with the type of symbiont, habitat and structural complexity of the lichen (Galun and Bubrick, 1984; Honegger, 1984, 1987).

In lichens with trebouxioid algae, three principal types of contact have been described (Fig. 6.3).

a) One or usually more peg-like projections of the fungus penetrate through the cell wall but not the cell membrane (Fig. 6.3a). These are characteristic of crustose lichens, especially those of simple thallus structure from very dry habitats; they are termed 'intracellular haustoria' in the lichen literature (Tschermak, 1941).

b) The fungus forms small plug-like projections which do not penetrate the symbiont cell wall (Fig. 6.3b). These are characteristic of lichens with a squamulose structure and from less dry habitats; they are termed 'intraparietal haustoria' in the lichen literature (as also is type (c) below).

c) The hyphae attach to the symbiont cell surface by a specialized structure (Fig. 6.3c, e). There is often only one such attachment per symbiont cell, and as the symbiont cell divides, the hypha branches to form new attachment to the daughter cells (Fig. 6.3f). These are particularly characteristic of foliose and fruticose lichens, which may occasionally also have types (a) and (b) above (Malachowski *et al.*, 1980).

In all these types of contact, the outer layer of the fungal cell wall appears to extend over and invest the surface of the symbiont cell wall. This layer gives histochemical reactions for protein and fatty acid polyesters (Honegger, 1986b), and may have crystals of secondary metabolic products on its outer surface (Fig. 6.2e).

Additionally, two other types of contact have been described in lichens of the genus *Peltigera*. In species containing the alga *Coccomyxa*, the fungus never penetrates the symbiont cell wall, and this has been correlated with the presence of the highly resistant carotenoid pigment sporopollenin in the wall of *Coccomyxa* (Honegger, 1986a). There is close wall-to-wall contact between host and symbiont (Fig. 6.3g), but no apparent formation of specialized attachment structures. In species containing the cyanobacterial symbiont *Nostoc*, thin-walled fungal hyphae enter the gelatinous sheath which encloses the symbiont colonies, but they do not come into contact with the outer peptidoglucan/protein layer of the cyanobacterial cells (Fig. 6.3h).

The specialized attachments between the fungal hyphae and trebouxioid algae probably represent the basis for the persistent contamination of isolated symbionts with fragments of hyphae and also for the differences in surface characteristics (e.g., lectin-binding, see 6.5.3) between freshly isolated symbionts and those which have been in long-term culture. The different type of contact in *Peltigera* species may account for the ease with which their symbionts can be isolated from homogenates and thus for their value in experimental studies of host-symbiont interactions (see 6.4.1.2).

6.3 Physiological characteristics of the lichen thallus

This section summarizes the salient features of the physiology of lichens, with particular emphasis on how they are adapted to the habitats in which they grow. In such experimental studies, lichens are generally treated as if they were single organisms, but many of the conclusions have a direct bearing on our understanding of the interactions between the partners.

6.3.1 Growth rates and longevity

Lichens grow very slowly. The annual increase in diameter rarely exceeds 1 mm for most mature crustose forms, and 2 cm for some of the faster

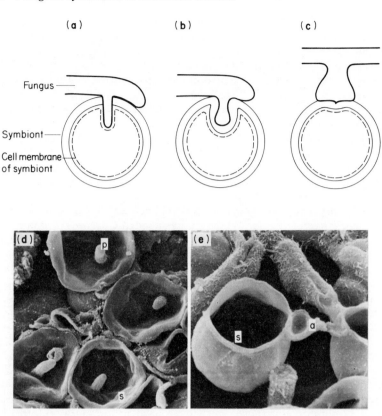

Fig. 6.3   Some types of contact between fungus and symbiont in lichens. **(a)–(c)** Various types of fungal projections into symbiont cells (see text 6.2.3). **(d)** Scanning electron micrograph of projections (p) into the *Trebouxia* symbionts (s) of *Lecanora chlarona*, see **(a)** above. (Photo of R. Honegger.) **(e)** Scanning electron micrograph of attachment (a) of fungus of *Parmelia acetabulum* to its *Trebouxia* symbionts. (Photo R. Honegger.)

growing foliose species. Such rates are up to a thousand-fold slower than those of non-lichen fungi in culture (Table 6.2). Many thalli of large diameter are very old, up to several centuries in temperate climates and several thousands of years in the antarctic (Beschel, 1955). Comprehensive studies of cell division in host and symbiont have not been conducted, but there is no evidence for rapid turnover in either partner. Lichens may therefore be the most long-lived of any symbiosis.

6.3.2   Adaptation to fluctuating moisture conditions

Lichens desiccate rapidly in dry conditions, sometimes to a water content as low as 2–5% dry weight. With the onset of a rain shower, they absorb water quickly, reaching a maximum content typically in the range of about

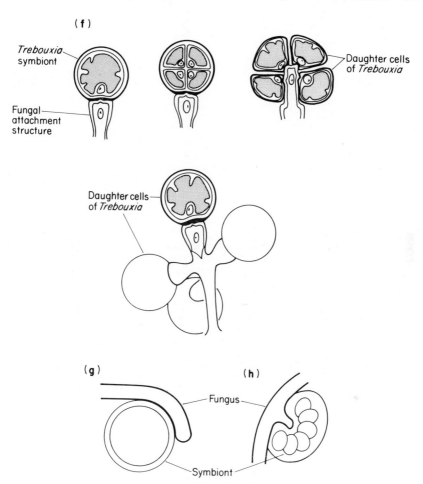

Fig. 6.3(f) Diagram showing division of a *Trebouxia* symbiont and the development of new fungal attachment structures on to the daughter cells, causing the latter to be separated from each other. (After Honegger, 1984.) **(g)** Close wall-to-wall adhesion, but no formation of appressoria or penetration of symbionts. The diagram here shows the relationship between the fungus of *Peltigera aphthosa* and its *Coccomyxa* symbionts. (After Honegger, 1984.) **(h)** Hyphae enter gelatinous sheaths enclosing colonies of cyanobacterial symbionts, but do not come into contact with symbiont cell walls. This diagram shows relationship between the fungus of *Peltigera* sp. and *Nostoc* symbionts.

150–300% dry weight. They can also slowly absorb water vapour from humid atmospheres; and for desert species, dew is a crucially important source of water (Lange *et al.*, 1970).

Most lichens therefore undergo frequent cycles of drying and wetting in nature. Attempts to maintain lichens in a healthy condition in the laboratory

Table 6.2 Growth rates of lichens compared to nonsymbiotic fungi (after Hawskworth and Hill, 1984).

	Maximum radial increase	
	$mm\ yr^{-1}$	$\mu m\ h^{-1}$
Lichens in natural habitats		
Parmelia conspersa (foliose)	5.5	0.6
Rhizocarpon geographicum (crustose)	0.5	0.06
Fungi in culture		
Neurospora crassa (anamorph)	–	4400
Aspergillus niger	–	133
Penicillium chrysogenum	–	76

show that growth (Harris and Kershaw, 1971), photosynthesis and phosphate uptake (Farrar, 1976a) are favoured by fluctuating rather than constant moisture conditions. Metabolic activities recover very quickly when dry lichens are immersed in water. Metabolism of externally supplied $KH_2{}^{32}PO_4$ is detectable within 10 seconds (Farrar, 1976b), and respiratory gas exchange within two to four minutes (Smith and Molesworth, 1973). Respiration rates may temporarily exceed those of controls, a phenomenon known as 'resaturation respiration'; this is more pronounced in lichens from moist habitats (Table 6.3). Also during the initial immersion of dry lichens in water, solutes passively leak from the thallus for 40–120 seconds until control of membrane permeability is re-established (Table 6.3). Such extensive leakage

Table 6.3 Effects of rewetting dry lichens. When air-dry lichens are immersed in water, two processes occur which lead to some loss of soluble carbohydrates. (a) Respiration rises to a level above that of control, undried, lichens for a period of one to several hours; this excess respiration is termed 'resaturation respiration'. (b) There is a brief period before membrane integrity (and hence permeability barriers) are re-established, so that some solutes (including carbohydrates) leak passively from the thallus. One of the roles of the provision of photosynthate from symbionts is to make good these losses. This Table summarizes the result of laboratory experiments and shows how the intensity varies with the degree of dryness of the habitat. (Data from Smith and Molesworth, 1973; Farrar 1976a,b; Smith, 1979.)

Lichen	Habitat	Excess loss of CO_2 from resaturation respiration ml per g. dry wt	Leakage of previously fixed [14]C	
			Period of passive leakage	Fixed ^{14}C lost by leakage (%)
Peltigera polydactyla	Moist woodland floor	3.9	120 sec	15
Hypogymnia physodes	Trees in open woodland	0.54	60 sec	7
Xanthoria aureola	Exposed tiled roof	0.16	–	–
Rocella sp.	Exposed coastal rocks in tropics	–	40 sec	4

is unlikely to occur often in nature, since it is rare for dry lichens to be suddenly immersed in water. However, it is very likely that localized leakage may occur within the thallus in areas where, for example, a rain drop strikes, and it offers a possible mechanism for the movement of substances between host and symbiont.

Experimental studies on the interaction between host and symbiont are usually carried out under constant moisture conditions, but it is important to remember not only that moisture conditions fluctuate in nature, but also that such fluctuation may often be a requirement for healthy growth. Some earlier experiments on the laboratory synthesis of lichens proceeded more successfully if cultures are subjected to slow, alternating periods of wetting and drying (Ahmadjian, 1962).

6.3.3 Photosynthesis, respiration and net productivity

The photosynthetic rate per unit chlorophyll of lichen symbionts is comparable to that of nonsymbiotic algae and cyanobacteria. However, the rate per unit thallus surface area or weight is low (approximately 10–20% of the value for shade-adapted leaves) because the symbionts comprise only 5–10% of the volume of the thallus and because they have a relatively low chlorophyll content per cell compared to nonsymbiotic species.

The rate of photosynthesis depends critically upon water content. Maximum rates are usually achieved at 50–80% of saturation, the lower values being in species with a thicker and denser thallus structure. Above and below the optimum water content, photosynthesis probably declines because of increased structural resistance to carbon dioxide diffusion (Snelgar *et al.*, 1981). As conditions become drier, lichens can continue photosynthesizing at lower water potentials than nonsymbiotic algae in the same habitat (Brock, 1975), perhaps due to a beneficial effect of internal thallus structure and organization in maintaining a moister environment for the symbionts. Dry lichens with algal symbionts can absorb sufficient moisture from water vapour for photosynthesis to occur, but those with cyanobacterial symbionts require liquid water (Lange and Ziegler, 1986). Respiration also varies with water content, but is often at a maximum at full thallus saturation when rates are in the range 0.2–2.0 mg CO_2 g^{-1} dry weight h^{-1}.

The photosynthetic rates in lichens, although low, cannot in themselves explain the extraordinarily low growth rates and net productivity of these associations. A substantial proportion of carbon is probably lost after fixation. One possibility is that lichens are much more often moist at night (because of dew) than day, so that CO_2 losses will be greater than in plants which do not dry out and can photosynthesize throughout the day. Resaturation respiration and passive leakage of solutes (Table 6.3) may also contribute to loss of fixed carbon. A net loss of biomass was measured in the tundra lichen *Cetraria cucullata* over an unusually dry period of 20 days when most rewetting was by dew (Lechowicz, 1981). Similar losses during the summer are routinely observed in *Peltigera polydactyla* (Smith, 1961).

6.3.4   Absorption of nutrients

Lichens can absorb large amounts of substances from solution. For example, *Peltigera polydactyla* can take up 25% of its own dry weight of glucose from a 10 mM solution in 24 hours (Smith, 1975). Absorption from dilute solutions is also efficient: *Hypogymnia physodes* absorbed phosphate at higher rates than barley roots from 1 μM KH_2PO_4. In solutions of 0.1 mM KH_2 $^{32}PO_4$, the lichen took up phosphate at a steady rate for four days, absorbing a total of 0.5 mg phosphate per 100 mg dry weight, none of which was exchangeable when the lichen was transferred to non-radioactive phosphate solutions.

Thus, lichens are unlikely to be deficient in key nutrients, and can take advantage of both organic and inorganic sources in the habitat. The fungal host is usually considered to be primarily responsible for the massive uptake observed.

6.3.5   Soluble carbohydrates

Lichen fungi contain high concentrations of polyols such as mannitol and arabitol (which, together with the disaccharide trehalose, are the principal soluble carbohydrates of Ascomycotina). The polyols are probably in saturated solution, and generate a high osmotic potential which would be advantageous under conditions of environmental water stress. It is also possible that under conditions of severe desiccation, the hydroxyl groups of polyol molecules may be able to replace those of water in helping to maintain the structural integrity of membranes (Farrar, 1976b). The algal symbionts are also rich in polyols, but these are different from those in the fungus: trebouxioid symbionts contain ribitol, and *Trentepohlia* contains erythritol.

6.3.6   Secondary metabolic products

These compounds (sometimes known as 'lichen substances' or 'lichen acids') are produced by the fungal partner and usually occur as extracellular crystalline products. They are only produced when the fungus is in symbiosis (Fig. 6.4), and most of them are derivatives of phenolic carboxylic acids, e.g., depsides, tridepsides, depsidones, dibenzofurans and usnic acids (Culberson, 1969, 1970; Culberson *et al.*, 1977). They are of great importance in the taxonomy of lichens.

Many of the compounds appear to serve a defensive function, making lichens unpalatable to grazing insects and molluscs and inhibiting overgrowth by plants such as mosses; some, such as usnic acid, have powerful antibiotic properties. The crystals are hydrophobic and so help maintain air chambers even in saturated thalli (see 6.2.2). Pigmented compounds deposited in the upper cortex may help protect symbionts from high light intensities.

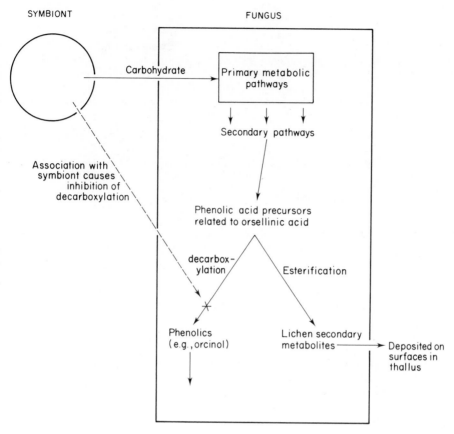

Fig. 6.4 Formation of secondary metabolic products by lichen fungi in symbiosis (after Culberson and Ahmadjian, 1980). These products are not formed by fungi cultured in isolation, and it is believed that association with the symbiont results in inhibition of decarboxylation of phenolic acid precursors, and instead they become esterified to form secondary metabolic products.

6.4 Movement of metabolites between the partners

The movement of fixed nitrogen from cyanobacterial symbionts to the host is described in Chapter 5 (5.3.3).

6.4.1 Photosynthate transport from symbiont to fungus

6.4.1.1 The extent of transport

The movement of photosynthate from symbiont to host was first demonstrated experimentally with *Peltigera polydactyla* (Fig. 6.1d); this has cyano-

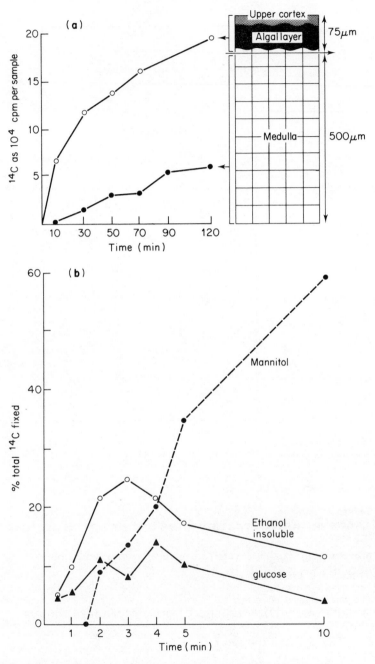

Fig. 6.5 Experiments on the movement of photosynthate from symbiont to host in *Peltigera polydactyla* (see Fig. 6.1.d). **(a)** Movement from the symbiont layer to the fungal medulla. Discs (7 mm diameter) cut from the thallus are floated on solutions of NaH^{14}CO$_3$ in the light. At intervals, samples are removed, the medulla separated from the rest of the disc, and the amount of fixed ^{14}C it contains is measured. **(b)** Pattern of incorporation of fixed ^{14}C

(c)

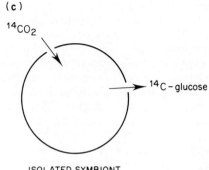

$^{14}CO_2$

^{14}C - glucose

ISOLATED SYMBIONT

^{14}C-glucose $\longrightarrow$ ^{14}C-mannitol

ISOLATED HOST

(d)	% Fixed ^{14}C released to medium	% Fixed ^{14}C recovered from mannitol
Untreated control	0.4	c.70%
Treated with digitonin during photosynthetic ^{14}C fixation	5.3 (as ^{14}C-glucose)	trace
Treated with digitonin after photosynthetic ^{14}C fixation	42.3 (mostly as ^{14}C-mannitol)	trace

in the intact thallus. Thallus discs are incubated as in (a), then removed at rapid intervals, killed immediately in hot ethanol, and the distribution of radioactive compounds studied by autoradiography of paper chromatograms of extracts of discs. Mannitol is a fungal product. (c) Production of glucose by isolated symbionts and its utilization by the host. Freshly isolated symbionts release 20% of their fixed ^{14}C as glucose; portions of medulla rapidly absorb ^{14}C-glucose from solution, converting 80% of it to mannitol. (d) Inhibition of host metabolism. The detergent digitonin inactivates eukaryotic membranes because it binds to the sterol groups which they contain; it has no effect on prokaryotic membranes which lack sterols. Since the symbiont of *P. polydactyla* is prokaryotic, digitonin can be used in the intact lichen as a selective inhibitor of the fungus. If it is used during ^{14}C fixation, then products released by the cyanobacterial symbionts leak into the medium because the fungus cannot absorb them. If used after ^{14}C fixation, soluble products formed by the fungus from symbiont photosynthate are released.

bacterial (*Nostoc*) symbionts, but the experiments formed the basis for subsequent research into lichens with algal symbionts. Discs cut from the thallus were floated in the light on aqueous solutions of ^{14}C-sodium bicarbonate (NaH^{14}CO$_3$). At intervals, discs were removed from the solutions and the fungal medulla dissected away from the overlying symbiont layer and upper cortex. Ten minutes after the start of the experiment, photosynthetically fixed ^{14}C was detectable in the medulla, and after 2 hours, appreciable fixed ^{14}C accumulated in this purely fungal tissue (Fig. 6.5a). Most of the ^{14}C in the medulla was incorporated into mannitol (Smith, 1980), a fungal carbohydrate which does not occur in the *Nostoc* symbiont. Incorporation of ^{14}C into mannitol could therefore be used as an indicator of photosynthate movement to the host in the intact thallus. In further experiments, radioactive mannitol was detected in lichen discs within 90 seconds of their immersion in NaH^{14}CO$_3$ solutions, and the rate of subsequent accumulation of ^{14}C in mannitol was about 70% of the rate of photosynthetic ^{14}C fixation. At thallus water contents below full saturation, a substantially smaller proportion of fixed ^{14}C accumulates in mannitol in *P. polydactyla* (MacFarlane and Kershaw, 1982). This has been interpreted as evidence for reduced photosynthate movement in lichens at lower water contents. An alternative explanation is that ^{14}C no longer accumulates primarily in mannitol because mannitol is probably at saturating concentrations in thalli with lower water contents (Smith, 1979), and other host metabolites may become the main sink for the accumulation of photosynthate.

Autoradiographic techniques which avoid the loss of water soluble compounds have also been used to study the movement of photosynthetically fixed ^{14}C (Tapper, 1981). These give a more accurate picture of ^{14}C movement since they measure all labelled compounds, and not just soluble fungal carbohydrates. In *Cladonia convoluta*, which has *Trebouxia* symbionts, more than 90% of the fixed ^{14}C was released from the symbionts, and about one third was in the upper cortex above the symbiont layer, and about two thirds in the underlying medulla.

Results of ^{14}C tracer experiments with a range of lichens suggest that a substantial proportion of the ^{14}C photosynthetically fixed by algal and cyanobacterial symbionts is released to the host. However, such experiments do not show the absolute *quantity* which moves, because the specific activity of neither the carbon dioxide at the site of fixation in the symbiont, nor the compounds moving from symbiont to host can be determined. Furthermore, it is not known if compounds continue to move from symbiont to host in darkness (as occurs, for example, in green hydra, see 2.2.2.2). Almost all laboratory experiments have been conducted with saturated thalli of temperate species at room temperature. More experiments are therefore needed to show whether movement continues to be substantial under the ecologically more realistic conditions of lower temperatures and reduced water contents.

6.4.1.2 The identity of the mobile compounds and the 'inhibition technique'

In *Peltigera polydactyla*, four lines of experimental evidence suggest that photosynthetically fixed carbon moves from symbiont to host as a single compound, glucose. Firstly, when the *Nostoc* symbionts are isolated from homogenates of the thallus by centrifugation and washing (Drew and Smith, 1967), they release fixed ^{14}C to the medium exclusively as glucose (Fig. 6.5c). Secondly, isolated portions of fungal medulla rapidly absorb ^{14}C-glucose, immediately converting much of it to ^{14}C-mannitol. Thirdly, in short-term photosynthesis experiments with intact lichen discs, fixed ^{14}C is incorporated into glucose before it begins to accumulate in mannitol (Fig. 6.5b). Fourthly, when lichen discs are incubated in solutions of digitonin (which inactivates membranes of the host but not those of the cyanobacterial symbionts) the photosynthetic products that leak out of the discs into the medium consist almost entirely of glucose (Fig. 6.5d, and see also 5.3.3).

Studies on a wide range of other lichens confirmed that photosynthate released by symbionts is always primarily in the form of a single compound, the identity of which depends on the identity of the symbiont. Cyanobacteria, such as the *Nostoc* symbiont of *P. polydactyla*, release glucose but algae release polyols, the identity of which varies with the genus of alga (Table 6.4).

Table 6.4 Types of carbohydrate moving from symbiont to fungus in lichens. This Table summarizes the results of experiments on 42 lichen species, and shows that the type of mobile carbohydrate depends upon the identity of symbiont: cyanobacteria release glucose, but algal symbionts release polyhydric alcohols (polyols).

| Symbiont | Symbiont genus | Number of lichens investigated | | Mobile carbohydrate | Formula |
		Genera	Species		
Algae	*Trentepohlia*	4	6	erythritol	$C_4H_{10}O_4$
	Trebouxia	10	13		
	Myrmecia	2	4	ribitol	$C_5H_{12}O_5$
	Coccomyxa	3	3		
	Hyalococcus	1	2		
	Stichococcus	2	2	sorbitol	$C_6H_{14}O_6$
Cyanobacteria	*Nostoc*	5	10		
	Calothrix	1	1	glucose	$C_6H_{12}O_6$
	Scytonema	1	1		

A rapid preliminary identification of the mobile compound can be made by the 'inhibition' or isotope trapping technique (Fig. 6.6a). This depends on the presence of specific carriers by which the mobile compound crosses membranes. These carriers can also mediate the exchange between external and internal molecules of the compound by the process of 'exchange diffusion'. The 'inhibition' technique operates in the following way. If *P. polydactyla* is incubated in 1% (w/v) ^{12}C-glucose during ^{14}C fixation, the non-radioactive glucose saturates all the fungal uptake sites by virtue of its high concentration, and also exchanges with ^{14}C-glucose in the symbiont cells. No ^{14}C-mannitol is formed because ^{14}C-glucose is prevented from entering the fungus and instead it diffuses into the medium (Fig. 6.6). The effect is very specific; no hexose other than glucose elicits ^{14}C-glucose release and inhibits ^{14}C-mannitol accumulation. The 'inhibition technique' is used to make a preliminary identification of the mobile carbohydrate in previously unstudied lichens by incubating them in solutions of a range of different carbohydrates during ^{14}C fixation. The carbohydrate which elicits substantial release of fixed ^{14}C to the medium and prevents ^{14}C incorporation into fungal carbohydrates is very likely to be the mobile compound.

6.4.1.3   Mechanism and pathways of photosynthate release

Several lines of evidence suggest that carbohydrate is released from symbionts by carrier-mediated active transport. The operation of the 'inhibition technique' (see 6.4.1.2 above) is indicative of specific membrane carriers. Release from the *Trebouxia* symbiont of *Cladonia convoluta* is abolished by inhibitors such as dinitrophenol, arsenate and fluorocarbonyl-cyanidephenylhydrazone (FCCP) (Tapper, 1981), suggesting that it is an energy-dependent process. However, one of the most important characteristics of active transport, movement against a concentration gradient, has not yet been demonstrated rigorously.

An important feature is that the massive release of a specific carbohydrate is not exhibited by symbionts in culture. On isolation from the lichen, the proportion of fixed ^{14}C released by symbionts progressively declines and is paralleled by an increased incorporation of ^{14}C into intracellular material, especially polysaccharides. Within 6–12 hours after isolation, symbionts resemble nonsymbiotic forms and release only about 5% of their fixed ^{14}C (Fig. 6.7); a variety of compounds is released and often these do not include the mobile carbohydrate in symbiosis. In this respect, lichen symbionts resemble many of the algal symbionts of aquatic protists and invertebrates (Chapters 2 and 3). However, procedures which induce photosynthate release in isolated *Chlorella* (incubation at low pH) or *Symbiodinium* symbionts (addition of aqueous extracts of host) have not been successful with isolated lichen symbionts.

In cyanobacterial symbionts, the principal product of nitrogen fixation, ammonia, is released to the host because the activity of the cyanobacterial enzyme of ammonia assimilation, glutamine synthetase, is repressed in symbiosis (see 5.3.3). Possibly, carbohydrate may be released by an analogous mechanism, in which pathways of polysaccharide synthesis in symbionts become altered or repressed so as to generate a surplus of the mobile compound. One specific suggestion (Hill, 1972) is that cell wall synthesis is modified so that carbohydrates (which are already destined for an extracellular location) are diverted from wall manufacture to release. Consistent with this hypothesis, fixed ^{14}C in the *Nostoc* symbionts of *Peltigera polydactyla* passes rapidly through a pool of ethanol-insoluble compounds

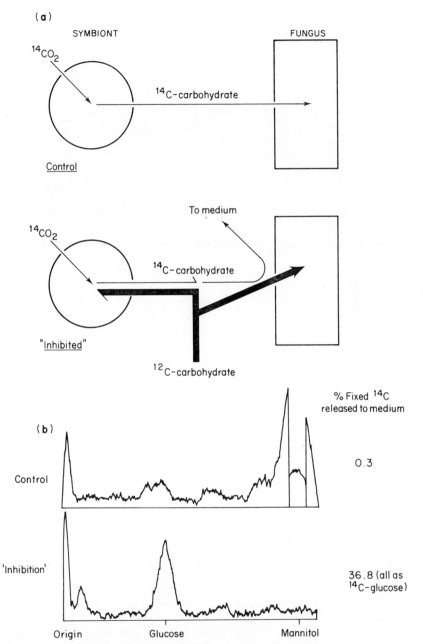

Fig. 6.6 'Inhibition technique' (also known as isotope trapping technique). **(a)** Mechanism. (For detailed explanation see 6.4.1.2.). Rapid screening to identify mobile carbohydrates carried out by incubating lichens in solutions of a range of likely carbohydrates during ^{14}C fixation, and seeing which causes the release of substantial fixed ^{14}C to the medium. **(b)** Effects of 'inhibition' in *Peltigera polydactyla*. The mobile compound is glucose, which the fungus converts to mannitol. With a high concentration of ^{12}C-glucose in the medium, these scans of one-dimensional radio-chromatograms show that formation of ^{14}C-mannitol is prevented, and mobile ^{14}C-glucose is released to the medium.

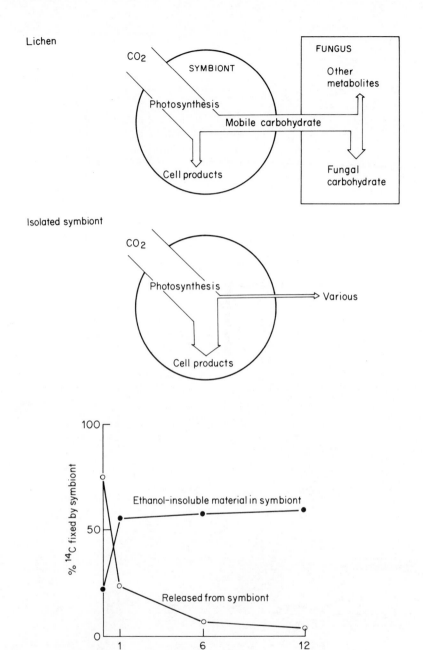

Fig. 6.7 Effects of removal from symbiosis on carbohydrate release from lichen symbionts. After separation from the fungus, carbohydrate release from symbionts declines sharply with time. The width of the arrows in the upper diagrams indicate the relative amount of carbon moving along each pathway. This figure illustrates results of experiments on the *Coccomyxa* algal symbionts of the lichen *Peltigera aphthosa* (Smith, 1974).

(probably polysaccharide) before release as glucose (Fig. 6.5b). Against this hypothesis is the fact that polyols, the mobile carbohydrates of algal symbionts, are not components of their cell walls (although they do occur as intracellular soluble carbohydrates).

A related question is the pathway by which photosynthate moves from symbiont to fungus. If the various types of contact between fungal hyphae and trebouxioid algae (6.4.2, and Fig. 6.3) are the principal sites of photosynthate transfer, it is surprising that a large area of surface contact between the partners is not developed (as occurs, for example, in the various kinds mycorrhizal projections (e.g. Figs 7.2d and 7.4)).

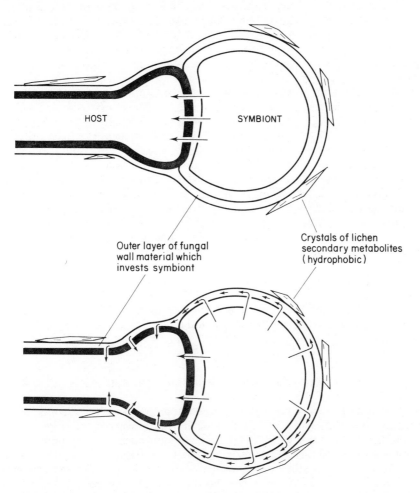

Fig. 6.8 Diagram to show possible routes (arrowed) of transfer of carbohydrate from symbiont to host when fungal attachments are as in Figs 6.3 c and e. The relative thickness of the layer of fungal wall material which invests the symbiont has been exaggerated.

Since the trebouxioid algal symbionts are invested with a layer of fungal wall material, the outer surface of which may bear crystals of hydrophobic secondary metabolic products, it seems unlikely that photosynthate released from the symbiont passes across this surface and into the surrounding space, especially since the latter may be air-filled. Two possibilities remain (Fig. 6.8): firstly, the region of host/symbiont contact, although relatively small in area, is nevertheless the site of a photosynthate transfer which is insufficiently large to require an extensive area of contact; or secondly, photosynthate is released over the surface of the symbiont, entering the outer investing layer of fungal material, and then diffusing along this to reach the fungal cytoplasm. The tendency for greater penetration of host into symbiont cells in lichens from very dry habitats (6.2.3) raises the question of whether 'haustoria' have particular functions in host/symbiont interactions in thalli with reduced water content. A better understanding of photosynthate transfer under such conditions requires a clearer picture of the distribution of water between host and symbiont as thalli dry out.

Richardson *et al.* (1968) found that in the 'inhibition technique' (6.4.1.2), three types of lichens could be recognized depending upon the rate at which the mobile ^{14}C-carbohydrate was released to media containing the appropriate ^{12}C-carbohydrate: 'fast', in which 20–40% of the fixed ^{14}C was released in 3 hours and was typical of lichens containing *Nostoc*; 'intermediate', in which 10–15% was released in 3 hours and was typical of lichens containing *Coccomyxa*; and 'slow', in which 2–4% was released in 3 hours and 20–45% in 24 hours, and included lichens containing trebouxioid symbionts. These differences are correlated with different types of host/symbiont contact (Fig. 6.3). The 'slow' rate of ^{14}C release in lichens with trebouxioid symbionts may arise from the outer layer of hydrophobic material which covers the symbiont and which may prevent the ^{14}C-carbohydrate in the 'inhibition' medium from gaining direct access to the site of photosynthate transfer. Instead, the ^{12}C-carbohydrate may follow a relatively long diffusion path through hyphal walls in the thallus to reach the site of transfer. Again, a better understanding of the pathways of water movement in the thallus is needed.

6.4.2 Movement of other substances from symbiont to host

The experiments which have been carried out on transport from symbiont to host are not sufficiently sensitive to detect the movement of either small quantities of substances such as vitamins, or substances which do not incorporate newly fixed carbon. It therefore remains possible that symbionts may provide some essential micronutrients. For example the lichen alga *Coccomyxa* in culture releases more biotin than related nonsymbiotic algae, and this may be significant since lichen fungi (like many other fungi) require biotin for growth in culture.

6.4.3 Movement of substances from host to symbiont

It has long been claimed that the fungal host provides its symbionts with mineral nutrients, but there is no experimental evidence either for the movement of nutrients or for the requirement by the symbionts for host-derived compounds. The growth of symbionts is so slow that their needs could probably be satisfied by the normal mineral content of rainwater. The speed with which externally supplied bicarbonate ions enter the symbiont in photosynthesis (Fig. 6.5b) illustrates how easily symbionts could absorb from water permeating the thallus.

On the other hand, lichen fungi have a marked ability to absorb and accumulate mineral ions from solution (6.3.4 and Smith, 1962). Although laboratory experiments suggest that they do not release back to the medium any minerals they absorb from solution, solutes are passively released from dry lichens for a brief period if they are rapidly rewetted (6.3.2). Within the thallus, substances passively released from hyphae during rewetting might be available for uptake by the symbionts.

6.5 Establishment of the lichen association

6.5.1 Reproduction and development of lichens in nature

Little is known about the reproduction of lichens in nature, partly because their very slow growth would require observations over prolonged periods in the field. Three methods are possible. Firstly, small fragments of thalli may break off and become dispersed by wind or along raintracks down trees and rocks. Secondly, quite a number of lichens produce special propagules, soredia (Fig. 6.2c), in powdery areas of the thallus, the shape and location of which are characteristic for the species. Each soredium consists of one or a few symbiont cells with some attached fungal hyphae. Soredia have been observed in nature to germinate and begin developing into new thalli. Thirdly, sexually produced fungal spores released from fruit bodies (Fig. 6.2b) could encounter cells of the symbiont, and the synthesis of a new lichen could result suggesting that synthesis can be a successful method of per-petuating the symbiosis, even though free-living lichen symbionts have been rarely reported (6.1). Recent descriptions of lichen synthesis in nature have clarified various ways in which this problem may be overcome. Galun (1987) observed fungal spores of *Xanthoria parietina* and free-living cells of its *Trebouxia* symbiont on the bark of trees on which lichen grows. By removing the surface microflora with scotch tape and examining under a scanning elec-tion microscope (SEM), she observed fungal hyphae surrounding groups of dividing symbiont cells, then various stages of synthesis from the formation of soredia-like structures to the development of small thalli. By immunological techniques, she was able to distinguish between symbionts and other unicellular algae. 'Incompatible' combinations between hyphae and nonsymbiotic algae were frequently observed; these developed to the

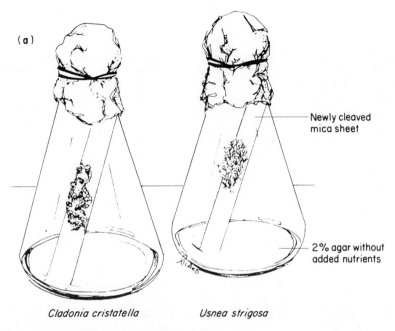

(a)

Newly cleaved
mica sheet

2% agar without
added nutrients

Cladonia cristatella   *Usnea strigosa*

Fig. 6.9   Axenic synthesis of lichens. **(a)** Techniques of resynthesis. The flasks are maintained at 21°, 95% Relative humidity, under a light regime of 12 h light: 12 h dark at 3 Klux intensity, and the host and symbiont inoculated on to thin sheets of newly cleaved mica, (Ahmadjian, 1982.)

soredial stage but not beyond. Ott (1987) also studied *X. parietina*, and observed hyphae from germinating spores acquire their algal symbionts from soredia of other lichen species, as well as from thalli of *Physcia*, a lichen which commonly grows associated with *X. parietina*. Like Galun, she observed frequent encounters between hyphae and nonsymbiotic algae which usually developed as far as the soredial stage. At the soredial stage, 'compatible' associations became enveloped in a jelly-like mucilage but 'incompatible' ones did not. Jahns (1987) studied the foliose lichen *Solorina crocea* which grows on moss. Balls of fungal hyphae occasionally became detached from the underside of the thallus (which lacks a lower cortex), and the hyphae then ramified amongst the microbial community at the base of the moss clumps, eventually acquiring cyanobacterial symbionts. No observer appears to believe that lichen symbionts have a permanent free-living existence, so that the release of symbionts from lichens in nature may be commoner than would be suggested by the solitary report of such an occurrence in the literature (Slocum *et al.*, 1980).

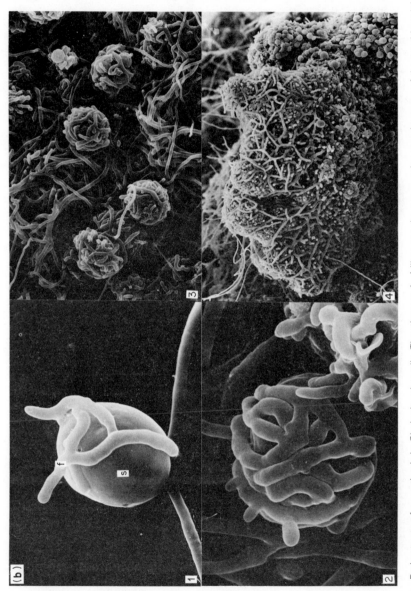

Fig. 6.9(b) Early stages of resynthesis in *Cladonia cristatella*. The pictures 1–4 illustrate the progressive envelopment of the symbiont (s) by the fungus (f). *Photograph* V. Ahmadjian.

6.5.2   Artificial synthesis of lichens in the laboratory

It has proved surprisingly difficult to synthesize a taxonomically identifiable lichen in the laboratory from cultures of its components. After many unsuccessful attempts by a variety of researchers during the past century, Ahmadjian (1983) has become the first to develop techniques which are consistently successful for at least the partial synthesis of a number of different lichen species. Pure cultures of host and symbiont are inoculated on to freshly cleaved strips of mica as shown in Fig. 6.9a. It is particularly important for the initiation of a lichen synthesis that the concentration of nutrients is low; under nutrient-rich conditions the partners grow independently and show no tendency to associate. Earlier studies (Ahmadjian, 1962) had shown that slow alternate drying and wetting promoted synthesis, but moisture conditions were not deliberately varied in the more recent methods.

The laboratory synthesis of *Cladonia cristatella* in Admadjian's recent experiments (Fig. 6.9b) proceeded in the following stages.
a)   Fungal hyphae and algal symbionts come into contact.
b)   Hyphae encircle the symbionts. This stage is non-specific as hyphae respond in a similar manner to a variety of nonsymbiotic algae and glass beads of similar size.
c)   Hyphae branch, and continue to envelop symbionts to form soredium-like bodies (Fig. 6.9b). The symbionts become surrounded by a gelatinous matrix of fungal origin. Penetration of algal cells by 'haustoria' (6.2.3) commences.
d)   Distinct small leaf- or scale-like structures ('squamules') are formed; the natural thallus is formed of dense squamules. Squamule formation involves tissue differentiation by the fungus (especially development of cortex and medulla), and the symbionts are confined to a distinct layer. Secondary metabolites (6.3.6) characteristic of lichens are formed.
e)   In a few samples, synthesis proceeds as far as the initiation of fungal fruit bodies.

There are a number of differences between natural and artificially synthesized squamules of *C. cristatella*. The latter have less extracellular matrix, but symbionts are encircled to a much greater degree by hyphae, and haustorial penetration is more frequent. The hyphae in artificial squamules lack 'concentric bodies', organelles of distinctive appearance (Fig. 6.10a) but uncertain function which are possessed by almost all ascomycete lichen fungi in nature, but are very rare in non-lichen fungi.

The specificity of the fungus of *Cladonia cristatella* for its symbiont (*Trebouxia*) has also been studied in laboratory synthesis experiments. Of nine *Trebouxia* spp. inoculated with the fungus, three were killed, one proceeded to stage 3 above and four as far as stage 4; no association was initiated with any of the 12 *Pseudotrebouxia* spp., but with the nonsymbiotic alga *Friedmannia israelensis*, synthesis to stage 3 was attained (Ahmadjian and Jacobs, 1981). This agrees with field observations (6.5.1) that lichen fungi are not highly specific in at least the early stages of lichen development.

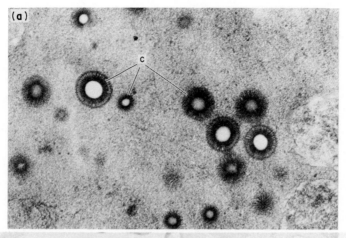

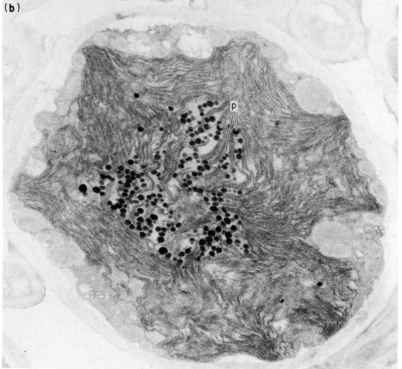

Fig. 6.10 Structural features of lichen fungi and algae which are common in the lichenized state but rare or absent in the free-living state. Electron micrographs provided by E. Peveling. **(a)** Concentric bodies (c) in lichen fungi. These are 300 nm in diameter, with an electron-transparent core surrounded by two concentric electron-dense bands and ray-like projecting structures. They are particularly abundant at cell division, so it has been proposed that they have a role in wall synthesis. **(b)** Pyrenoglobuli (p) in lichen algae. These are lipid-containing globules, 40–100 nm diameter, which are distributed throughout the pyrenoid. It has been proposed that they serve as respiratory substrates under conditions of water stress.

Table 6.5 Effects of lichen formation upon the fungus and its symbionts.

	Morphology		Fine Structure	Physiology	Reproductive behaviour
	Gross	Cell/Tissue differentiation			
Fungus	Adopts highly characteristic thallus shape (see Fig. 6.1)	Differentiation into cortex, medulla, and other tissues	'Concentric bodies' (Fig. 6.10a) formed;	Characteristic secondary metabolic products of lichens are formed (Fig. 6.4)	Sexual stages and associated structures formed
Algal symbionts	Filaments become shorter, sometimes reduced to unicells (see Table 6.1)	–	Pyrenoglobuli (Fig. 6.10b) formed; cell walls become thinner	Fixed carbon accumulates mainly in soluble compounds; release of a specific carbohydrate induced	Motile stages repressed.
Cyanobacterial symbionts	Filaments become shorter, often contorted	In cephalodia, proportion of heterocysts shows marked increase (see Table 5.3)	Cell sheathing structures become reduced	''	?

6.5.3 Lectins and recognition

As with some other symbioses, the role of lectins in recognition has been investigated in lichens and has provided somewhat confusing results. Lectins isolated from *Peltigera polydactyla* and *P. canina* bound to the cultured symbionts (*Nostoc* spp.) from those lichens and also to the nonsymbiotic cyanobacterium *Gloeocapsa alpicola*, but not to 10 other nonsymbiotic cyanobacteria (Lockhart *et al.*, 1978). However, in a separate study, a lectin from *Peltigera horizontalis* bound to the cultured symbiont of this lichen and not to cultured symbionts of other lichens, but it did not bind to the freshly isolated symbiont of *P. horizontalis*. The lectin concanavalin A bound to cultured but not freshly isolated cells of a number of symbionts of lichens (Galun and Bubrick, 1984). The differences in lectin-binding properties of cultured and freshly isolated symbionts could be due either to effects of symbiosis on the symbiont cell walls themselves, or to the likelihood that the walls of freshly isolated symbionts are contaminated by fungal material. Not only lichen symbionts, but also lichen fungi can bind a range of lectins (Marx and Peveling, 1983).

Several authors (Ahmadjian and Jacobs, 1981; Galun and Bubrick, 1984) doubt that lectin-mediated recognition is important in the contact phase of selectivity between fungus and symbiont.

6.5.4 Effects of lichenization: comparisons of the partners in symbiosis and in culture

The complexity of interactions between host and symbiont is well illustrated by the various ways in which their structure, reproduction and physiology in symbiosis differs from that in culture (Table 6.5). The structure and reproductive behaviour of the symbiont becomes simpler in symbiosis, but that of the host becomes more complex. The formation of secondary metabolites only in symbiosis (Fig. 6.4) shows that physiological interactions extend beyond carbohydrate flow from symbiont to host.

Table 6.5 illustrates why studies of the partners in isolated culture adds little to our understanding of the lichen symbiosis unless it is accompanied by investigations of the intact lichen and its development.

7
Fungi in symbiosis II. As symbionts: mycorrhizas

7.1 Introduction

Mycorrhizas are associations between fungi and plant roots (or other underground structures). Part of the fungal mycelium is in the host tissue, and part is in contact with the surrounding soil and usually spreads into it. Host growth is almost always enhanced compared to uninfected plants of the same species. Mycorrhizas occur in some bryophytes (especially liverworts), many pteridophytes, all groups of gymnosperms, and nearly all families of angiosperms (examples of families in which only a few species are regularly and heavily infected include the Juncaceae, Cyperaceae, Caryophyllaceae, Chenopodiaceae and Cruciferae). Many taxa of fungi are also involved including representatives of the Zygomycotina, Ascomycotina, Basidiomycotina, and Deuteromycotina.

In most terrestrial habitats, except those which are very wet or where the soil is particularly nutrient-rich, the great majority of plants are mycorrhizal. For example, there is direct evidence that over 70% of plants in the British flora can be mycorrhizal (Harley and Harley, 1986). Mycorrhizas are more common as nutrient absorbing organs than are uninfected plant roots (Harley and Smith, 1983), and the mycorrhizal condition probably represents the most abundant type of symbiosis in the world.

7.2 Types of mycorrhizas

Four main types of mycorrhizas will be recognized here, based partly on the morphology of the infection and partly on the kind of host plant (see Fig. 7.1 and Table 7.1). Some host plants, and also some fungal symbionts, can be involved in the formation of more than one type of mycorrhiza (Table 7.2).

Except when vegetative growth is dormant (as in winter or other unfavourable seasons), roots are actively and continuously growing, so that a mycorrhiza is not a static association. The relationships between host and symbiont portrayed in Fig. 7.1 are those of the 'mature phase' in a continuously changing relationship.

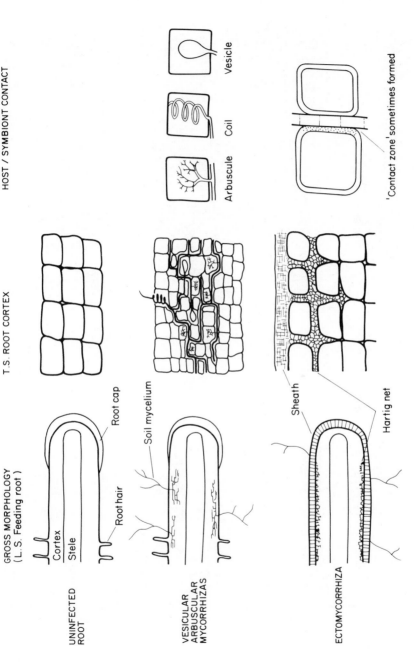

Fig. 7.1 The principal morphological features of mycorrhizas (continued).

Fig. 7.1 (continued)

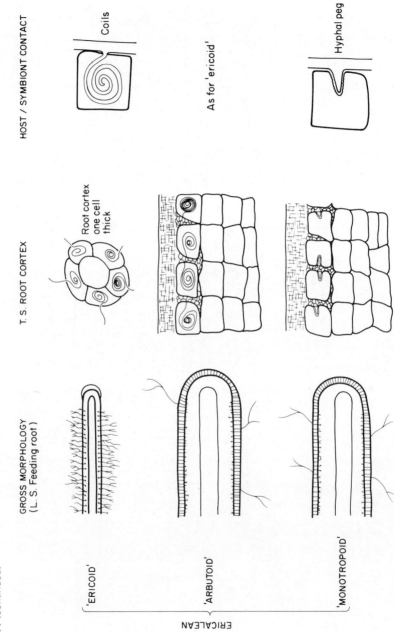

Fig. 7.1 (continued)

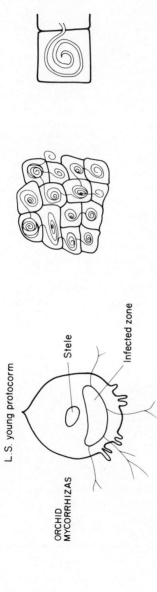

ORCHID
MYCORRHIZAS

L.S. young protocorm

Stele

Infected zone

Coil

Table 7.1　Summary of characteristics of main types of mycorrhizas.

| | STRUCTURE | | | |
	Sheath	Hartig Net	Host cell penetration	Host range
Vesicular-arbuscular mycorrhizas	−	−	+ (Arbuscules and coils)	Many plant species, including representatives of bryophytes, pteridophytes, gymnosperms and many angiosperms
Ectomycorrhizas	+	+	−	Many trees and shrubs, especially of temperate regions. Including: Pinaceae, Betulaceae, Fagaceae } N. Hemisphere; Eucalypts, Caesalpinoideae, Dipterocarpaceae } S. Hemisphere and montane regions of tropics
Ericoid	−	−	+ (Coils)	Members of Ericales with fine hair roots, especially Ericoideae, Vaccinoideae, Rhododendroideae, Epacridaceae and Empetraceae
Arbutoid	+	+ (Limited to epidermal layer)	+ (Coils)	Members of Ericales with sturdier roots, including *Arbutus*, *Arctystaphylos*, and *Pyrolaceae*
Monotropoid	+	+ (Limited to epidermal layer)	+ (Pegs)	Achlorophyllous members of Ericales such as *Monotropa*, *Sarcodes*, *Plerospora*
Orchid mycorrhizas	−	−	+ (Coils – also called 'pelotons')	All members of the Orchidaceae

(Ericalean: Ericoid, Arbutoid, Monotropoid)

Symbiont range	Nutritional interactions		Ecological distribution
	Symbiont → Host	Host → Symbiont	
4 genera of Zygomycotina, all from Endogonaceae: *Glomus* *Acaulospora* *Gigaspora* *Sclerocystis*	Mineral nutrients, especially phosphate	Carbohydrate	Very wide, and from arctic to tropical forests, especially on mineral soils
Many fungi, including species from: 25 Families of Basidiomycotina 7 Families of Ascomycotina 1 genus of Zygomycotina (*Endogone*)	Mineral nutrients	Carbohydrate	Regions where host growth is seasonal or otherwise periodic
Many isolates sterile in culture (including *Oidiodendron*): one has been identified as *Hymenoscyphus* (Ascomycotina)	Nutrients, especially ammonia and organic nitrogen	Carbohydrate	Many grow on acid, peaty soils where nitrogen may be more limiting to host growth than phosphate
	Probably mineral nutrients	Probably carbohydrate	
Those identified so far are mostly Basidiomycotina which also form ectomycorrhizas	Carbohydrates and mineral nutrients	None known	
Many isolates form sterile mycelia referable to 'form' genus *Rhizoctonia*, induced to form sexual stages, referable to about 8 genera of Basidiomycotina including some pathogens	Juvenile achlorophyllous hosts:– carbohydrates and mineral nutrients	None known	Very wide, but especially in tropics, where hosts have many life forms, including lianes and epiphytes
	Adult photosynthetic hosts:– probably mineral nutrients	None known	

7.2.1   Vesicular-arbuscular mycorrhizas

These are by far the commonest type and have been observed in over 1000 genera of plants from over 200 families. Law and Lewis (1983) estimated that 200 000–250 000 species of flowering plants have the potential for forming this kind of symbiosis.

The name 'vesicular-arbuscular' derives from structures formed by the infecting fungus in the host tissue (Fig. 7.2a). 'Arbuscules' are dichotomously branched projections into host cells which do not rupture the host cell membrane (Fig. 7.2b); additionally, some hyphal coils may also occur in host cells (Fig. 7.2a) in many infections. 'Vesicles' are terminal or sometimes intercalary swellings which may either lie between host cells or within them (Fig. 7.2c). Vesicles are rich in lipids, and have been ascribed a storage and reproductive function. Hyphae within the root are connected to an external soil mycelium which may extend several centimetres from the root surface.

The fungi all belong to a single family of Zygomycotina, the Endogonaceae. The fungi are assigned to the genera *Glomus*, *Gigaspora*, *Acaulospora* and *Sclerocystis*, and about 70 species have been recognized, largely on the characteristics of their spores. These spores are abundant in many soils, and are unusually large (up to 500 μm in diameter, depending on the species) so that they can be isolated by sieving soil, a common method of obtaining inocula for experiments. None of the fungi appears to exist saprophytically away from the host for more than a brief period. To date, none has been brought into permanent axenic culture, an important obstacle to certain kinds of experimental investigation.

Roots usually become infected either by hyphae from nearby roots or from resting spores present in the soil. The spores germinate to produce one or a few germ tubes which grow through the soil but do not exhibit directional growth until a few millimetres from the root surface. The advancing germ tube may then branch into a fan-shaped complex of hyphae. When a hyphal tip encounters the root surface, it swells to form an appressorium, from which a hypha penetrates into the cortex (Fig. 7.2a), ramifying both between and through cells. The longitudinal spread of the infection is usually limited to within about 5 mm of the original penetration point, and it has been suggested that the host regulates the rate of growth of the fungus (Buwalda *et al.*, 1984). Hyphae are confined to the cortex, and never penetrate the stele. The internal mycelium may account for 4–17% of the dry weight of the mycorrhiza. The root apical meristem is never infected, but the region just behind it is much more susceptible to infection than the rest of the root system. Hyphae can also spread along the surface of the root creating further penetration points. Even in a heavily infected root, penetration points are sparse, usually about 5 per cm root.

The infection does not alter the morphology of the root or its external appearance and root hairs may still be formed. Within the root, a single fungal species may show different morphology of infection in different hosts. For example, when *Glomus fasciculatum* infects maize, the hyphae and vesicles are mainly intercellular, and the arbuscules terminal, whereas in

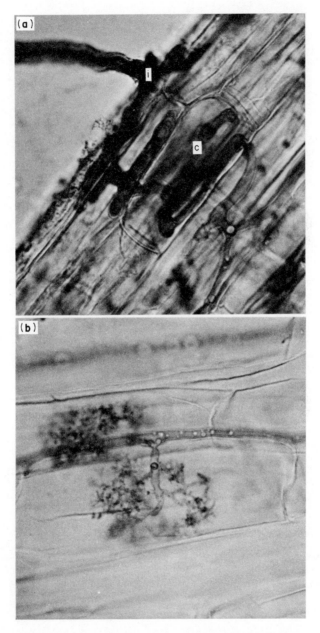

Fig. 7.2 Vesicular–arbuscular infections. **(a)** Light micrograph of an infection point (i) of the fungus *Glomus mosseae* on roots of leek. Note hyphal coils (c) in outer cortical cells. **(b)** Light micrograph of an arbuscule of *Glomus mosseae* in cortical cell of a root of leek. *Photographs* K. Hardie (continued).

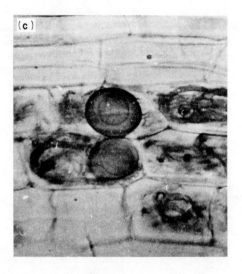

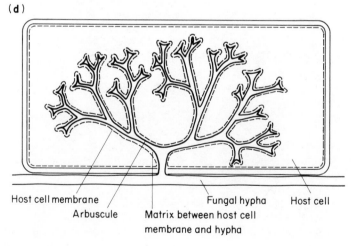

Host cell membrane   Fungal hypha   Host cell
       Arbuscule   Matrix between host cell
                        membrane and hypha

Fig. 7.2(c) Vesicles of a vesicular–arbuscular mycorrhizal fungus in roots of yew. *Photograph* J.L. Harley. **(d)** Diagram to illustrate extensive area of contact between host and symbiont in arbuscules. Note that the plasma membranes of host and symbiont are not in direct physical contact but are separated by a matrix (see 7.3.1.2).

the tulip tree (*Liriodendron*), the hyphae and vesicles pass through cells, and the arbuscules are formed on lateral branches from coiled hyphae.

The soil mycelium originates entirely as branches from the penetration points on the root surface. Once the internal infection is established, the soil mycelium begins to expand at a greater rate, and may eventually be twice as extensive, producing 50–130 cm hyphae per cm of root. The soil mycelium also produces asexual spores, which may be borne either singly on the surface of hyphae or in fruiting structures (sporocarps), depending on the species. The possibility that sexual reproduction occurs has not been investigated.

7.2.2 Ectomycorrhizas

Almost all the host plants are trees and shrubs living in areas where plant growth is seasonal or otherwise intermittent (Table 7.1). Ectomycorrhizas are thus especially characteristic of forest trees of temperate and subarctic regions, but are also found on tropical and subtropical trees in areas where vegetative activity is restricted during some period of the year for edaphic, climatic or other environmental reasons; in tropical and equatorial forests at lower altitudes where growth is continuous, vesicular-arbuscular mycorrhizas predominate. Meyer (1973) estimated that 3% of flowering plants are ectomycorrhizal, but they include species which dominate significant areas of the global land surface.

The characteristic feature of ectomycorrhizas is the form which the infection takes on the ultimate branch tips or absorbing regions of the root system which, in uninfected roots, produce root hairs. Instead, in ecto-mycorrhizas, the absorbing region is invested with a sheath of fungal tissue (Fig. 7.3a) which also encloses the root apex. Fungal hyphae extend inwards from the sheath into the outer 2–3 cell layers of the cortex in the form of labyrinthine branch systems known as the *Hartig Net* (Fig. 7.3a, b), passing between host cells and not penetrating them. These infected root tips are often known as 'ectomycorrhizal organs', and the proportion of fungus in them may be substantial: 25% of total dry weight in pine, and 40% in beech. Some hyphae extend outwards from the sheath to connect to a soil mycelium. The extent to which this occurs is variable, and sometimes there are only a few connections.

In many trees, the branches of the root system can be divided into those of potentially unlimited growth ('long' roots) and those of potentially restricted growth ('short' roots). Ectomycorrhizal organs occur on short roots, although fungal hyphae occur in other parts of the root system and form a reservoir from which new short roots are infected.

Numerous fungi can form ectomycorrhizas (Table 7.1). Many of the mush-rooms and most of the subterranean fungal fruit bodies (such as truffles) found in temperate woodlands are formed by ectomycorrhizal fungi. The only Zygomycotina to form ectomycorrhizas are *Endogone* spp., from the same family as the genera of vesicular-arbuscular fungi.

Most ectomycorrhizal fungi can be cultured. In contrast to their nonsym-

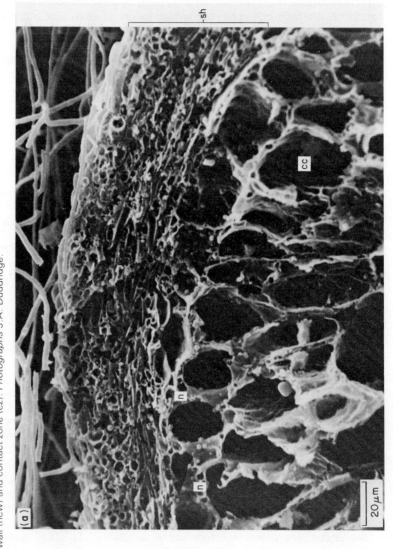

Fig. 7.3 Ectomycorrhizas. **(a)** Scanning electron micrograph of a transverse fracture through an ectomycorrhiza of *Pinus* showing the fungal sheath (sh), and Hartig net (n) between outer cortical cells (cc). **(b)** Transmission electron micrograph of the outer cortical area of a mycorrhizal short root of *Larix kaempferi* (Japanese Larch), showing Hartig net (n) between cortical cells (cc). The net may form a pseudoparenchymatous fungal sheet (pfs). Note host cell wall (hcw) and contact zone (cz). *Photographs* J.A. Duddridge.

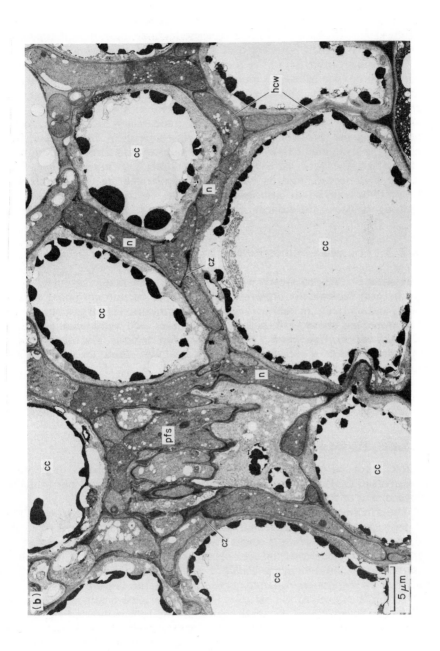

(b)

biotic relatives they are very slow-growing, have complex vitamin and amino acid requirements, and they are unable to break down cellulose to any significant extent. Probably as a result of these features, most do not appear to exist away from their hosts for prolonged periods as soil saprophytes.

The primary infection of the roots occurs soon after the young seedlings have become established. Exudates from roots of both ectomycorrhizal and nonsymbiotic hosts stimulate the growth of ectomycorrhizal fungi and enhance the generally low rate of spore germination. A weft of hyphae forms around the root system, and expands to accomodate new root growth. At the point along the root where protoxylem vessels begin to differentiate, just behind the apex, intercellular penetration begins so as to form the developing Hartig Net. The Net is usually limited to the outer cortical region; occasionally it may spread inwards but it never penetrates the endodermis and beyond. In contrast to pathogenic infections, mycorrhizal fungi seem to prolong the life of the adjacent cortical cells.

7.2.3   Ericalean mycorrhizas

The order Ericales are mostly woody shrubs or trees, many of which belong to or form ecologically important communities on nutrient-poor, usually peaty and acid soils, in habitats such as heaths, moors. The largest family, the Ericaceae, has about 1350 species, and contains such well-known genera as *Rhododendron*, *Vaccinium*, *Calluna*, *Erica* and *Arbutus*. The other families include a number of evergreen perennials, and also plants devoid of chlorophyll such as *Monotropa*.

Three different types of mycorrhizas are formed by the Ericales (Fig. 7.1 and Table 7.1), but they are considered together because the host plants are taxonomically related and many have broadly similar habitat preferences.

7.2.3.1   Ericoid mycorrhizas

These occur on plants which have very fine, hair-like roots, e.g., most members of the Ericoideae, Vaccinoideae and Rhododendroideae of the Ericaceae, and of the Epacridaceae and Empetraceae.

The structure of the fine roots is very simple: a small stele is surrounded by a pericycle and endodermis, outside which is a very thin cortex, 1 to 3 cells deep whose outer surface is covered with a thick mucigel. There are neither root hairs nor epidermis, and the root cap is reduced or absent. The diameter of the root is about 40 μm in *Calluna*, 50–100 μm in *Pernettya*, and slightly greater in *Rhododendron* and *Vaccinium*. In the mature phase of the infection, every cell of the cortex is filled with extensive coils of hyphae; in *Calluna* about 42% of the total volume of the root is infected (Read and Stribley, 1973). There are numerous hyphal connections between the root and the soil since each infected cell usually has at least one penetration point. Thus, there are very many more penetration points (about 2000 per cm root in *Calluna*) than in vesicular-arbuscular infections.

The fungi form slow-growing, dark-coloured mycelia in culture. A few of the isolates produce fruiting bodies referable to the genus *Hymenoscyphus* (Ascomycotina) (Read, 1974), but some of the others may have different affinities, such as *Oidiodendron* (Deuteromycotina). *Clavaria* spp. (Basidiomycotina) grow closely associated with some hosts, and hyphae on *Rhododendron* (*Azalea*) roots have been shown to be immunologically related to *Clavaria*.

Infection begins by growth of the fungus from the soil to form a sparse network of hyphae spreading over the root, and at the same time spreading between and into the cortical cells. The apical meristem itself is free of infection in actively growing roots. The hyphae spread through the mucigel covering the root surface, penetrating cortical cells from the outside rather than spreading from cell to cell within the cortex. No appressoria are formed by hyphae before they penetrate cells. Infection is often sparse at the beginning of a growing season, but increases markedly as the season progresses.

7.2.3.2   Arbutoid mycorrhizas

These occur on members of the Arbutoideae and Pyrolaceae which have sturdier roots than those described above. The root system of arborescent forms is divided into long and short roots (see 7.2.2), the latter being infected in a manner resembling ectomycorrhizas in that they are enclosed in a fungal sheath. A Hartig Net is also formed, but this differs from that of ectomycorrhizas by its restriction to the outer epidermal layer and by abundant penetration into cells by coils of hyphae. Most fungi of arbutoid mycorrhizas also form ectomycorrhizas on other hosts (Table 7.2). It is not known why the same fungus regularly penetrates cells in one family of host but not in another.

Mycorrhizas of very similar structure to arbutoid mycorrhizas are found in juvenile conifers. They involve members of the Deuteromycotina, and have been termed ectendomycorrhizas (Harley and Smith, 1983). They are not considered further here.

7.2.3.3   Monotropoid mycorrhizas

Monotropa seeds do not germinate and develop unless infected by a fungus. The adult host plants are usually herbaceous and they lack chlorophyll. Monotropoid mycorrhizas resemble arbutoid in having a sheath and a Hartig Net limited to the epidermal layer, but differ in that the penetration into host cells are in the form of simple pegs (Duddridge and Read, 1982) and not coils. Monotropoid mycorrhizas function in a fundamentally different way from other ericalean mycorrhizas since the fungus is the donor and not the recipient of carbohydrate (see 7.5.2). The fungi can form ectomycorrhizas on non-ericaceous hosts.

Table 7.2 **(a)** Examples of mycorrhizal fungi able to form more than one type of symbiosis (after Harley, 1984, and Duddridge, unpublished).

Fungus	Mycorrhizal associations formed	Pathogenic associations
Many Basidiomycotina	Ectomycorrhizas	
Boletus sp.	Ectomycorrhiza on pine	
	'Arbutoid' mycorrhizas	
	Monotropoid mycorrhizas on *Monotropa hypopytis*	
Armillaria mellea	Orchid mycorrhiza on achlorophylloces sp. (e.g. *Gastrodia elata*)	Destructive parasite of woody and herbaceous plants
	Monotropoid mycorrhiza on *Monotropa uniflora*	
Rhizoctonia solani	Orchid mycorrhiza on many species	Destructive parasite of many herbaceous plants
	–	
Cenococcum geophilum	Ectomycorrhizas on many hosts (including some which otherwise have vesicular-arbuscular infections)	Mycorrhizas with host cell penetration as in *Stellaria holostea*

(b) Examples of host genera in which some species form both ectomycorrhizas and vesicular-arbuscular mycorrhizas in some cases simultaneously

Acacia	*Crataegus*	*Juniperus*	*Salix*
Acer	*Cupressus*	*Leptospermum*	*Sorbus*
Adiantum	*Eucalyptus*	*Populus*	
Alnus	*Fraxinus*	*Prunus*	
Casuarina	*Helianthemum*	*Pyrus*	

7.2.4 Orchid mycorrhizas

All orchids are infected with fungi at an early stage of their life, when the entire young plant is still underground and non-photosynthetic. As in monotropoid mycorrhizas, the plant receives carbohydrate from the fungus so that host/symbiont relationships are very different from other kinds of mycorrhizas. Many orchids remain infected after they become adult and photosynthetic, but this stage has received little experimental study. Although orchids do not develop in nature unless infected by a fungus, they can be grown aposymbiotically in the laboratory.

The Orchidaceae are one of the largest families of flowering plants, with over 730 genera and more than 20 000 species. The family is cosmopolitan, but is especially abundant in the tropics. It is appropriate for an account of their mycorrhizas to begin with seed germination and the subsequent infection of the developing embryo.

Orchid seeds are remarkably small, ranging from 0.3 to 14 μg in weight, and comprising no more than 8–100 cells (a single flower capsule may produce up to four million seeds). Upon germination, the seed undergoes a few cell-divisions but then does not develop further unless infected by a fungus. This usually occurs when a hypha penetrates a cell at the suspensor end, away from the meristem. The infection then spreads from cell to cell

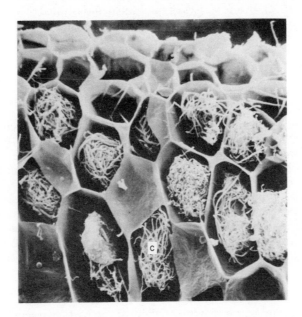

Fig. 7.4 Branched coils (c) or 'pelotons' formed by orchid mycorrhizal fungi inside host cells of *Neottia nidus-avis*. Scanning electron micrograph, R. Honnegger.

until much of the protocorm except the growing point becomes infected. Within host cells (which remain healthy) the fungal penetrations develop into coils (often called 'pelotons') (Fig. 7.4). Subsequently, a central column of conducting tissue differentiates, and fungal infection becomes particularly concentrated in the basal region of the protocorm (Fig. 7.1). Roots which grow out may become infected either from the fungus in the protocorm, or independently from the soil. As development continues, some orchids form storage tubers which, in contrast to the absorbing roots, are uninfected. The length of time before this subterranean structure produces foliage leaves is very variable: just under a year in *Orchis morio*, and as long as ten years in *O. ustulata*. Some orchids remain permanently non-photosynthetic.

Many orchid seeds, even if infected with a compatible fungus, fail to develop, either because the infection kills the plant or because the orchid reacts against the infection and its defence mechanisms eliminate the fungus. Presumably, the very large numbers of seeds produced by the host allows for many unsuccessful infections.

Orchid fungi are easily isolated into culture, but many produce sterile mycelia which are assigned to the 'form' genus *Rhizoctonia*. Recently, a number of isolates have been induced to produce sexual stages which show that they belong to genera of the Basidiomycotina such as *Corticium*, *Cerato-basidium*, *Sebacina*, *Tulasnella*, *Marasmius*, *Xerotus*, *Hymenochaete* and *Armillaria mellea*. It is remarkable that some strains of these fungi such as *A. mellea*, *Ceratobasidium* and *R. solani* (now known to be the imperfect form of *Thanatephorus cucumeris* (Basidiomycotina)) are parasites on other plants (Table 7.2). In a few cases, it has been demonstrated that strains parasitic on other plants will form mycorrhizas with orchids.

7.3   Contacts between host and symbiont

7.3.1   Morphology of cell-to-cell contact

There are two principal types of cell-to-cell contact between host and symbiont in mycorrhizas (Figs. 7.1, 7.2, 7.3 and 7.4): (a) intercellular contact between host cells and hyphae ramifying through the cortex; and (b), the more intimate contact of various fungal projections into host cells (arbuscules, coils or 'pelotons', and haustoria). These projections are termed 'intracellular' in the mycorrhizal literature, but differ from true intracellular symbionts because they remain connected to extracellular hyphae and so the symbiont is not completely enclosed by the host cell. Some fungi and hosts can each be involved in more than one type of mycorrhiza (Table 7.2), so that the type of cell-to-cell contact is not rigidly determined by either partner.

7.3.1.1   Intercellular contact

In vesicular-arbuscular mycorrhizas, there are no particular modifications to hyphae in the cortex. Sometimes, host cell walls appear to become modified and fuse with the walls of the hyphae, but in other cases the partners lie side-by-side in close juxtaposition. In ecto-, arbutoid and monotropoid mycorrhizas, a specialized structure, the Hartig Net (Fig. 7.3), is formed in the region just behind the root meristem. This consists of sheets of hyphae organized into a labyrinthine system between the cortical cells, providing a large surface area of contact with the host. The host cells remain alive and metabolically active, and they are connected with each other by plasmodesmata. The outer layer of the host cell wall may sometimes appear modified when in contact with a hyphal wall (which occasionally may also be modified). These have been called 'contact zones', and are believed to result from fungal interference with, or inhibition of, host enzyme activity in forming wall polymers (Harley and Smith, 1983). 'Contact zones' are not always observed.

7.3.1.2 Projections into host cells

All mycorrhizal fungi, except those of ectomycorrhizas, insert projections into host cells during the mature phase of the association (Figs 7.1, 7.2 and 7.4). These projections never penetrate the host plasmalemma (Fig. 7.2d), and are always relatively short-lived (4–14 days in vesicular-arbuscular, 1–11 days in orchid, and up to 5–6 weeks in ericoid mycorrhizas). The host cell is viable and usually shows signs of greater metabolic activity such as increased volume of nucleus and cytoplasm. The fungal projections eventually degenerate, but it is not known if this results from autolysis or whether the host cell plays an active role. Except in ericoid mycorrhizas, host cells remain alive after the projections degenerate, and in orchids and vesicular-arbuscular mycorrhizas they may undergo repeated cycles of penetration.

The two main kinds of projections are highly branched structures such as arbuscules (Fig. 7.2b, d), and hyphal coils (Figs 7.2a, 7.4). The former are characteristic of vesicular-arbuscular fungi, although many of these can also form coils. But whatever the shape of the projection, its morphological relationship to the host cell is essentially the same. There is usually a matrix between the host cell membrane and symbiont cell wall which contains fibres and vesicles. It is as if host cell wall formation has been disrupted but the host has retained the ability to secrete carbohydrates and polymerize them into fibrils (Harley and Smith, 1983). In some cases, a collar is formed around the base of the projection, reminiscent of that described for haustoria of pathogenic fungi. This collar may seal the space between host and symbiont. Monotropoid mycorrhizas present a somewhat different picture, and with a sequence of changes which follows the development of the host (Duddridge and Read, 1982). The peg-like projections do not penetrate host cell walls, but instead the host cell wall invaginates around them. The peg continues to grow, while at the same time, the invaginated host cell wall forms extensive branched ingrowths reminiscent of 'transfer cells' (characteristically found in plants in regions where there are extensive nutrient fluxes across cell membranes). At about the time of flower production, the tips of the projections appear to burst, releasing their contents into sacs enclosed by host cell membranes. Hyphae from the sheath also then invade and colonize cortical cells.

Projections into host cells are very likely to be important in nutrient movements between the partners, but because of the structural complexity and intimacy of the association, direct experiments are difficult. However, it has been demonstrated, for example, that when a host cell membrane invaginates around the branches of an arbuscule, its ATPase activity increases (Marx *et al.*, 1982).

7.3.2   How do mycorrhizal fungi penetrate host tissues?

In culture, mycorrhizal fungi (except the orchid symbionts) have little or no ability to break down cellulose and pectin (principal components of plant cell walls), even though many of their nonsymbiotic relatives in the Ascomycotina and Basidiomycotina can do so. This raises the question of how mycorrhizal fungi penetrate into roots. Hyphae enter the cortex behind the root apex, in a region where host cell division has ceased but secondary wall formation continues, with carbohydrate secreted by the host cell membrane being polymerized and added to the middle lamella. It appears from electron microscopy that the often wedge-shaped tips of the hyphae force their way between the cells by hydrostatic pressure, and that localized production of cellulase and pectinase at the hyphal tips is unlikely. Harley and Smith (1983) suggest that during this process, when walls of host and symbiont become tightly pressed together, proteins on the surface of the hypha may inhibit or complex with host enzymes responsible for wall synthesis. This hypothesis may explain why fungi enter the root just behind the apex, how hyphae can then penetrate between host cells, and it could account for the appearance of the 'contact zone' and matrix. It also suggests a possible mechanism whereby carbohydrates originally destined for wall formation are made available to the fungus (7.5.1.2).

7.4   Effects of mycorrhizal infection on the host

7.4.1   Improvements in host vigour

Numerous pot experiments have demonstrated that, on nutrient-poor soils, plants with ecto- and vesicular-arbuscular mycorrhizas nearly always have greater dry weights than uninfected plants and a higher content of some of the important mineral nutrients (Fig. 7.5, Table 7.3). On nutrient-rich soils, mycorrhizas usually have little or no effect, and the degree of infection of roots is often much less. Mycorrhizal plants usually have a lower root/shoot ratio, but the actual size of their root system is larger because the overall plant size is larger.

Experiments comparing mycorrhizal and non-mycorrhizal plants growing in soil are not always straightforward. The wide distribution of mycorrhizal

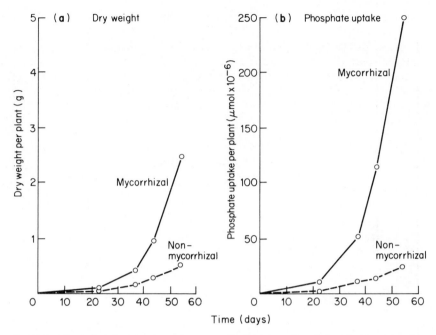

Fig. 7.5 Effect of vesicular–arbuscular mycorrhizas on growth and phosphate uptake of onions during a growth period of 54 days (After Harley, 1984; data of Sanders and Tinker, 1973). The rate of phosphate inflow (mol cm^{-1} root length s^{-1} × 10^{-14}) into mycorrhizal roots in two experiments was 11.5–13.0, and into non-mycorrhizal roots 3.2–4.2.

symbionts means that care has to be exercised in selecting a soil in which the relevant type of mycorrhiza-forming fungus is absent. Some methods of soil sterilization have a deleterious effect on soil structure and properties, with a consequent impairment of plant growth. For example, many experiments comparing plants with and without ericoid mycorrhizas using soil sterilized by heat or steam treatment gave conflicting results. The acid and peaty soil on which host plants grow has a high organic matter content, and when heated, it both releases some nutrients and produces toxic degradation products. If the soil is sterilized by γ-irradiation, clear improvements in host growth resulting from infection could be demonstrated consistently (Table 7.3).

A note of caution is required about two aspects of the experiments illustrated in Fig. 7.5 and Table 7.3. Firstly, they are almost all conducted as pot experiments with single species of plants. In nature, the soil is heavily colonized by roots of other plants, many of which are also mycorrhizal and some may even be linked to the same fungal mycelium. The interactions between host plants are likely to be complex, and the problem will be discussed in 7.5.1.3 and 7.9. Secondly, experiments on ectomycorrhizas are always conducted with seedlings because of the various and obvious difficulties of handling mature trees and shrubs and, consequently, there is no experimental evidence of the effects of infection on the vigour of adult hosts.

Table 7.3 Examples of experimental results showing effects of mycorrhizal infection on host plant growth.

Type of infection	Control soil		Soil with phosphate supplement	
	Uninfected	Mycorrhizal	Uninfected	Mycorrhizal
Ectomycorrhizal				
Pinus strobus seedlings after 1 year's growth in Prairie soil (Hatch, 1937)				
Dry wt (mg)	303	405	—	—
Nitrogen content (% dry wt)	0.85	1.24	—	—
Phosphorus content (% dry wt)	0.074	0.196	—	—
Potassium content (% dry wt)	0.425	0.744	—	—
Vesicular-arbuscular				
Maize plants on poor soil				
Length of ear (cm)	14.0	22.0	19.5	22.7
No. grains/ear	31	354	279	321
1000 grain wt (g)	2.4	19.8	23.7	20.9
Vesicular-arbuscular plus rhizobium				
Stylosanthes guyanensis in poor soil (pH 6.5) after 10 weeks' growth. All plants previously inoculated with rhizobium, and grown on sterile (irradiated) soil (Mosse *et al.* 1976)				
Dry wt (mg)	93	580	310	610
Total P per plant (mg)	77	1077	383	1791
No. rhizobium nodules per plant	0	34	7	37
Ericoid				
Vaccinium macrocarpon after 6 months (Read and Stribley, 1973)				
Dry wt per plant (mg)	184	235	—	—
% nitrogen in shoots	0.46	0.84	—	—

7.4.2 Depressions in host vigour

There have been various reports that young seedlings infected with ecto- or vesicular-arbuscular mycorrhizal fungi sometimes show a temporary depression in vigour (manifested as a reduction in dry weight and/or size compared to uninfected plants) (Harley and Smith, 1983). However, as the host grows and more foliage is developed, competition for photosynthetically fixed carbon becomes less severe and the deleterious effects of the infection are outweighed by the advantages it brings to host nutrition. The initial temporary depression in host growth was attributed by Harley (1969) to competition with the symbiont for limited supplies of carbon.

7.5 Nutritional interactions

7.5.1 Ectomycorrhizas, vesicular-arbuscular and ericoid mycorrhizas

7.5.1.1 Flow of mineral nutrients from fungus to host

The major factor limiting plant growth on poor soils is the supply of essential mineral elements, commonly N, P and K. Addition of these elements as fertilizers to most natural soils results in improved plant growth. The effect of mycorrhizal infection on mineral content and growth of plants has for long been taken to indicate that an important consequence of infection is increased efficiency of uptake into the host of any nutrients in short supply (Hatch, 1937).

Many experiments have been concerned with the uptake of phosphate; the

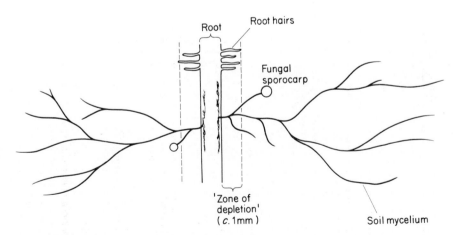

Fig. 7.6 Diagram to show how the soil hyphae of vesicular–arbuscular mycorrhizal fungi extend beyond the 'zone of depletion' of available phosphate (see 7.5.1.1) to exploit a larger volume of soil than root hairs.

relatively few experiments on other nutrients such as nitrogen show that their uptake is also enhanced by mycorrhizas. Phosphate is a nutrient required in relatively large amounts by plants. Much of the phosphate in the soil is in an insoluble form not readily available to plants, and it is frequently in low concentration (micromolar or less) in the soil solution. Inorganic phosphate tends to be immobile because it binds to soil colloids, or is fixed as aluminium and iron phosphates. Consequently, roots may take up phosphate from the soil more quickly than phosphate diffuses to them, resulting in formation of a 'zone of depletion' (Nye and Tinker, 1977) around them (Fig. 7.6). Uptake into the root is then severely limited by the slow rate of diffusion of phosphate into the zone. Because the external mycelium of a mycorrhizal fungus grows through this zone into the soil beyond, its uptake is not limited, especially if hyphae continue to grow and explore new volumes of soil.

Early experiments were conducted with ectomycorrhizas. Direct demonstrations by Melin and co-workers that various nutrients could move from the mycelium of a mycorrhizal fungus to a tree seedling were made with the system illustrated in Fig. 7.7. Later, a detailed series of laboratory studies of

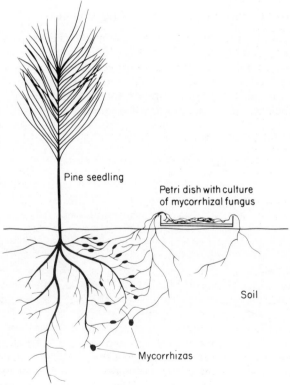

Fig. 7.7 Experimental system used by Melin and his co-workers to study movement of isotopically labelled nutrients between ectomycorrhizal fungi and their hosts (see Melin, 1958).

the uptake of phosphate and other nutrients was made by Harley and co-workers (Harley and Smith, 1983) using excised mycorrhizal root tips of the beech tree. The rate of uptake of phosphate from very dilute solutions (i.e., at concentrations comparable to those in the soil) by mycorrhizas was approximately 4–6 times higher than by uninfected roots; similar results were later obtained for *Pinus radiata* (Bowen and Theodoru, 1967). In beech mycorrhizas, 90% of the phosphate taken up accumulated initially in the fungal sheath, and then moved slowly into the host tissue by processes which were oxygen-dependent and sensitive to metabolic inhibitors. The sheath was shown to function as a storage organ, passing phosphate to the host in the absence of any external source. This was further illustrated in intact seedlings of *P. radiata* by experiments in which mycorrhizal and non-mycorrhizal seedlings were supplied with $^{32}PO_4$ for a period, and then transferred to a phosphate-free medium (Morrison, 1962). In non-mycorrhizal plants, ^{32}P passed rapidly to the shoots for a few days, and then transport ceased. In mycorrhizal plants, the isotope was transported to the shoots at a steady rate over a 21 day period.

More recently, various experiments have shown that the hyphae of vesicular-arbuscular mycorrhizas also transport ^{32}P from the soil to the host. The soil mycelium is particularly important, and it takes up phosphate actively from dilute solutions at high rates comparable to ectomycorrhizal and nonsymbiotic fungi. The movement of phosphate and other ions along the soil hyphae to the root has been investigated in experiments in which the root system of a plant is confined in soil inside a porous container, the pores of which are of a size which permits passage of hyphae through them but not roots. When $^{32}PO_4$ was added to the soil outside the container, it was not transported to uninfected roots, but ^{32}P could be detected in host tissues of mycorrhizal roots within 2 days; transport occurred along hyphae up to 7 cm from the root. In natural conditions, hyphae have been observed to extend at least 2 cm away from the root. The rate of phosphate movement along hyphae is about 100 times faster than can be explained by simple diffusion. The flux of other ions such as calcium is much slower, suggesting that there may a specific mechanism for the translocation of certain ions such as phosphate.

In studies of the uptake of ^{15}N from the soil, Ames *et al.* (1983) found that flux rates of nitrogen along hyphae of vesicular-arbuscular fungi to be similar to those of phosphorus. Smith *et al.* (1985) found that mycorrhizal infection increased the glutamine synthetase activity of clover and onion roots, and they suggested that this enzyme, which has a high affinity for ammonia, may be important in the uptake of ammonia by soil hyphae.

In vesicular-arbuscular mycorrhizas, the mechanism by which phosphate and other ions are transferred from symbiont to host within the root is not known. Arbuscules are very likely to be a site of transfer since they have a large surface area of contact with the host, with the host cell membrane surrounding each branchlet (Fig. 7.2d). Further, ^{32}P becomes concentrated in arbuscules during transport experiments and the arbuscule tips lack polyphosphate (i.e., as if it had already been unloaded); the host cell also shows signs of increased metabolic activity.

In essence, the soil mycelium of vesicular-arbuscular mycorrhizas exploits large volumes of soil for scarce nutrients (Fig. 7.6). One could argue that, for an uninfected plant to exploit a comparably large volume of soil, the costs of forming the requisite amount of root tissue must be greater than the costs of accomodating fungal symbionts, and this may explain why so very many plants have this type of mycorrhiza.

The extent to which ectomycorrhizas develop a soil mycelium is very variable. It appears to be very extensive in some cases, but negligible in others. The latter invites comparison with the situation in vesicular-arbuscular mycorrhizas described above. Smooth-surfaced ectomycorrhizas are particularly common in the litter layer of woodlands, often occurring between decaying leaves or leaf fragments. This is a quite different environment from. the underlying mineral soil, and the release of minerals from decaying leaves may be quite rapid and periodic. Harley and Smith (1983) consider that, in such situations, the intense exploitation of the litter layer by ectomycorrhizas will lead to efficient trapping of nutrients without an extensive soil mycelium. But whatever the extent of the soil mycelium, all nutrients must pass through the sheath, so that the fungus affects uptake in some way.

Ericoid mycorrhizas have received rather less experimental investigation. They resemble vesicular-arbuscular mycorrhizas in exploiting large volumes of soil for scarce nutrients. However, nitrogen may sometimes be more limiting to host growth than phosphate because the soils in which they live are often very acid and, at pH values below 4.0, nitrogen mineralization rates are low and ammonium ions (which are relatively immobile) predominate over nitrate. Mycorrhizal plants of *Vaccinium* have higher nitrogen contents (as % dry weight) than non-mycorrhizal (Read and Stribley, 1973), and in sand culture they take up more ammonium. There is also some evidence that ericoid mycorrhizas may be able to utilize nitrogen from the organic soil fraction to a greater extent than non-mycorrhizal plants; organically complexed nitrogen represents by far the greatest reserve of nitrogen in heathland.

Arbutoid mycorrhizas have been little studied.

7.5.1.2   Flow of carbohydrates from host to fungus

A number of experiments have shown that ^{14}C fixed photosynthetically in the foliage of hosts is subsequently recovered from mycorrhizal fungi, but none gives direct evidence of the mechanism of transfer between host and symbiont nor of the amounts of carbohydrate involved. Since mycorrhizal fungi show limited or no ability to utilize cellulose, hemicellulose or pectin in culture, they probably gain little of their organic carbon requirements from the soil, and the host is probably the major and possibly the only source. Indirect estimates of the quantity of carbohydrate flowing from plants to mycorrhizal fungi are substantial, and the ecological significance of this is discussed in 7.9.

In ectomycorrhizas, the experimental system in Fig. 7.7 was used to demonstrate that ^{14}C fixed by the pine seedling moved to the fungal

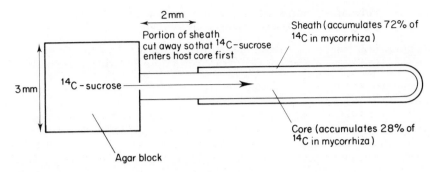

Fig. 7.8 Experimental feeding of excised *Fagus* roots with ^{14}C-sucrose (Lewis and Harley, 1965).

mycelium. In laboratory experiments, Lewis and Harley (1965) placed agar blocks containing 10% ^{14}C-sucrose (to simulate the high concentration of sugar in the phloem) on the ends of excised mycorrhizal roots of the beech (Fig. 7.8). The ^{14}C-sucrose moved into the host tissues, and a substantial proportion of the ^{14}C was later recovered from the fungal sheath as trehalose, glycogen and mannitol, all characteristic fungal carbohydrates. In whole plants, a higher proportion of photosynthate may be translocated to ecto-mycorrhizal than to uninfected roots (Table 7.4).

Vesicular–arbuscular mycorrhizas have been less easy to study, although fixed ^{14}C has been recovered in the mycelium and as fungal lipids from spores. Tinker (1984) concluded that estimates by various authors showed that the amount of photosynthate passing from host to fungus was in the range 4–10% of the total. As in ectomycorrhizas, there is evidence for increased translocation of photosynthate to roots of mycorrhizal plants, and also of an increase in rate of photosynthesis per unit area of leaf. The causes of these increases are probably complex.

In ericoid mycorrhizas, ^{14}C transport from host to fungus occurs, but if fungi are supplied with ^{14}C-labelled amino acids, then the isotope moves in the opposite direction from fungus to host. This reflects the role of the fungus in the nitrogen nutrition of the host (see 7.5.1.1).

Table 7.4 Effect of ectomycorrhizas on translocation of carbon from shoots to roots of *Pinus strobus* (after Nelson, 1964). Distribution of fixed ^{14}C measured after 12 hours in darkness following photosynthetic [14]CO_2 fixation. Because roots of mycorrhizal plants are more extensive, the amount of ^{14}C in roots relative to their weight was also assayed.

	Percentage distribution of [14]C		
	Shoots	Roots	In roots relative to weight
Mycorrhizal	46	54	17.4
Non-mycorrhizal	95	5	4.6

7.5.1.3   Flow of carbohydrates and minerals between hosts along interconnecting mycorrhizal hyphae

Experimental evidence is accumulating that when a mycorrhizal fungus is connected to two separate plants (either of the same or different species),

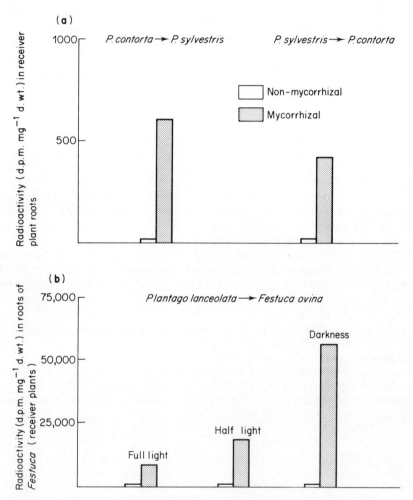

Fig. 7.9 Movement of carbohydrate between host plants connected to the same mycelium of a mycorrhizal fungus. **(a)** Ectomycorrhizas. Pairs of seedlings of *Pinus contorta* and *P. sylvestris* were grown together, some pairs ('mycorrhizal') connected by the mycorrhizal fungus *Suillus bovinus*, other pairs ('non-mycorrhizal') not infected. In each pair, 'donor' plant fed with 10 μCi NaH^{14}CO$_3$ for 96 hours. Data of Finlay and Read (1986). **(b)** Vesicular–arbuscular mycorrhizas. Donor plant was *Plantago lanceolata*, recipient *Festuca ovina*. 'Mycorrhizal' pairs interconnected by the fungus *Glomus caledonium*. Donor plants exposed to 30 μCi^{14}CO$_2$ for two days. 'Half Light' plants covered with muslin cloth. Data of Francis and Read (1984).

both carbohydrate and mineral nutrients can move from one host to the other via the interconnecting hyphae. Isotopes (^{14}C, ^{32}P) are supplied to one plant (the 'donor'), and their accumulation in the connected plant (the 'receiver') is monitored and compared with uninfected control plants (Fig. 7.9). Francis and Read (1984) showed that movement of ^{14}C from a donor was greatly increased if the receiver was shaded, implying that movement occurred along a gradient of concentration from enriched sources to depleted sinks. The velocity of transport of ^{14}C exceeded 20 cm h^{-1}, and over distances exceeding 20 cm (Finlay and Read, 1986). In studying the movement of mineral nutrients, Francis *et al.* (1986) found that recipient plants were enhanced with respect to nitrogen as well as phosphorus, although in almost all cases, the incremental gain in phosphorus exceeded that in nitrogen.

7.5.2   Orchid and monotropoid mycorrhizas

Unlike the previous associations, the mycorrhizal fungus of orchids transports carbohydrate as well as mineral nutrients to the host when the latter is in the nonphotosynthetic protocorm stage (Fig. 7.10). The fungi can utilize cellulose and, under experimental conditions, can grow on filter paper as a sole carbon source, nourishing a protocorm at the same time. Orchid seedlings which have been reared aposymbiotically are unusual amongst flowering plants in being able to utilize the fungal sugar trehalose. Adult, photosynthetic orchids often continue to have mycorrhizal infections, but the relationship between host and symbiont has received very little study. Recently, Alexander and Hadley (1985) found that while adult plants of the orchid *Goodyera repens* remain infected by mycorrhizal fungi, they are fully autotrophic and neither receive nor provide carbohydrate to their fungal symbionts. However, Alexander *et al.* (1984) showed that infected adult plants receive up to 100 times more phosphorus than non-mycorrhizal. When the growth of the fungus was inhibited by a fungicide, the growth of the orchid was also reduced.

Monotropoid hosts, like orchid protocorms, lack chlorophyll. Their fungal symbionts also form ectomycorrhizas on trees, and the fungi appear to transport carbon compounds and other nutrients from the tree to the monotropoid hosts. Thus, when ^{14}C-glucose and $^{32}PO_4$ were supplied to pine and spruce, these isotopes were recovered within 5 days from *Monotropa* plants growing 1–2 m away (Bjorkman, 1960). When *Monotropa* is separated from its neighbouring trees by metal plates, it grows poorly compared to those which have not had their hyphal connections severed. Although traditionally regarded as a 'saprophyte', *Monotropa* is in fact a parasite (through the medium of its symbiont) on surrounding trees.

7.6   Other interactions

Most ectomycorrhizas recover from drought more quickly than uninfected roots (Harley and Smith, 1983). For example, uninfected root tips of *Pinus*

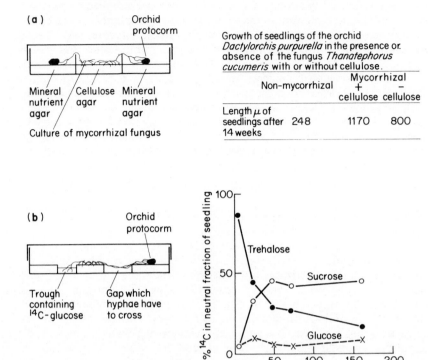

METHODOLOGY

RESULTS

(a)   Orchid protocorm

Mineral nutrient agar / Cellulose agar / Mineral nutrient agar

Culture of mycorrhizal fungus

Growth of seedlings of the orchid *Dactylorchis purpurella* in the presence or absence of the fungus *Thanatephorus cucumeris* with or without cellulose.

	Non-mycorrhizal	Mycorrhizal + cellulose	Mycorrhizal − cellulose
Length μ of seedlings after 14 weeks	248	1170	800

(b)   Orchid protocorm

Trough containing ^{14}C-glucose

Gap which hyphae have to cross

Trehalose

Sucrose

Glucose

% ^{14}C in neutral fraction of seedling

Time (hours)

Fig. 7.10   Translocation of carbohydrate to orchid seedlings (after S.E. Smith 1967). **(a)** Fungi using cellulose as a carbohydrate source (which the host plant cannot utilize). **(b)** Supplying ^{14}C-glucose to the fungus. Trehalose is a fungal sugar, and sucrose is a plant sugar. The graph shows that in seedlings ^{14}C in trehalose falls as that in sucrose rises, indicating conversion from fungal to plant sugars.

strobus and *P. taeda* became dormant after a period of severe stress and showed no renewed growth for 14 days, but mycorrhizal roots renewed growth within 3 days of relief of stress. The mechanisms involved have not been investigated. Tritiated water was transported relatively rapidly (27 cm h^{-1}) along fungal strands from mycorrhizas synthesized with *Pinus sylvestris* (Duddridge *et al.*, 1980); these strands have some tissue differentiation and a structure which might facilitate water conduction. There is evidence that vesicular-arbuscular infections also improve host tolerance of water stress in some cases.

Mycorrhizal fungi dominate the rhizosphere to the exclusion of other fungi, even though they grow very slowly and can utilize only a restricted range of carbon sources. This has led to speculation that the fungi might produce substances antagonistic to other fungi, but only a few species of those examined have been found to do so in culture. In some (but not all) cases, presence of vesicular–arbuscular fungi has reduced the incidence of pathogenic infection of roots.

In culture, some ectomycorrhizal fungi (like many other fungi) may produce plant growth regulators ('plant hormones') including indole acetic acid, ethylene, and substances with cytokinin activity. It has been suggested that some of the morphological and physiological changes in the root resulting from infection are caused by growth regulators produced by the symbiont, but unfortunately, it has so far proved impossible to discover whether this ever occurs in the intact symbiosis.

Plants with ericoid mycorrhizas grow in acid soils where low pH causes an increase in the availability of metals like aluminium and copper, often to levels toxic to many non-ericaceous species. Mycorrhizal plants of *Calluna*, *Vaccinium* and *Rhododendron* in culture were much more tolerant to high levels of copper (up to 50 mg l^{-1}) and zinc (up to 100 mg l^{-1}) than non-mycorrhizal (Bradley *et al.*, 1982). Tolerance probably results from binding of heavy metals to the carboxyl groups of the pectic interfacial matrix between fungus and host (Read, 1983).

7.7 Specificity, recognition and the establishment of infection

7.7.1 Specificity

Specificity between host and symbiont in most mycorrhizal associations is low or very low. There is no case known in which a single strain of fungus is restricted to a particular host genotype.

Amongst ectomycorrhizas, there are many potential symbionts and a wide range of hosts embracing several phyla. Investigation in the field of the extent to which a particular host or symbiont is restricted in its choice of partner depends upon accurate identification of the symbiont, which is based largely on the characteristics of the fruit body. However, the fruit bodies of many fungi appear for only brief periods, and not always every year. Even so, there are relatively few examples where fruiting bodies of one species of symbiont only occur in association with one genus of host; one such example is *Alpova diplophloeus* which only associates with species of *Alnus*, and this has been upheld in culture experiments. It was once thought that *Suillus grevillei* only associated with *Larix* sp. but apart from recent reports of its occasional association with *Pinus* sp. it forms ectomycorrhizas in culture with *Pseudotsuga mensziesi* and arbutoid mycorrhizas with two species of the Ericales.

Specificity of host and ectomycorrhizal fungi for their partners is almost always lower when tested in laboratory culture than when examined in the field. In the laboratory, Godbout and Fortin (1985) synthesized ectomycorrhizas of aspen with 29 species of fungi from 12 different genera, while field observations had recorded only 5 associated species. Some species of pine and birch will associate with over 40 species of fungi in laboratory experiments.

In orchid mycorrhizas, tests in culture combined with some field obser-vations suggest that, as in ectomycorrhizas, the level of specificity is variable but generally low, and a similar picture emerges from studies of ericoid and arbutoid mycorrhizas.

Field and laboratory studies of specificity in vesicular–arbuscular mycorr-hizas show that, with few exceptions, a fungus isolated from one host infects any other plant capable of forming these mycorrhizas, so that specificity is very low. Molina *et al.* (1978) investigated the mycorrhizal fungi associated with 6 species of grass (*Festuca*) species in various sites in the Western United States and Canada. Nearly all plants examined had 75% or more of their fine roots infected and it was common to find two or sometimes more species of fungus associating with a single plant. They concluded that no specificity of any mycorrhizal fungus for any *Festuca* species can be inferred. As with other mycorrhizal fungi, some symbionts are more effective at promoting host growth than others so some degree of ecological specificity (11.7) might be expected. It presumably explains why, for mycorrhizas in general, specificity in the field is higher than when tested in culture.

7.7.2   Recognition

There has been very little experimental work on recognition in mycorrhizas, but the available evidence suggests that, as for other symbioses, it involves a number of different stages (Harley and Smith, 1983; Harley, 1984; Duddridge, 1985). Thus, while spores of mycorrhizal fungi germinate more readily in the presence of roots, the effect is not usually specific to mycorr-hizal hosts; mycorrhizal fungi will spread along the root surfaces of non-mycorrhizal plants; and ectomycorrhizal fungi form sheaths around silicone tubes (Read and Armstrong, 1972). The generally very low specificity raises the question of the extent to which fungi are positively recognized by the host, or whether the host fails to recognize them as pathogens so that they do not trigger host defence systems. Harley and Smith (1983) suggested that there is an interaction between symbiont and host cell wall proteins within the tissues (see 7.2.1.2.) and this could also be a component of recognition. Modifica-tion of host cell walls occurs widely in mycorrhizas, not only at intercellular contact, but also temporarily during penetration of the cells by projections.

7.7.3   Factors affecting the development of infection

Many experiments have shown that the degree of infection of root systems by vesicular–arbuscular and ectomycorrhizal fungi decreases sharply in soils of high nutrient status, such as cultivated soils receiving heavy applications of fertilizer. Plants usually achieve greater dry weights if optimum amounts of phosphate are added to the soil than if they have vesicular–arbuscular mycorrhizas. It is the concentration of phosphate within the plant rather than in the soil which primarily determines the degree of vesicular–arbuscular infection (e.g., if plants growing on poor soil have foliar applications of phosphate, infection is reduced). Some experiments on ectomycorrhizas suggest that infection may be promoted by high concentrations of soluble carbohydrate in the root.

In most mycorrhizas, the region immediately behind the apical meristem, where cell division has just ceased, is much more susceptible to infection than other parts of the root. The meristem itself is never infected.

Observation of the development of the symbiosis in the laboratory is hampered by the fact that in many methods it is relatively slow and occurs in an opaque and finely granular medium such as the soil. However, rapid synthesis of ectomycorrhizas has recently been achieved in transparent plastic pouches containing a defined medium (Fortin *et al.*, 1980), and this technique should enable considerable advance in the study of mycorrhizal interactions.

7.8 Effects of mycorrhizal association on root nodulation

Many nodulated legumes are normally infected with vesicular–arbuscular mycorrhizal fungi under natural conditions; only a very few, such as *Lupinus* are rarely infected. In pot experiments, vesicular-arbuscular mycorrhizas greatly increase nodulation by legumes growing on poor soils (Table 7.3). Since legumes require phosphate for nodulation, the primary effect of mycorrhizal formation is probably through improved phosphate nutrition of the host. Secondary effects presumably arise because host growth is increased, including a more extensive root system. Although rhizobial and vesicular-arbuscular infections occur in similar regions of the root, hyphae do not extend into nodules. Plants infected with both rhizobia and vesicular-

Table 7.5 Estimates of the quantitative importance of mycorrhizas as sinks in the circulation of carbon in ecosystems (Harley and Smith, 1983).

Spruce forest

Estimate based on the data of Rommell (1939) on sporophore production:–
Carbohydrate consumption of ectomycorrhizas equivalent to 10% potential timber production.

Beech forest

Estimates of CO_2 production, based on data of Harley, 1969 and Moller *et al.*, 1954:–
CO_2 emission per year by beech root systems $= 500-900$ kg ha^{-1} y^{-1}
CO_2 emission per year by ectomycorrhizal sheaths $= 100-250$ kg ha^{-1} y^{-1}

Abies amabilis forest

Data of Vogt *et al.*, 1982:–
Total net primary production 24 870 kg ha^{-1} y^{-1} dry mass
Total mycorrhizal fungus produced 3260 kg ha^{-1} y^{-1} dry mass

arbuscular fungi have higher rates of photosynthesis than uninfected controls. Harris *et al.* (1985) found that in six-week-old soyabeans infected with both rhizobia and *Glomus*, there was a 52% increase in the carbon assimilation rate g^{-1} leaf, and this was associated with an increase in the specific rate of carbon incorporation into plant biomass of 18%, and into nodules and mycorrhiza of 12% and 17% respectively.

Many non-legumes with *Frankia* nodules are also often heavily infected with vesicular-arbuscular mycorrhizas, and there is some evidence that infection promotes nodulation.

7.9   Ecological significance of mycorrhizas

Most plants normally have mycorrhizas, and they are probably the normal route of entry for most of the mineral nutrients absorbed from the soil into many types of natural vegetation. Mycorrhizal fungi are undoubtedly very abundant in the soil, although direct estimates of their biomass have never been made. Since their organic carbon requirements are provided by host plants, this must be a significant component of the circulation of carbon in the ecosystem. The few indirect estimates of the quantities involved (Table 7.5) show mycorrhizal fungi to be an important sink for carbon.

Root densities in soil are often high, especially in closed communities. Since mycorrhizal fungi are generally of very low specificity, it is very likely that interconnections between plants by mycorrhizal fungi are abundant in nature. The role of these interconnections in the transfer of carbohydrates and minerals between plants in natural vegetation may be very important (see 7.5.1.3), although this topic is largely unexplored. For example, rapid infection by mycorrhizal fungi and the consequent acquisition of carbohydrate from surrounding plants could be of vital importance to the survival of young seedlings in shaded situations. There is the intriguing possibility that mycelial networks could be one route by which fixed nitrogen is transferred from pasture legumes, which are often heavily mycorrhizal, to other plants.

Pot experiments consistently show that the growth of mycorrhizal plants on poor soils is enhanced compared to uninfected. However, in nature, the significance of mycorrhizas may be more complex than this, and the role of interconnecting hyphae as conduits for the flow of carbohydrates and minerals between plants may have a key role in the structure of certain types of vegetation. Harley (1984) visualized the possibility of complex interconnections between diverse groups of plants linked to a number of different mycelial networks. Plants linked to a common mycelium would not compete directly for nutrients in the soil, but compete indirectly through their ability to act as a sink for nutrients absorbed from the fungus and to release less carbohydrate to the fungus than their competitors. This is again speculative, but it could revolutionize our understanding of how plants interact in natural vegetation.

8
Symbiosis in animal guts

8.1 Introduction

The guts of many animals harbour an extensive microflora. Many of the microorganisms are transient; they enter the gut with the food but fail to persist because they are expelled with the faeces or because they are killed by digestive enzymes, low pH or the anaerobic conditions which occur in certain regions of the gut. Other microorganisms are 'more-or-less' permanent residents of the gut, well-adapted to the unusual environmental conditions and indeed many of them rarely occur in any other habitat. They are not removed with the passage of food, either because their division rate is sufficiently high to replace cells that are lost or because they adhere to the gut wall. These permanent residents comprise the gut symbionts. With few exceptions among invertebrate hosts (e.g., see 8.4.1), the gut symbionts are exclusively extracellular.

The effect of different gut symbionts on the well-being of the host varies enormously. Some are pathogenic or otherwise overtly detrimental to the host (they are not considered further here). Other symbionts are not harmful and many, especially those which have metabolic capabilities not possessed by the host, are clearly advantageous. Some animals are absolutely dependent on their gut symbionts for digestion of food. For example, herbivorous vertebrates and most phytophagous insects lack the enzymes which can degrade structural plant polysaccharides (such as cellulose, hemicellulose and pectin) which form the bulk of their diet. The gut symbionts hydrolyse these polysaccharides to their constituent sugars, which are then degraded anaerobically to produce volatile fatty acids (VFAs), such as acetic, propionic and butyric acids. The VFAs pass through the gut wall into the host tissues and are assimilated. The gut symbionts which break down plant material are maintained under anaerobic conditions; under aerobic conditions, many would die, while the remainder would degrade sugars to carbon dioxide and water, and the host would derive no nourishment. The gut symbionts of herbivorous animals are usually housed in an enlarged anaerobic portion of the gut, in which food is retained for many hours, while the slow microbial degradation of insoluble plant polysaccharides is effected.

Gut symbionts can also contribute to the nitrogen needs of the host, particularly in herbivorous animals whose diet of plant material is usually nitrogen-poor. The symbionts may utilize host waste nitrogenous products (e.g., urea, uric acid) or, more rarely, atmospheric nitrogen to synthesize amino acids and other nitrogenous compounds that can be metabolized by the host. Symbionts may also provide vitamins and other essential micro-nutrients. For example, the intestinal flora of rodents synthesize vitamins of the B complex and vitamin K (Schaedler, 1973) and the actinomycete *Nocardia rhodnii* in the midgut of the blood-sucking insect *Rhodnius* provides vitamins of the B complex (Koch, 1967).

Animals can be divided into those in which the main site of microbial activity is in the foregut, and those where it is in the hindgut. Foregut symbiosis has the advantage that surplus microbial biomass can subsequently be digested in more distal regions of the gut, but in hindgut symbiosis the surplus microbes are voided in the faeces and lost to the host. Despite the potential advantage, foregut symbiosis occurs in only a minority of animals, presumably because it is less likely to evolve in the gut region where host digestive processes are most active.

In contrast to the associations described in earlier chapters, many gut symbioses involve a variety of microorganisms, which may include bacteria, spirochaetes, actinomycetes, protozoa and sometimes fungi, all within a single host. The microorganisms constitute a complex community in which the various components interact with and are dependent upon each other. Both the species composition and population size of gut symbionts may also vary with diet and physiological condition of the host. The diversity of gut symbionts has been related to the complexity of both the food ingested and the gut environment.

This chapter will be restricted to symbioses in vertebrates and insects, and primarily those species which are dependent on a plant diet. Of all gut symbioses, most is known about the foregut symbiosis in ruminant mammals and this is discussed first (8.2), followed by a description of hindgut symbioses in vertebrates (8.3) and insects (8.4).

8.2   Foregut symbioses in herbivorous mammals

8.2.1   Introduction (Bauchop, 1977)

Major foregut symbioses have evolved independently in four orders of mammals, including at least three times within the order Artiodactyla (Table 8.1). The hosts are herbivores, living on a diet rich in plant structural poly-saccharides, for example, grasses and foliage. In all cases, part of the foregut (oesophagus and/or cardiac region of the stomach) has become enlarged and modified to form a multi-chambered anaerobic organ which contains a dense population of bacteria and, in some species, protozoa. The chambers contain a high concentration of volatile fatty acids (VFAs) (Table 8.1), which are the main products of microbial fermentation of plant material. Despite the VFAs, the pH of the chambers is maintained at a value close to neutrality which is suitable for continued microbial activity. This is achieved by the

Table 8.1 Characteristics of foregut symbiosis in herbivorous mammals (Bauchop, 1977).

The Host	No. of chambers[†]	Weight (% total body weight)	pH	Concentration of VFAs[1] (mM)	Symbionts bacteria	Symbionts protozoa
Order Marsupialia Family Macropodidae (kangaroos)	3	15	4.6–8.0	100–140	+	+
Order Primatia Subfamily Colobinae (colobus monkeys)	3	10–20	5.5–7.0	90–220	+	–
Order Edentata Family Bradypodidae (sloths)	2	20–30	5.2–6.7	40–95	+	–
Order Artiodactyla Family Hippopotamidae	3	?	5.0–5.7*	110–120	+	+
Family Camelidae	2	10–17	6.4–7.0	80–120	+	+
Suborder Ruminantia (e.g. deer and cattle)	3	10–15	6.0–7.0	90–140	+	+

[†] excluding the true stomach.
* values from carcasses, probably underestimates of pH in living animals.
[1] VFA = volatile fatty acid.

copious amounts of saliva, rich in compounds of high buffering capacity (e.g., bicarbonate, phosphate), produced during mastication of the food and transported from the mouth to the fermentation chambers. The surface area of food particles available for microbial attack is very great because the host grinds and chews the food to a small size before it is swallowed. In camels and ruminants, the food may be returned to the mouth after a period of fermentation and ground more finely yet. This behaviour is called rumination or 'chewing the cud'.

The foregut symbiosis in mammals of the suborder Ruminantia has been the subject of extensive study because this group includes many domestic animals of economic importance, such as cattle and sheep. Although the foregut symbioses in other herbivorous mammals have the same basic characteristics (Table 8.1), they have received scant experimental interest and will not be considered further.

8.2.2   Foregut symbiosis in ruminants

8.2.2.1   Introduction (Hungate, 1966)

The complex stomach of ruminants consists of four chambers: the rumen, reticulum, omasum and abomasum (Fig. 8.1). The main fermentation chamber is the rumen which, with its contents, comprises 8–13% of the body

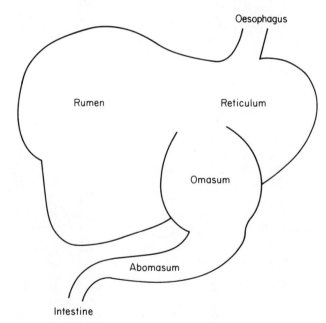

Fig. 8.1 Structure of the ruminant stomach. Food enters the rumen and reticulum from the oesophagus and then passes sequentially through the omasum and abomasum.

weight of the animal. The rumen fluid, known as 'liquor', is maintained at constant pH and temperature, and contains the microbial symbionts which degrade and ferment the ingested food particles. Most of the VFAs produced pass through the rumen wall into the host tissues. The gaseous phase above the liquor consists largely of carbon dioxide and methane produced by fermentation and, as a result, the liquor is an anaerobic environment with a redox potential of -250 to -450 mV. The small quantities of oxygen taken into the rumen dissolve in the liquor and are rapidly metabolized by facultative aerobic bacteria. Surplus gas is removed by belching. The rumen contents are regularly mixed by rhythmic contractions of the muscular gut wall. Periodically, portions of the liquor are passed to the omasum, where water, bicarbonate (from the saliva, see 8.2.1) and the remaining VFAs are absorbed by the sheet-like layers of tissue which traverse this chamber. The buffering capacity of the digesta is thereby reduced before entry to the abomasum (the true stomach), where acidic gastric digestion takes place. About one-third of the symbiont population is passed to the abomasum every day and digested. The alimentary tract posterior to the stomach is not substantially different from that of other mammals.

8.2.2.2 Methods used to study the rumen symbiosis (Hobson, 1977)

Because many of the gut symbionts are obligate anaerobes, techniques which rigorously exclude oxygen are needed to isolate and culture them. Only limited information can be gained from studying single species, and in order to investigate how combinations of symbionts interact, continuous cultures of species mixtures in 'model rumens' have been used. Even these fall short of portraying the complexity of the rumen ecosystem, so direct methods of studying rumen contents have been developed, such as cannulation. This consists of inserting a small tube into the rumen so that samples can be withdrawn at any time. Investigation of rumen metabolism of ingested food can be simplified by feeding the animal on partially purified diets containing constituents which can be determined readily. For example, the protein zein has the unusual property of solubility in alcohol and has been used to investigate the conversion of food protein to symbiont protein (which is alcohol-insoluble); and diets of pure cellulose aid in the study of polysaccharide breakdown in the rumen.

Largely by these methods, a broad picture of the nutritional interactions between ruminant mammals and their symbionts is emerging, though many details still remain to be established.

8.2.2.3 Microbial breakdown of food in the rumen

The diet of ruminants is generally dominated by carbohydrates. For example, summer grass in temperate regions contains 10–35% cellulose, 10–25% hemicellulose, 2–12% lignin and 25% soluble sugars, per unit dry weight. There is now a substantial body of information on the biochemistry and enzymology of carbohydrate metabolism by rumen symbionts and the principal pathways are shown in Fig. 8.2. The refractive plant polysaccharides are degraded by the microorganisms to their constituent monosaccharides. These and the ingested soluble sugars are then fermented by a variety of pathways, of which glycolysis to pyruvic acid (the Embden-Meyerhof pathway) is the most important. Pyruvic acid is metabolized to yield a range of end products: VFAs (particularly acetic, propionic and butyric acids), carbon dioxide and methane. After absorption into the host tissues, the VFAs are substrates for aerobic ATP production (with a net total of 3.6–5.6 moles ATP formed per mole hexose sugar) and various biosynthetic pathways. Propionic acid, the only VFA which can be converted into carbohydrate, is of key importance because very little free glucose or other sugar is absorbed from the gut of ruminants.

Components of the diet other than carbohydrate are also metabolized by the rumen symbionts. About half of all ingested protein is degraded to ammonia, carbon dioxide and VFAs by proteolysis, deamination and fermentation reactions. Some dietary lipids, including triglycerides, phos-

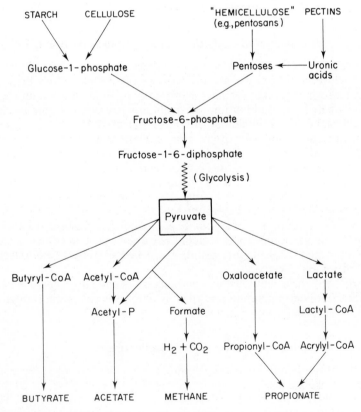

Fig. 8.2   Pathways involved in the degradation of plant polysaccharides by rumen symbionts. Modified from Rook and Thomas (1983).

pholipids and sulpholipids, are hydrolysed to yield free fatty acids. These are then hydrogenated by a fermentation reaction to saturated fatty acids (especially palmitic and stearic acids), which are utilized by the host in lipid biosynthesis. The symbionts also metabolize a number of secondary plant products, often altering their toxicity to the host. For example, they may detoxify alkaloids in the plant *Heliotropum* that otherwise cause chronic liver damage but convert the secondary product miserotoxin in the vetch *Astragalus miser* var. *serotonus* to a product which is lethal to the host (Prins, 1977).

8.2.2.4 Methane production in the rumen

Methane comprises a significant proportion (30–40% in cattle) of the gas in the headspace above the rumen liquor. It is produced by methanogenic bacteria which reduce carbon dioxide, with formic acid (Fig. 8.2) or hydrogen gas as the hydrogen donor. These reactions provide energy for the growth of the methanogenic bacteria, but the methane produced is a waste product, utilized by neither symbionts nor host. Although it has been estimated that 10% of the energy intake of the host is lost in methanogenesis, it may be nevertheless advantageous because it removes hydrogen gas from the rumen (Prins and Clarke, 1980) and so maintains the equilibrium of some reversible reactions in favour of hydrogen production. Of particular importance is the oxidation of reduced pyridine nucleotides (e.g., $NAD(P)H \longrightarrow NAD(P) + H$), which is involved in the pathways of synthesis of some fermentation products. Methanogenic bacteria may also serve this function in associations with ciliate protozoa (see 9.3).

8.2.2.5 Contribution of rumen symbionts to the nitrogen economy of the host (see Fig. 8.3)

The rumen symbionts degrade dietary nitrogenous compounds mainly to ammonia. The ammonia is utilized as a nitrogen source by the symbionts and, to a lesser extent, it is absorbed by the host and utilized in the synthesis of non-essential amino acids. Much of the nitrogen assimilated by the symbionts is ultimately recovered by the host through the digestion of surplus micororganisms in the abomasum (see 8.2.2.1). This produces a more balanced mix of amino acids than in the original diet. In particular, symbionts contain the amino acids cysteine and methionine, synthesized from inorganic sulphate in the diet. Some of the microbial nitrogen (e.g., in cell wall components) is not susceptible to host digestion.

The main waste nitrogenous product of ruminants is urea. Some urea is excreted in the urine and some is transported in the bloodstream, either directly to the rumen or to the salivary glands, from which it passes to the rumen with saliva (Fig. 8.3). Many rumen microorganisms can degrade urea to ammonia, which is metabolized as described above. In animals maintained on nitrogen-poor diets, the amount of endogenously-produced urea recycled in this way can be increased up to 50% (Houpt, 1970).

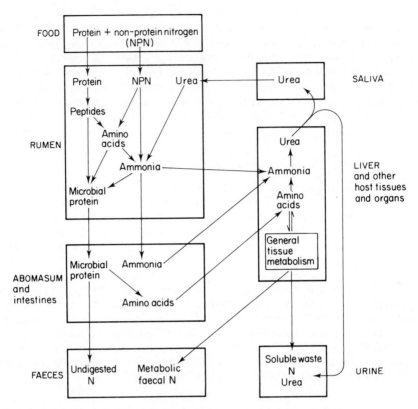

Fig. 8.3 Interactions between nitrogen metabolism of ruminants and their rumen symbionts (see text for full details). Modified from Rook and Thomas (1983).

Fixation of atmospheric nitrogen by rumen symbionts has been reported but is not of quantitative importance to the host.

8.2.2.6 Vitamin synthesis by rumen symbionts (Hungate, 1966)

Certain rumen symbionts can synthesize vitamins of the B complex, vitamin C and fat-soluble vitamins, and these vitamins are made available to the host when the microorganisms are digested. Consequently, ruminants have no dietary requirement for these micronutrients under normal conditions.

8.2.2.7 The role of different types of symbiont in rumen metabolism

About 200 species of bacteria (not all of which may be 'authentic' rumen microbes) and 50 species of protozoa have been isolated from the rumens of various domestic animals. There are usually about 10^9–10^{10} bacteria and

10^4-10^5 protozoa per ml rumen liquor. Some animals also contain phycomycete fungi.

The bacterial flora consists principally of Gram-negative, nonsporing anaerobes, a group whose taxonomy is notoriously difficult to unravel. Identification and classification of the rumen bacteria is further hampered because some forms are not known in any other habitat and because some taxonomically important morphological and physiological features may vary between different isolates and change with long-term culture *in vitro*. Despite these problems, several taxa have been identified as important components of the rumen flora. For example, *Bacteroides* species display great metabolic diversity and degrade cellulose, hemicellulose, pectin, starch and protein. *B. succinogenes* represents 5-20% by weight of the total bacterial population and, with the ruminococci (e.g., *Ruminococcus flavefaciens, R. albus*), is probably of key importance in the degradation of plant cell wall components, especially cellulose (Macy, 1981). *Butyrovibrio* species also degrade plant fibrous material, with butyrate as the usual end product. Other bacteria, especially *Selenomonas*, utilize carbohydrates that can be fermented rapidly (e.g., dietary starch and soluble sugars, and products of polysaccharide hydrolysis by other bacteria) and the selenomonads are particularly abundant in animals fed on high starch diets (e.g., cereals) (Hespell and Bryant, 1981). *Bacteroides, Butyrovibrio* and *Selenomonas* species also contribute to the deamination of protein; selenomonads and the Gram-negative vibrio *Anaerovibrio lipolytica* are significant in glycerol fermentation (Hobson, 1977); species of *Ruminococcus, Eubacterium* and *Fusocillus* have been implicated in the hydrogenation of fatty acids (Kemp *et al.*, 1975); and *Methanobacterium ruminantium* is a common methanogen (Prins and Clarke, 1980). By contrast, the bacteria involved in urea degradation are Gram-positive, oxygen-tolerant species, probably staphylococci or micrococci (Wallace *et al.*, 1979).

The rumen protozoa (e.g., Fig. 8.4) are dominated by two groups of ciliates: members of the order Entodiniomorphida and two genera (*Isotricha* and *Dasytricha*) of the order Trichostomatida which are often referred to as 'holotrichs' (Williams, 1986). The rumen protozoa are obligate anaerobes and can survive only in physical environments that closely resemble the rumen (low redox potential, 37-42°C, pH 6-7). Complex, heterologous media containing bacteria are required for the maintenance of entodiniomorphids *in vitro*. The holotrichs are relatively easy to culture for short periods but their long-term maintenance has proved very difficult (Coleman, 1979). Protozoa related to the rumen symbionts have been isolated from anaerobic chambers in the foregut of camels (see Table 8.1) and in the hindgut of some herbivorous vertebrates (see 8.3.2) but they are unknown in habitats other than vertebrate digestive tracts.

The protozoa contribute to the breakdown of carbohydrate in the rumen. The entodiniomorphids phagocytose particles of plant fibre and starch grains and hydrolyse them to their constituent sugars, which are either released into the rumen liquor (and utilized by rumen bacteria) or fermented by the protozoa to VFAs. The surfaces of some entodiniomorphid species harbour

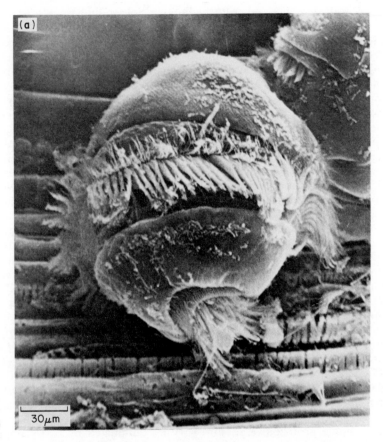

Fig. 8.4 *Ophryoscolex caudatus*, one of the cellulolytic rumen protozoa. **(a)** Scanning electron micrograph to show external appearance of protozoon. The material in the background is a partially digested dietary plant fragment. Many of the small particles on the surface of the protozoon are bacteria (see Fig. 8.4b).

methanogenic bacteria (Vogels *et al.*, 1980), which may enhance carbohydrate degradation by removing hydrogen (see 8.2.2.4). The carbohydrates utilized by holotrichs are principally soluble sugars, for example, glucose, fructose, galactose, which are degraded to VFAs (although *Isotricha* also takes up starch) (Coleman, 1979). The nitrogen requirements of the protozoa are probably met by phagocytosis of rumen bacteria and uptake of free amino acids from the liquor.

Protozoa may be responsible for 30–60% of fermentation in the rumen (Hungate, 1966). However, most studies have found that when ruminants are freed of their protozoa, either by preventing infection of young animals (see 8.2.2.8) or by treatment with chemicals which selectively kill protozoa (Hobson, 1977), their growth and vigour is unaffected (Eadie and Gill, 1971;

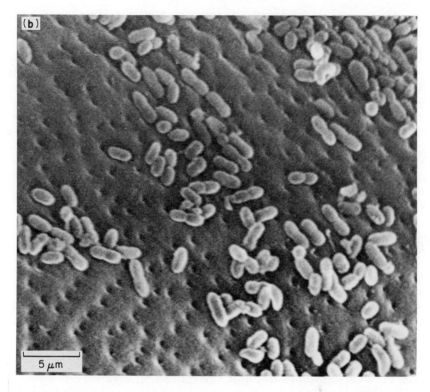

Fig. 8.4(b) Bacteria attached to the pellicle of the protozoon. *Photographs* G.S. Coleman and F.J. Hill

Hungate, 1966). This suggests that although the protozoa are *important*, they are not *essential* components of the rumen flora (Williams, 1986) and the symbiotic bacteria can take over their functions.

Anaerobic phycomycetes have been identified adhering to particles of plant material in the rumen of cattle and sheep and they have been implicated in the breakdown of plant fibre (Bauchop, 1979). However, recent studies on cattle fed on different antibiotics which specifically inhibit the fungal or bacterial populations suggest that the rumen bacteria are far more important than the fungi in fibre degradation (Windham and Akin, 1984).

8.2.2.8 Acquisition of gut symbionts by the young ruminant (Hungate, 1966)

The gut of the neonate ruminant is essentially devoid of microorganisms, but it is colonized rapidly when the animal starts to feed. The first gut symbionts are bacteria (usually lactobacilli, coliforms and streptococci) which can utilize milk products. They occur predominantly in the abomasum and intestine because milk is transported directly from the oesophagus to the abomasum by closure of a special structure, the gastric groove, which bypasses the rumen.

When the young animal begins to eat solid food, the rumen increases in size, matures and is colonized by microorganisms capable of polysaccharide degradation to VFAs. The composition of the rumen flora gradually changes to that of the adult animal. The young animal acquires rumen symbionts directly from adults, which always contain some rumen microorganisms in their mouths because they regurgitate and masticate partially digested food (see 8.2.1). The microorganisms are transmitted either in saliva when the young animal is licked by an adult or by aerial passage of drops of saliva that have fallen or been blown from the adult's mouth. Bacteria can be transmitted long distances in air-borne droplets of saliva but the transmission of protozoa, particularly the larger species, is dependent on direct contact.

8.3   Hindgut symbioses in vertebrates

The primary role of the hindgut in all vertebrates is the absorption of water and ions from food material that has not been digested and assimilated in more proximal regions of the gut. Because the hindgut is essentially non-enzymatic and anaerobic, it is also a common site for colonization by microorganisms and development of a fermentation chamber.

8.3.1   Distribution of hindgut symbioses among vertebrates

Hindgut symbioses occur in many herbivorous mammals, including rodents, lagomorphs, horses, elephants and ruminants (McBee, 1977). In all cases, the microbial symbionts are housed in a single outpocketing, the caecum, at the proximal end of the hindgut, where they ferment plant material to VFAs. Although hindgut symbioses are considered theoretically to be less efficient than those in the foregut (8.1), many herbivorous mammals are markedly dependent on their caecal symbionts for nutrition and some groups are highly successful in terms of numbers of species and number of individuals. Hindgut microorganisms are of negligible importance to carnivorous mammals, whose diet can be digested readily by the animal's complement of enzymes; their significance to omnivores is intermediate. These differences are reflected in the relative capacity of the hindgut of herbivores, omnivores and carnivores (Table 8.2).

The usual sites of gut symbiosis in birds are the paired caeca (McNab, 1973) – although the emu is reported to contain microbial symbionts in its small intestine (Herd and Dawson, 1984). However, fermentative digestion is less common among birds than mammals and avian fermentation chambers are generally smaller. This is probably because the weight of a large fermentation chamber and the enclosed slowly-degrading plant material greatly increases the energy required for flight. (The power necessary for flight

Table 8.2 Relationship between gut capacity and diet in mammals (based on data from Stevens 1977).

Animal	Ratio of total gut length to body length	Average absolute capacity of gut region (l)		
		foregut (stomach)	midgut (small intestine)	hindgut (caecum, colon & rectum)
Ox (ruminant)	20:1	253	66	38
Horse (non-ruminant herbivore)	12:1	18	64	130
Pig (omnivore)	6:1	8	9	10
Dog (carnivore)	4:1	4	2	1

increases by a factor of 2.24 for a doubling in body weight.) For example, even in those galliform species (e.g., grouse, ptarmigan) whose diet is high in plant fibre, the caeca comprise less than 6% of the body weight (Gasaway, 1976); this is half the value for many herbivorous mammals (McBee, 1977). One might expect that flightless herbivorous birds would have particularly large and well-developed fermentation chambers, but there is insufficient information to examine this possibility in detail. Although the ostrich and rhea exhibit modifications of the hindgut suggestive of fermentation (McLelland, 1979), other flightless species, such as the takaha, apparently thrive on plant material without significant microbial fermentation (Morton, 1978).

The incidence of hindgut symbiosis among lower vertebrates (reptiles, amphibia and fish) is generally held to be low (McBee, 1977) and most herbivorous species are believed to derive sufficient nourishment from their diet by consuming large amounts of food and extracting only the readily digestible components. For example, the grass carp *Ctenopharyngodon idella* eats its own body weight of vegetation daily and so obtains only a small proportion of the energy potentially available in its diet (Hickling, 1966). However, there is evidence for gut symbiosis in the surgeon fish *Acanthurus nigrofuscus* (Fischelson *et al.*, 1985) and in herbivorous lizards of the family Iguanidae. The hindgut of these iguanids is divided by transverse folds into a series of consecutive pockets, which slow the rate of passage of digesta and provide a stable habitat for microorganisms (Iverson, 1980).

8.3.2 Types of hindgut symbionts

The density, taxonomic identity and metabolic capabilities of hindgut symbionts resemble those of the rumen (8.2.2.7). In most animals, the dominant hindgut symbionts are Gram-negative, anaerobic bacteria (e.g., *Bacteroides*, *Eubacterium*, *Lactobacillus*), many of which can degrade cellulose and other plant polysaccharides (Clarke, 1977). Ciliate protozoa are also conspicuous components of the hindgut flora in some species, such as the horse (McBee, 1977), the Californian quail (McNab, 1973), the common iguana (Troyer, 1982) and the surgeon fish (Fischelson *et al.*, 1985). Anaerobic phycomycetes have been isolated from the horse caecum (Orpin, 1981).

8.3.3   Contribution of hindgut symbionts to host nutrition

8.3.3.1   Fermentation of plant polysaccharides

There is a considerable evidence that the hindgut symbionts of many vertebrates degrade cellulose and other plant polysaccharides to VFAs by the same pathways as in the rumen (Fig. 8.2). Acetic, propionic and butyric acids, together with other VFAs at a total concentration of 0.1–0.2 M have been demonstrated in the caeca of many hosts, including ptarmigan and grouse, domestic fowl, rodents, lagomorphs and the horse (McBee, 1977; Stevens, 1977; Yang *et al.*, 1970). A proportion of VFAs is absorbed through the hindgut wall into the host tissues and not lost in the faeces. VFAs in similar proportions to those in the caeca have been detected in the portal blood of chickens (McNab, 1973) and ^{14}C-labelled VFAs introduced to the caecum of rats are metabolized and exhaled as ^{14}C-carbon dioxide (Yang *et al*, 1970). The estimated contribution of hindgut fermentation to the energy needs of the host varies from less than 2% in the human (McBee, 1977) to 10–12% in rabbits (Hoover and Heitmann, 1972) and 25% in the horse (Stevens, 1977).

8.3.3.2   Conservation of nitrogen

The hindgut symbionts in many animals are believed to degrade host nitrogenous wastes (e.g., urea, uric acid) to ammonia, which is then assimilated by the host and utilized in amino acid synthesis. This is comparable to the process of nitrogen recycling which occurs in the rumen symbiosis (8.2.2.5 and Fig. 8.3). Strong evidence for nitrogen recycling by the hindgut symbionts has been obtained in birds. For example, the droppings of chickens that have been caecetomized or reared free of microorganisms contain more nitrogen than those of untreated birds (Coates and Fuller, 1977).

8.3.3.3   Vitamin synthesis

Hindgut symbionts of chickens and a number of mammals, including rodents, lagomorphs and humans have been implicated in the synthesis of B group and K vitamins, but the significance of this to the host has not been quantified (McBee, 1977).

8.3.3.4   Coprophagy

Although at least a proportion of the soluble metabolites such as VFAs pass directly to the host from the hindgut, most of the more complex microbial products are lost in the faeces. In some animals, notably rodents and lago-morphs, these products are recovered by coprophagy, i.e. the reingestion of faeces derived from the caecum. These caecal pellets differ in appearance from the usual faecal pellets and are not dropped but delivered directly from the anus to the mouth. If coprophagy by rats or rabbits is prevented, the animal exhibits an increased requirement for B and K vitamins and the ability of the rabbit to digest cellulose and utilize dietary protein is also reduced (McBee, 1977). Coprophagy of caecal pellets also occurs in prosimian primates, marsupials, domestic fowl and iguanine lizards; the role of this behaviour in the nutrition of these groups deserves further study.

The caecal pellets often contain viable symbionts and coprophagy by young animals of pellets produced by older conspecifics is an important mode of transmission of hindgut symbionts in many species (Coates and Fuller, 1977; Troyer, 1982).

8.3.4 The nutritional cost of hindgut symbionts to the host

Although hindgut symbionts contribute to the nutritional well-being of verte-brates in very many cases (see 8.3.3), they may also impose certain costs. Rodents and chickens freed of their usual microbial flora can still be main-tained in a healthy condition and, under certain conditions, these aposym-biotic animals may even exhibit greater survival and growth than untreated individuals. For example, aposymbiotic guinea pigs survive on a vitamin C-free diet for longer than individuals infected with the normal gut microflora (Fig. 8.5). It is believed that the gut symbionts degrade vitamin C and so increase host demand for this vitamin.

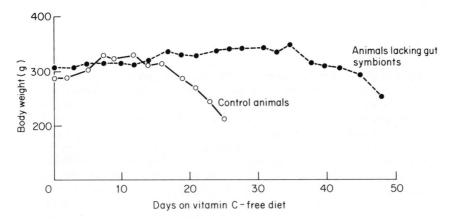

Fig. 8.5 Maintenance of guinea pigs on a vitamin C-free diet. The mean body weights of animals experimentally freed of gut symbionts and of control animals which possessed hindgut flora are shown. The control animals could not be maintained for longer than 4 weeks (from Levenson *et al.*, 1962).

8.3.5 Non-nutritional effects of hindgut symbionts on the host

There are numerous morphological differences between animals freed of their gut flora and untreated animals, and many of these can be attributed to the absence of gut symbionts. In particular, the wall of the small intestine of aposymbionts is thin, the shape of the epithelial cells is altered and the microvilli are small and regular in shape (Coates and Fuller, 1977).

Gut symbionts increase the resistance of the host to bacterial infections and disease in a variety of ways (Savage, 1977; Schaedler, 1973). For example, colonization of the gut by invading microorganisms is often prevented because the indigenous symbionts are more successful in the competition for nutrients or epithelial attachment sites. Components of the normal gut flora also enhance peristalsis of the gut and this impedes attachment of potential pathogens to the epithelium. However, the gut symbionts have been implicated in the development of certain diseases and malignancies of the digestive tract. In particular, certain microorganisms in the large intestine of mammals may produce carcinogens from dietary or endogenous compounds and alter the growth cycle of epithelial cells. In the latter respect, changes in the pattern of proliferation of cells similar to those associated with the development of the cancerous state have been demonstrated in aposymbiotic rodents experimentally infected with intestinal microorganisms (Savage, 1977).

8.4 Gut symbiosis in insects

8.4.1 Introduction

In those insects which have gut symbiosis, the more-or-less permanent population of frequently diverse types of symbionts is usually restricted to one region, most commonly the hindgut. In some omnivorous and many phytophagous species, this region forms a large anaerobic chamber for the fermentation of cellulose and other plant polysaccharides. Examples include termites (Breznak, 1984), cockroaches (Bracke *et al.*, 1979), the scarab beetle *Oryctes* (Bayon, 1980) and larvae of the cranefly *Tipula* (Klug and Kotarski, 1980). Midgut symbioses are relatively rare, probably because digestive enzymes are released in this region, and also a chitinous peritrophic membrane is produced which encloses the food and separates it from the gut wall. Nevertheless, the midgut of *Triatoma* and *Rhodnius* (bloodsucking bugs of the family Reduviidae) harbours Gram-positive bacteria and, in *Rhodnius*, the actinomycete *Nocardia rhodnii* (Dasch *et al.*, 1984); actinomycetes occur between the midgut wall and peritrophic membrane in the higher termite *Cubitermes severus* (Bignell *et al.*, 1980). Foregut symbioses are also uncommon and, in contrast to vertebrates, they are not characteristic of any large insect group. The reason for this is unclear. Although the wall of insect foreguts is relatively impermeable to aquatic fluids and hydrophilic molecules, the pH of this region in most insects is higher than in the vertebrate stomach and apparently not inhospitable to microbial colonization

(Bignell, 1984). In a few species, the location of the symbionts changes during the life cycle of the host. For example, the bacterial symbionts of the tephritid fly *Dacus oleae* are found in the midgut caeca of the larvae, but in an enlarged oesophageal pouch (the cephalic organ) and hindgut of adults (Buchner, 1966).

As in vertebrates, the gut symbionts of most insects are *extracellular*, either lying free in the lumen or adhering to the gut wall (e.g. see Fig. 8.1). However, there are a few examples of *intracellular* gut symbionts (Buchner, 1966), such as the anobiid beetles, which live on timber or other plant products and contain the yeast *Taphrina* in blind-ended caeca arising from the midgut (Jurzitza, 1979) (see also 10.2.2). Some of the yeast cells are extracellular and others are enclosed within hypertrophied epithelial cells at the distal end of the caeca. Dietary studies of one species, *Sitodrepa panicea*, suggest the symbionts provide vitamins and amino acids (Jurzitza, 1979; Koch, 1967). However, some of the yeast cells are in a disintegrating state (Jurzitza, 1979) and the relative contribution of biotrophy and digestion of the yeasts to host nutrition is unknown.

Of all the gut symbioses among insects, only those in termites and cockroaches have been studied in any detail, and they are described below.

8.4.2 Termites

8.4.2.1 Introduction

Most of the approximately 2000 species of termites (order Isoptera) live in the tropics. Termites are scarce at higher latitudes and entirely absent in many temperate countries. They are social insects with several morphologically different castes, including sterile workers and soldiers and the reproductive king and queen. They are phylogenetically distant from the other social insects (of the order Hymenoptera – ants, bees, wasps) but are closely allied to the cockroaches (order Orthoptera). The termites are divided into six families, five of which comprise the 'lower' termites and the sixth the Termitidae or 'higher' termites, which represents 75% of all termite species. All lower termites and many higher termites are dependent on hindgut symbionts for the degradation of their diet of plant material (e.g., wood, leaves, roots, humus), but members of one group of higher termites (subfamily Macrotermitinae) cultivate fungi as a food source.

Biochemical and microbiological studies of termites have concentrated on the worker caste because they can be obtained in large numbers. Since they feed the other castes, the workers are of central importance to the nutrition of the entire colony.

8.4.2.2 The symbionts of termites

The symbionts are housed in an enlarged portion of the termite hindgut called the paunch (Fig. 8.6). This region is anaerobic, for example, the redox

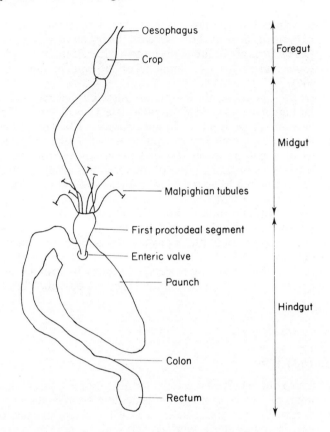

Oesophagus

Crop

Foregut

Midgut

Malpighian tubules

First proctodeal segment

Enteric valve

Paunch

Hindgut

Colon

Rectum

Fig. 8.6   Digestive tract of worker caste of the lower termite *Kalotermes flavicollis* (from McBee, 1977).

potential is – 23 to – 298 mV in *Zootermopsis nevadensis* (Bignell, 1984), and all the symbionts are obligate or facultative anaerobes. An enteric valve proximal to the paunch prevents mixing of the paunch contents with the aerobic midgut.

The paunch of lower termites contains protozoa and bacteria. The protozoa are predominantly flagellate species of two orders, Trichomonadida and Hypermastigida (Fig. 8.7); 'lower' termites of the family Kalotermitidae also contain flagellates of the order Oxymonadida (e.g., *Oxymonas, Pyrsonympha*) (Honigberg, 1970). Many of these protozoa are found only in the hindguts of lower termites. The bacterial symbionts include members of the family Enterobacteriaceae, the genera *Bacteroides, Bacillus, Streptococcus* and *Staphylococcus*, and spirochaetes and methanogens (e.g., *Methanospirillum*) (Breznak, 1982). The densities of the symbionts are very high, up to 10^7 protozoa and 10^9–10^{10} bacteria per ml gut volume. Most of the symbionts lie free in the lumen but some species adhere to the gut wall and certain motile

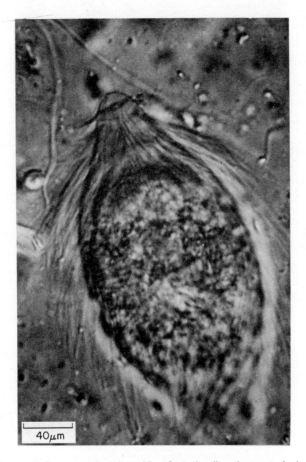

Fig. 8.7 Protozoon (hypermastigote) symbiont from the digestive tract of a lower termite.

forms, especially spirochaetes, are attached to food particles or associated with the surface of protozoa, on which they confer motility (see 9.2 and Figs. 9.1 and 9.2).

Higher termites have bacterial symbionts similar to those in lower termites and often actinomycetes, but they lack the flagellate protozoan symbionts of lower termites (Breznak, 1982).

8.4.2.3 The role of gut symbionts in the degradation of plant material

It has been estimated that 60–90% of the plant material ingested by termites is utilized (Breznak, 1984). This is comparable to or exceeds the values for ruminants and other herbivorous vertebrates.

In contrast to the situation in ruminants (8.2.2.7), the protozoa in termites are essential for the degradation of cellulose and related compounds. This

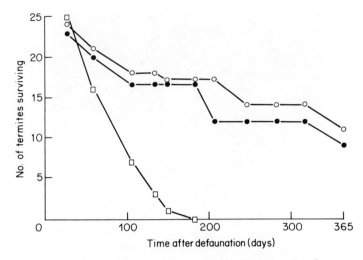

Fig. 8.8   Survival of refaunated *Zootermopsis* maintained on a diet of cellulose. Twenty five days after defaunation by exposure to oxygen, termites were infected with protozoan symbionts from untreated termites (23 individuals; closed circles), axenic culture of *Trichomitopsis termopsidis* (24 individuals; open circles) and heat-killed *T. termopsidis* (25 individuals; open squares) and their survival was assayed over one year (Yamin and Trager, 1979).

was first indicated by the pioneering experiments of Cleveland (1925), who selectively killed the protozoan symbionts by exposing termites to high oxygen levels. Although the bacterial flora of the treated insects was unaffected, these protozoa-free ('defaunated') animals did not survive for more than a few weeks on the standard diet of wood or cellulose. Recently, it has been shown that when defaunated termites are reinfected with protozoa their survival is prolonged (Fig. 8.8).

The protozoan symbionts phagocytose fragments of plant material and degrade the cellulose and other carbohydrates anaerobically to acetic acid, hydrogen and carbon dioxide. Acetic acid at a concentration of 60–80 mM and traces of other VFAs (butyric and propionic acids) are found in the hindgut of *Zootermopsis* and *Reticulitermes* (Odelson and Breznak, 1983). The VFAs are probably absorbed through the gut wall into the insect tissues and metabolized aerobically.

Bacteria are frequently observed within the protozoan symbionts of termites and for many years it has been unclear whether it is the protozoa or enclosed bacteria which are cellulolytic. This problem has been resolved by the isolation into axenic culture of a number of protozoa, including *Trichomitopsis termopsidis* and *Trichonympha sphaerica*, from the termite *Zootermopsis*. The bacteria-free protozoa are actively cellulolytic under anaerobic conditions, producing acetic acid, carbon dioxide and hydrogen (Yamin, 1981).

The bacterial symbionts of lower termites might contribute to host nutrition in the following possible ways.

a) The bacteria may serve as a source of food for the cellulolytic protozoa. This would imply that at least a proportion of the bacteria within the protozoa (see above) are undergoing digestion. In support of this proposal, termite protozoa in culture require heat-killed bacteria from termite hindguts or the rumen of cattle (Yamin, 1981).

b) The bacteria may help to create the environmental conditions in the hindgut that enhance cellulolytic activity by the protozoa. For example, the utilization of hydrogen by methanogenic bacteria may promote the synthesis of VFAs by mechanisms also believed to operate in the rumen symbiosis (Breznak, 1984) (see 8.2.2.4).

c) Some bacteria may be directly involved in the degradation of lignin, although no anaerobic pathway of its degradation is known. There are a number of reports of lignolysis by termite gut contents, for example Butler and Buckerfield (1979), and one possibility is that sufficient oxygen diffuses into the hindgut with the bolus of food to sustain aerobic lignin degradation by bacteria which can tolerate microaerophilic conditions.

d) Some bacteria fix atmospheric nitrogen or recycle host nitrogenous waste products and so contribute to the nitrogen needs of the termite.

With the exception of (d) (see 8.4.2.4), the evidence for these proposed functions of symbiotic bacteria is circumstantial.

Considerably less is known about the role of gut symbionts in higher termites, largely because it is difficult to maintain these insects under laboratory conditions. Since higher termites lack protozoan symbionts (8.4.2.2), their bacterial flora have often been assumed to be cellulolytic. However, this view is supported by little evidence. Most cellulase activity in higher termites is associated with the salivary glands and midgut, and the enzymes are probably produced by the insect (Breznak, 1984).

8.4.2.4 The role of gut symbionts in the nitrogen economy of termites

As in herbivorous vertebrates, gut symbionts allow termites to thrive on a nitrogen-poor diet of refractory plant material. There is now clear evidence that the hindgut bacteria recycle nitrogenous wastes of the insect by a mechanism analogous to those in vertebrates (8.2.2.4 and 8.3.3.2) and that, unlike the vertebrate symbioses, nitrogen fixation by the symbionts also makes a major contribution to the nitrogen economy of some termites.

The major excretory product of nitrogen metabolism in most terrestrial insects is uric acid. Uric acid synthesis by termites has been demonstrated, but the acid is not excreted even though termite tissues lack uricase, the enzyme usually involved in uric acid degradation (Potrikus and Breznak, 1980a). However, uricolytic activity has been detected in gut homogenates of *Reticulitermes flavipes* (Potrikus and Breznak, 1981). The activity is reduced tenfold if the population of hindgut bacteria is depleted by antibiotic treatment (Fig. 8.9), suggesting that the uric acid is degraded by the bacterial

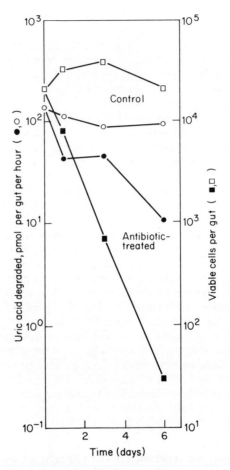

Fig. 8.9 Uricolytic activity of gut homogenates and viability of gut bacteria in *Reticulitermes flavipes* treated with antibiotics (penicillin G, chloramphenical and tetracycline). (Data from Potrikus and Breznak, 1981.)

symbionts. This interpretation is confirmed by the isolation of hindgut bacteria, including *Streptococcus*, *Bacteroides* and *Citrobacter*, which degrade uric acid anaerobically to ammonia, carbon dioxide and acetic acid (Potrikus and Breznak, 1980b). The importance of bacteria in recycling nitrogenous waste is further indicated by experiments using ^{14}C and [15]N (Potrikus and Breznak, 1981) in which the degradation of uric acid in the hindgut of the intact insect and subsequent assimilation of nitrogen by the termite tissues was demonstrated.

The fixation of atmospheric nitrogen has been demonstrated by the acetylene reduction assay (4.1.2) in many lower and higher termites (Breznak, 1984) and by ^{15}N methods in the higher termite *Nasutitermes corniger*

(Bentley, 1984). Several lines of evidence suggest that fixation is due to the bacterial symbionts of the hindgut: nitrogen fixing activity is associated with the gut contents and not animal tissues (Breznak *et al.*, 1973); fixation is abolished when termites are fed with antibiotics (Breznak *et al.*, 1973); and nitrogen fixing bacteria of the genera *Citrobacter* and *Enterobacter* have been isolated from termite hindguts (Breznak, 1982).

The fixation rate varies widely between different species. Thus, nitrogen fixation appears to be of negligible importance to the nitrogen economy of, for example, *R. flavipes* and *Labiotermes* sp., but may be significant in other species, e.g., *I. minor*, *T. trinervoides* and *N. corniger* (Table 8.3a). The level of fixation may also vary with the nitrogen content of the termite diet. For example, when the diet of *Coptotermes formosanus* is supplemented with ammonium or nitrate, nitrogen fixation can be reduced by up to two orders of magnitude (Table 8.3b). This effect cannot be explained by differences in the density of gut bacteria (Breznak *et al.*, 1973) and is probably due to repression of nitrogenase synthesis in the bacteria by the combined nitrogen sources.

Table 8.3 Nitrogen fixation by termites.

(a) Fixation rates by the worker caste of different species. Nitrogen fixation rates are calculated from acetylene reduction assays made on living animals. Where documented, the fixation rate of workers is usually comparable to or higher than those of other castes (Data from Breznak, 1984).

Species	Nitrogen fixation rate (g nitrogen (g fresh weight)$^{-1}$ d^{-1})	Time to double nitrogen* (years)
Reticulitermes flavipes	0.05	904
Labiotermes sp.	0.16	282
Cubitermes sp.	0.17	265
Armitermes sp.	0.36	126
Heterotermes sp.	0.94	48
Incisitermes minor	1.00–18.87	2–45
Coptotermes formosanus	0.16–49.39	1–238
Rhynchotermes permeatus	3.5	13
Trinervitermes trinervoides	6.86	7
Nasutitermes corniger	6.00–8.00	6–8

(b) Fixation rates of *Coptotermes formosanus* maintained on different diets. The termites were maintained on a diet of filter paper impregnated with basal salts and nitrogen supplements for 10 days prior to assay. (Data from Breznak *et al.*, 1973.)

Nitrogen supplement to diet	Nitrogen fixation rate (p mol nitrogen per termite h^{-1})
None	8.70
0.8 mg ammonium sulphate	5.40
8.0 mg '' ''	0.05
1.2 mg potassium nitrate	1.31
12 mg '' ''	0.05

* Time required for the insect to double its nitrogen content at the measured rate of nitrogen fixation.

The form in which the products of uric acid degradation and nitrogen fixation are assimilated by the termite tissues is unknown. There is evidence for the release of amino acids by intact protozoa and bacterial symbionts (Mauldin *et al.*, 1978) and the bacteria may also release ammonia (a product of anaerobic uricolysis, see above), which, as in ruminants (8.2.2.5), may be assimilated into non-essential amino acids by the host. The principal route of nitrogen transfer from symbionts to host in ruminant mammals, digestion of the symbionts (8.2.2.5), is unlikely to be important in termites because host digestive enzymes are not secreted into the hindgut and there is no substantial lysis of the symbionts.

8.4.2.5 The transmission of symbionts

The termite host needs to acquire a fresh complement of gut symbionts at each generation and also after each moult. This is because the symbiont population in the paunch is killed by exposure to oxygen when the exoskeleton, which includes part of the hindgut wall, is shed. Transmission of symbionts from one insect to another within the colony occurs by 'proctodeal trophyllaxis', i.e., the expulsion of a drop of fluid containing active symbionts from the hindgut of one individual for immediate ingestion by a second insect.

8.4.3 Cockroaches

8.4.3.1 Contribution of hindgut symbionts to nutrition of the host

Cockroaches (order Orthoptera) contain a complex hindut microflora, predominantly of obligate anaerobes, including cellulolytic and methanogenic bacteria (Bracke *et al.*, 1979). VFAs occur in the hindgut of *Periplaneta americana* (Bracke and Markovetz, 1980), suggesting that the symbionts degrade cellulose and other plant polysaccharides. *P. americana* also displays antibiotic-sensitive degradation of ^{14}C-cellulose and ^{14}C-hemicellulose to $^{14}CO_2$ (Bignell, 1977).

Most cockroaches are scavengers, able to survive on a great variety of nutritionally poor and unbalanced diets. To investigate the importance of the hindgut symbionts to cockroach nutrition, Bracke and coworkers (1978) fed *P. americana* with metronidazole, which selectively kills strict anaerobes. (General antibiotics, such as penicillin and chlortetracycline are not suitable for cockroaches because these insects also contain aerobic, intracellular 'mycetocyte symbionts' which contribute to host growth by the recycling of nitrogen and synthesis of vitamins and amino acids (see 9.10).) Metronidazole had no discernible effect on the size and vigour of adult *P. americana*, but nymphs raised on metronidazole from hatching had essentially sterile hindguts and grew more slowly than the untreated controls. The reasons for the difference in response of adults and nymphs have not been examined.

Some cockroaches, often known as 'woodroaches', live on a diet of wood.

The characteristics of the hindgut symbiosis in these insects are very similar to those in termites (Brooks, 1963). In particular, the woodroaches, like lower termites, contain protozoa of the orders Hypermastigida and Oxymonadida (but not trichomonads) (Honigberg, 1970) (see 8.4.2.2), which ferment cellulose and other polysaccharides. It has been suggested that the woodroaches and termites evolved from a common ancestor in which the gut symbiosis with protozoa had already been established.

8.4.3.2 Host control of the life cycles of protozoan symbionts in *Cryptocercus punctulatus* (Cleveland *et al.*, 1960)

The life cycles of the protozoan symbionts in one semicolonial species of woodroach, *Cryptocercus punctulatus* were studied in detail by Cleveland. In intermoult hosts, the protozoa reproduce asexually by fission but they become sexual when the host moults. Essentially all members of one protozoan species enter into the sexual cycle in synchrony and at a fixed time relative to the time of moulting (ecdysis) of the host, but the timing and detail of the cycle varies widely between different protozoan species. There is evidence that the cycle is controlled by ecdysone, the 'moulting hormone' of the host, which reaches a peak at ecdysis. Sexual forms of the symbionts can be induced in intermoult insects by injection of ecdysone and sexuality is abolished by the extirpation of the host neurosecretory cells which produce the hormone. It has not been possible to examine the effect of the hormone on the protozoa *in vitro*, so it is not known if its effect on sexuality is direct or indirect.

A conspicuous feature of the transformation of the asexual to sexual form in most protozoan species is encystment prior to gametogenesis. The highly resistant encysted phase persists through ecdysis and so the symbionts survive the aerobic conditions which occur at this time. Just after ecdysis, most insects expel a portion of the encysted symbionts in faecel pellets. Newly-hatched, symbiont-free nymphs feed on the pellets and thereby obtain a complement of symbionts.

The mode of transmission of the protozoan symbionts in *C. punctulatus* can be contrasted with lower termites (8.4.2.5), whose symbionts rarely become sexual or encyst (Honigberg, 1970). It is of little consequence to the individual termite that its gut symbionts die at ecdysis because that insect can acquire fresh symbionts from the other termites in the colony. However, individuals of *C. punctulatus* need to retain their symbionts because all members of the colony moult in synchrony and at the same time as the eggs hatch (Brooks, 1963). If their symbionts could not survive ecdysis, the entire colony's supply of symbionts would be lost.

9
Further associations between prokaryotes and animals or protists

9.1 Introduction

In addition to those described in previous chapters, there is a very wide variety of other associations involving prokaryote symbionts. This chapter describes a selection of associations with protist (9.2-9.7) or animal (9.8-9.12) hosts, chosen to illustrate the diversity of ways in which the partners of a symbiosis may interact.

9.2 Motility symbioses in flagellate protozoa

In motility symbioses, the movement of a host is powered by motile prokaryotes adhering to the host surface. This type of association occurs in certain flagellate protozoa which inhabit the hindgut of termites and woodroaches (8.4).

The first motility symbiosis to be described was the trichomonad protozoon *Mixotricha paradoxa* from the termite *Macrotermes darwiniensis*. *M. paradoxa* has four anterior flagella, but at first sight it also appears to be covered by cilia. Closer examination revealed that the 'cilia' are in fact small spirochaetes which undulate in unison whenever the host is actively swimming (Cleveland and Grimstone, 1964) (Fig. 9.1). The coordinated movement of the spirochaetes probably results from the tendency of all vibrating objects in close proximity to each other to beat in rhythm. *M. paradoxa* continues to move when its four flagella are motionless, showing that it is propelled by the motility of the spirochaetes. Further, *M. paradoxa* swims smoothly at constant speed, whereas other large flagellate protozoa which are dependent on their flagella for locomotion swim more slowly and jerkily with frequent interruptions and changes of speed. The flagella of *M. paradoxa* may act as a steering device.

The spirochaetes adhere to the posterior face of projections on the surface of *M. paradoxa* (Fig. 9.2) and as a result, their motility propels the host forwards. On the anterior face of each projection is a single flagellate rod-shaped bacterium (Fig. 9.2). The protozoon also bears a small number of large spirochaetes on its surface (Fig. 9.1) and several different bacteria in the cytoplasm (Ball, 1969). The variety of prokaryotes associated with *M.*

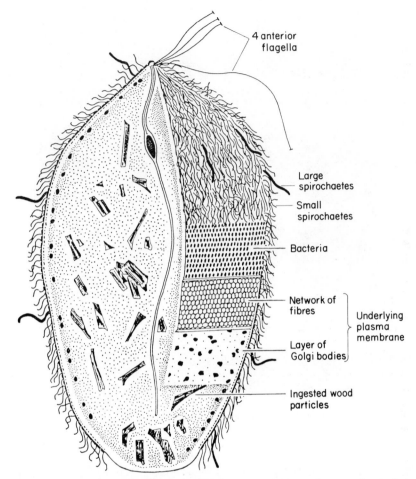

Fig. 9.1 Diagram of *Mixotricha paradoxa* and its motile symbionts. The organism is shown in longitudinal section on the left and at a series of progressively more superficial levels (passing from posterior to anterior ends) on the right (from Cleveland and Grimstone, 1964).

paradoxa led the American biologist Lewis Thomas to describe the association as 'not so much a symbiosis as a committee'.

Complex surface structures for the adhesion of motile symbioses have been identified in several protozoan gut symbionts, including the oxymonad protozoon *Pyrsonympha* from the termite *Reticulitermes flavipes* and a devescovinid protozoon in the woodroach *Cryptocercus cavifrons*. There is substantial variation in the taxonomic identity of the symbionts and structure of attachment sites in the different associations (e.g., see Tamm, 1980), suggesting that motility symbioses have evolved independently on a number of different occasions.

Organisms with one to several flagella can swim no faster than

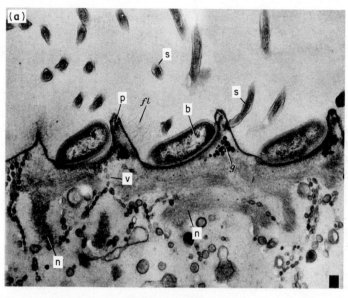

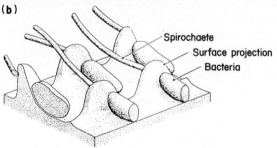

Fig. 9.2   Structural relationship between motile spirochaete symbionts, nonmotile bacterial symbionts and the surface of the host protozoon, *Mixotricha paradoxa* (after Cleveland and Grimstone, 1964). **(a)** Electron micrograph. p = surface projections, b = bacterium, s = spirochaete, n = fibrous network, v = chains of small vacuoles. **(b)** Diagrammatic reconstruction.

0.02–0.2 mm s^{-1}, whatever their body size. Swimming speed is increased by an order of magnitude when the organism is propelled by many motile structures, as is provided by cilia or motile prokaryotes.

9.3   Associations between methanogenic bacteria and anaerobic ciliate protozoa

A variety of anaerobic ciliates from anoxic marine sediments harbour bacteria, either on the surface or within the cell (Fenchel *et al.*, 1977). The

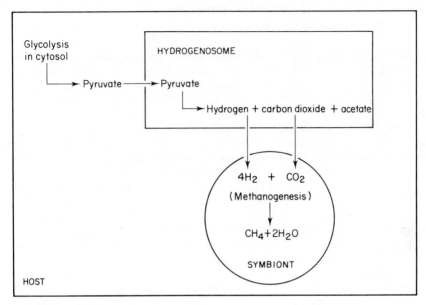

Fig. 9.3 Metabolic interactions between the anaerobic ciliate *Metopus striatus* and its methanogenic symbiont *Methanobacterium formicicum*, (as proposed by Bruggen *et al.*, 1984).

symbionts of several species have been demonstrated to be methanogens (i.e., capable of methane synthesis) (Bruggen *et al.*, 1983). In *Metopus striatus*, the intracellular symbiont has been identified as *Methanobacterium formicicum* (Bruggen *et al.*, 1984). In the intact association, the cells of *M. formicicum* are enclosed in membrane-bound vacuoles closely apposed to host organelles with the ultrastructural characteristics of hydrogenosomes (Bruggen *et al.*, 1984). It has been suggested that hydrogen, produced in the hydrogenosome, is utilized by the symbionts for methane and energy production (Fig. 9.3). By the proposed removal of hydrogen from the ciliate, methanogenesis in the symbionts provides more favourable conditions for oxidative reactions involving hydrogen production in the host. The symbionts thus act as an electron sink in an analogous fashion to the mitochondria of most aerobic eukaryotic cells.

Other anaerobic ciliates which have hydrogenosomes are certain entodiniomorphids and trichostomatids in the foregut of ruminant mammals (Yarlett *et al.*, 1983 and 1984) (see 8.2.2.7). Many entodiniomorphid species of the family Ophryoscolecidae bear a surface flora of methanogenic bacteria which may enhance the fermentative metabolism of the host by their utilization of hydrogen produced (Vogels *et al.*, 1980). However, such a relationship is not characteristic of all anaerobic ciliates containing hydrogenosomes, for no methanogens have been identified in association with trichostomatids (Bruggen *et al.*, 1984).

9.4   The role of symbiotic bacteria in respiration of *Pelomyxa palustris*

Pelomyxa palustris is a multinucleate 'giant' amoeba that lives in micro-aerophilic freshwater habitats. It has a number of unusual structural features. In particular, it lacks mitochondria and Golgi bodies. Micro-tubules, and hence the mitotic spindle, are absent from the nucleus, suggesting that the mechanism of chromosome segregation is atypical. *P. palustris* was once believed to be closely related to the multinucleate amoebae of the genus *Chaos*, but its characteristics are so different from all other amoebae that it is now considered as the sole member of a separate order (Pelobiontidae) or phylum (Caryoblastea) (Whatley and Whatley, 1983).

Three structurally distinct types of bacteria have been identified in membrane-bound vacuoles in the cytoplasm of *P. palustris*: a large Gram-negative form found either in association with glycogen granules or close to the nucleus, a small Gram-positive form distributed throughout the host cytoplasm, and a relatively uncommon Gram-negative bacterium (Chapman-Andresen and Hamburger, 1981).

Although *P. palustris* lacks mitochondria, it exhibits oxygen uptake and aerobic respiration (Chapman-Andresen and Hamburger, 1981), and several lines of evidence indicate that this is mediated by the bacterial symbionts. Cytochrome *c*, a component of the oxidative phosphorylation chain, has been detected in symbiont-rich fractions of *P. palustris* homogenate (Leiner *et al.*, 1968) and aerobic respiration in the intact association is abolished by inhibitors of bacterial respiration, for example, atabin, but not of eukaryote (i.e. mitochondrial) respiration, for example amytal, antimycin A (Leiner *et al.*, 1968). The small Gram-positive bacteria may be responsible for aerobic respiration because they increase in number when *P. palustris* is cultured under aerobic conditions, whereas the number of the large, Gram-negative bacteria is increased by partially anaerobic conditions (Chapman-Andresen and Hamburger, 1981). This difference between the two common symbionts and the close association of the large bacteria with glycogen granules have led to the proposal that the large bacteria function in the anaerobic mobilization of glycogen and the small bacteria utilize the end product (perhaps lactate) as substrate for aerobic respiration (Chapman-Andresen and Hamburger, 1981). It is not known whether the energy produced by the symbionts is made available to the host (e.g., in the form of ATP) and what degree of control the host has over energy production. One could envisage that the small Gram-positive symbionts serve the same function in *P. palustris* as the mitochondria of most eukaryotic cells.

9.5   Haem synthesis by the symbionts of trypanosomatid flagellates

Bacterial symbionts, sometimes known as bipolar bodies or diplosomes, occur in the cytoplasm of several species of trypanosomatid flagellates

Table 9.1 Haem requirement of *Blastocrithidia culicus* and *Crithidia oncopelti*. The protozoa were freed of their cytoplasmic symbionts by treatment with chloramphenicol. They were inoculated into the test media at density of 2×10^6 cells ml^{-1} and the yield was assayed at late logarithmic phase of growth. (Data from Chang and Trager, 1974).

| | Yield ($10^{-6} \times$ cells per ml) | | | |
| | *B. culicus* | | *C. oncopelti* | |
Medium	Symbiotic	Aposymbiotic	Symbiotic	Aposymbiotic
Complete*	140	20	65	20
Haem-free	130	no growth	65	no growth

* Trager's defined medium (which contains haematin), supplemented with 0.25% liver extract for the culture of aposymbionts.

(protozoa of the order Kinetoplastida), including two insect gut parasites, *Crithidia oncopelti* and *Blastocrithidia culicus*, (Chang, 1975). These trypanosomes, unlike related species which lack bacterial symbionts (e.g., *C. fasciculata*) have no dietary requirement for haem (Chang and Trager, 1974).

If *C. oncopelti* and *B. culicus* are freed of their cytoplasmic bacteria, they can no longer be maintained on haem-free media (Table 9.1). Further, the symbionts but not host cells contain enzymes for haem synthesis (Chang *et al.*, 1975). It is therefore likely that the symbionts satisfy the haem requirement of these protozoa. The symbionts probably provide further, as yet unidentified, nutrients to the host. This is suggested by the very slow growth rate of aposymbiotic individuals on the standard medium containing haem (Chang and Trager, 1974); their growth rate is enhanced (although not to the level of untreated cells) by a supplement of liver extract (see Table 9.1).

9.6 Associations in *Amoeba proteus*

A striking example of how the characteristics of an association can change rapidly has been described by Jeon (1980) in strain D of *Amoeba proteus*. In 1966, a stock of these amoebae (designated strain xD) was found to be infected with Gram-negative, rod-shaped bacteria, called X-bacteria. The bacterial cells were enclosed, either singly or in groups, by membrane-bound vacuoles in the host cytoplasm. When isolated from the amoebae, they were viable and could infect other amoebae (of the same or different strain) either by phagocytosis from the surrounding medium or experimentally by micro-injection, but they could not be maintained *in vitro* for more than a few hours. The X-bacteria were evidently harmful to the xD amoebae, which were smaller, more sensitive to starvation and mechanical stress, and grew considerably more slowly than did the uninfected stocks. The amoebae could be freed of the bacteria by incubation at high temperature, which killed the bacteria.

Table 9.2   Necessity of the association with X-bacteria for *Amoeba proteus* (data from Jeon and Ahn, 1976). Amoebae that had been infected with X-bacteria for 1 week to many years were freed of the symbionts by temperature shock. The association is considered necessary for the amoeba if it fails to grow after this treatment.

Time since infection	Percentage of amoebae which fail to grow in the absence of X-bacteria
1 week	4.2
6 months	18.2
12 months	34.2
18 months	90.4
More than 10 years*	100
Uninfected stock of amoebae	5.3

* the original xD strain of amoebae (see text).

Over the years after the infection was initially observed, the detrimental effect of the X-bacteria on the host diminished and, within 5–10 years, xD amoebae grew at comparable rates to the uninfected D amoebae. The morphology of the bacteria did not change, but their density in the host cells approximately halved. The amoebae of the fully established associations did not survive the removal of their bacterial population by temperature shock. More detailed experiments indicated that more than 90% of xD amoebae had become dependent on the bacteria within 18 months of the original infection (about 200 host generations) (Table 9.2). Thus, an association which was originally harmful to the host evolved into a relationship that was obligate for the host in a relatively short span of time.

Table 9.3   Survival of hybrid amoebae synthesized by nuclear and cytoplasmic transplantation between amoebae infected with X-bacteria (xD amoebae) and uninfected amoebae (D amoebae) (data from Jeon (1972)).
(a) Isolated nuclei injected into enucleated amoebae (cytoplasm)

Hybrid cell type		Viability (%)
Nucleus	Cytoplasm	
D	D	92
xD	xD	82
D	xD	91
xD	D	7

(b) A portion of cytoplasm injected into hybrid cells

Hybrid cell type		Viability (%)
Cytoplasm	Hybrid cell*	
D	D/D	96
xD	D/D	96
xD	xD/D	91

* strain of nucleus/strain of cytoplasm.

The physiological basis of the obligacy of the association is unclear, but nuclear and cytoplasmic transplantation experiments suggest it involves nuclear function. The data in Table 9.3a indicate that nuclei of xD amoebae require the cytoplasm of xD amoebae to survive and that the death of xD-nucleus/D-cytoplasm hybrids may be prevented by the addition of a portion of xD-cytoplasm containing X-bacteria to the hybrid amoebae. It is of interest that the X-bacteria derived from the well-established xD amoebae (for which the association is obligate) have changed such that they no longer reduce the growth rate or viability of newly-infected D amoebae (Table 9.3b).

A protein in xD amoebae that is absent from D amoebae and xD amoebae freed of X-bacteria has been identified (Ahn and Jeon, 1984). This protein (of unknown function) is probably synthesized by the X-bacteria and may be of importance in the interaction between host and symbiont.

The X-bacteria are one of a number of different cytoplasmic symbionts in amoebae (Ball, 1969). Some strains of *A. proteus* (including strain D) contain bacteria, often known by the generic term 'DNA bodies', which proliferate at the same rate as the host. These associations are specific, for the DNA bodies degenerate when they are experimentally brought under the control of the nucleus of a different host strain by nuclear transplantation (Jeon, 1975). Methods to obtain amoebae free of their DNA bodies or to culture these symbionts *in vitro* have not been developed.

9.7 Symbioses in the ciliate protozoon *Paramecium aurelia* (Preer *et al.*, 1974; Preer, 1981)

Members of the *Paramecium aurelia* species-complex, comprising 14 species, are used as model systems for the study of many biological problems because of their large size and amenability to genetic investigation. In the 1930s, Sonneborn demonstrated that certain strains of paramecia released an agent which killed 'sensitive' paramecia and that the 'killer' trait was an inherited characteristic transmitted in the cytoplasm and not the nucleus, although persistence of the 'killer' trait is dependent on the presence of a dominant gene not present in 'sensitives'. The cytoplasmic factor was called *kappa*, but for some time it was not clear if it was a plasmid, a virus or a larger particle. It is now known that *kappa* particles are Gram-negative bacteria of the genus *Caedibacter*. Other bacterial symbionts of the *P. aurelia* complex have also been identified. They vary in their morphology and taxonomic identity, host specificity and effect on sensitive paramecia (Table 9.4). Viable symbionts can be isolated from cell-free homogenates of paramecia by density gradient centrifugation but they cannot be maintained in culture.

Recent study of the killer trait has concentrated on *kappa*. Two types of *kappa* can often be seen in a single paramecium: 'brights', which appear refractile by phase contrast microscopy, and 'non-brights' (Fig. 9.4a). The proportion of brights varies with culture condition and strain of *kappa*. The refractile structure in brights is known as the R body and appears by electron microscopy as a coiled ribbon. DNA-containing virus-like particles are some-

Table 9.4 Symbiotic bacteria of *Paramecium aurelia* (from Preer, 1981).

Common name	Distinguishing morphological features of symbiont	Binomial name of symbiont	Host species	Nature of killing activity*
Kappa	Variable size, no flagella, 2–50% of population contain R bodies	*Caedibacter taeniospiralis* *C. pseudomutans* *C. varicaedens* *C. paraconjugatus*	*P. tetraurelia* '' *P. biaurelia* ''	Vacuolizer or hump Spin Spin, paralysis or vacuolizer Mate killer
Gamma	Very small (0.7 μm long), enclosed in extra set of membranes (endoplasmic reticulum?)	*Pseudocaedibacter minutus*	*P. octaurelia*	Vacuolizer
Lambda	Straight rods (5 μm long), covered in peritrichous flagella	*Lyticum flagellatum*	{*P. tetraurelia* *P. octaurelia*	Rapid lysis
Mu	Slender rods (1–4 μm long)	*Pseudocaedibacter conjugatus*	{*P. octaurelia* *P. primaurelia*	Mate killer
Delta	Rods with few flagella	*Tectobacter vulgaris*	*P. primaurelia*	None
Pi	Similar to *kappa* but no R bodies and more slender shape	*Pseudobacter falsus*	*P. tetraurelia*	None
Alpha[+]	Rod, crescent or spiral shape	*Holospora caryophila*	*P. biaurelia*	None

* Sensitive paramecia may be killed with no obvious prelethal effects ('rapid lysis'), after vacuolization of the cytoplasm ('vacuolizer') or abberant behaviour (spinning, 'hump', paralysis), or only during conjugation (mate killer).

[+] Unlike the other symbionts which are cytoplasmic, *alpha* is found in the macronucleus. When the macronucleus degenerates at host division, the *alpha* bacteria pass from the macronucleus fragments through the cytoplasm to the newly-produced macronucleus.

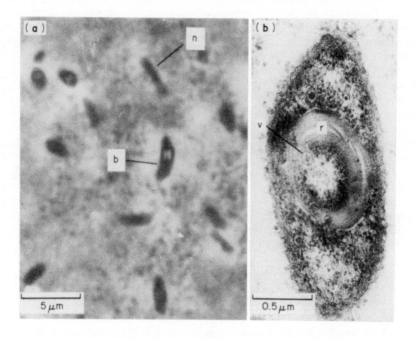

Fig. 9.4   *Kappa* symbionts of *Paramecium tetraurelia*. **(a)** Dark phase contrast micrograph of a paramecium showing: (b) 'bright' (with refractile body present) and (n) 'nonbright' (refractile body absent) *kappa* symbionts (*Caedibacter varicaedens*). (Photo by I. Gibson). **(b)** Transmission electron micrograph showing (r) refractile body and (v) vesicle containing virus. (Provided by I. Gibson.)

times found associated with R bodies (Fig. 9.4b). The virus particles have not been observed in non-bright *kappa* but since brights arise spontaneously from non-brights, it is possible that non-brights contain the virus in a latent form (e.g., integrated into the bacterial genome).

Only the bright form of *kappa* has killer activity; sensitive paramecia incubated with paramecia containing only non-bright *kappa* are not affected. By contrast, only the non-bright *kappa* can divide or be transmitted to other paramecia that can support *kappa*. The mechanism of killing by brights involves the release of the *kappa* from the host, probably via the cytostome (the cell 'mouth') and their phagocytosis by sensitive paramecia into a food vacuole. The R body then unfolds into a long ribbon, ruptures the vacuolar membrane and kills the paramecium. Although the virus associated with the R body is probably involved in the killing effect, no further virus particles are produced after the sensitive paramecium is killed. This suggests the process is not comparable to the usual course of viral infection in which many virus progeny are released on lysis of the host cell.

Symbionts with the killer trait have been found in paramecia in various parts of the world and a high proportion of natural populations of *P. tetraurelia* include *kappa*-bearing individuals. It has been proposed that the killer trait confers benefit on the host in competition with sensitive paramecia for food and other resources. Some investigators have disputed this suggestion on the grounds that, in the natural situation, the paramecia are at too low a density for the killer trait to be effective against sensitive individuals. However, in one ecological study, the paramecia were found to congregate in high densities around small, temporary resource patches and sensitive paramecia were never collected in the same sample as paramecia with the killer trait (Landis, 1981). These data suggest that the killer trait may be important in the exclusion of sensitive paramecia from a resource patch. This interpretation is supported by laboratory experiments in which *kappa*-bearing *P. tetraurelia* successfully outcompete sensitive individuals (Landis, 1981)

The symbionts may also be of direct nutritional benefit to the host. For example, *lambda*-bearing *P. octaurelia* can be maintained indefinitely on media free of folic acid and biopterin but require these nutrients if freed of the symbionts (Soldo *et al.*, 1982).

9.8 Associations in marine sponges

Almost all marine sponges except the hexactinellids contain bacteria, usually in intercellular spaces. The bacteria are structurally intact and metabolically active, as indicated by their incorporation of exogenous radioactive amino acids. The relatively massive sponges harbour a dense population of bacteria comprising 4–7 morphological types. For example, *Verongia* sp. contains five distinct forms of symbionts which comprise 38% of the total sponge volume. By contrast, the well-irrigated sponges of low tissue density contain small numbers of bacteria of a single morphological form (Vacelet and Donaday, 1977). A few sponges, for example, *Petrosia ficiformis*, have intracellular bacteria enclosed in membrane-bound vacuoles in distinctive host cells called bacteriocytes. The bacteriocytes may also contain cyanobacteria if the sponge is in a well-illuminated position (Fig. 9.5).

There is evidence that the associations between sponges and bacteria are specific. The symbionts in different individuals of one sponge species are identical in structure and often closely resemble those in other species but differ substantially from bacterial populations in the ambient water (Vacelet and Donaday, 1977; Wilkinson, 1978). The significance of the association to the sponge is unknown, and no attempt has been made to examine the vigour of sponges freed of their symbionts.

The symbiotic bacteria are transmitted directly from the parent sponge to its offspring during sexual reproduction (Fell, 1983). For example, the developing eggs of *Verongia cavernicola* phagocytose bacteria from the surrounding tissue and incorporate them into vacuoles in the peripheral ooplasm. Alternatively, as in *Chondrosia reniformis*, bacteria are transferred to the follicle cells which surround each egg. During embryogenesis,

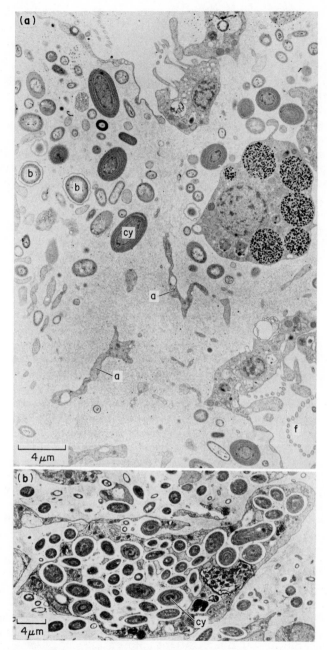

Fig. 9.5 Intracellular bacteria and cyanobacteria in two marine sponges. **(a)** *Aplysina aerophoba*. Note bacteria (b), cyanobacteria (cy), amoeboid cells of host (a), and feeding chamber (f) of host. **(b)** *Jaspis stelligera*. Cyanocyte with one large vacuole containing numerous cyanobacteria (cy). *Photographs* C.R. Wilkinson.

these cells become enclosed within the embryonic cells and at metamorphosis they are disrupted, liberating the bacteria into intercellular spaces of the young adult.

9.9   Symbionts of interstitial animals with reduced digestive tracts

There are several reports of invertebrates from anaerobic or microaerobic marine sediments that lack mouthparts and whose digestive tract is rudimentary or entirely missing but which contain bacteria (see Ott *et al.*, 1982). For example, the turbellarian *Paracatenula* (Sterrer and Rieger, 1974) and the nematode *Astronema jenneri* (Ott *et al.*, 1982) have bacteria in their rudimentary guts; the bacteria in the oligochaete *Phallodrilus leukodermatus* are subcuticular (Giere, 1981). The absence of structural specializations of the host epidermis or other surface layer (e.g., reduced cuticle, increased microvillar density) for the enhanced uptake of dissolved organic compounds suggests that the bacterial symbionts provide nutrients to the host, but the metabolic capabilities of the bacteria and their interactions with the host have not been investigated. There are close parallels between these symbioses and those described in 9.11.

9.10   Mycetocyte-symbioses in insects

9.10.1   The mycetocyte

Many insects contain symbiotic microorganisms within specialized cells, 'mycetocytes' (sometimes referred to as bacteriocytes), which may be scattered or aggregated together as a coherent structure, the mycetome.

Apart from the presence of symbionts in the cytoplasm, the cell structure of mycetocytes is not unusual; each cell contains a single nucleus, ribosomes, endoplasmic reticulum, Golgi bodies and lysosomes, and is capable of DNA, RNA and protein synthesis. The position of the mycetocytes in the insect body varies between different hosts (Buchner, 1966). For example, they are associated with the midgut wall of the human louse *Pediculus capitata*, in the Malpighian tubules of the weevil *Apion pisi*, in the fat body of cockroaches, and free in the haemocoel of aphids and leafhoppers.

9.10.2   Identity of the mycetocyte symbionts

Until recently, there has been much confusion over the identity of the mycetocyte symbionts, and some investigators have avoided the problem by calling them Blochmann Bodies (after F. Blochmann who observed bacteria-like particles in the egg cytoplasm of cockroaches). The early literature includes many reports of yeasts isolated into culture from mycetocytes (Buchner, 1966; Koch, 1967) (the terms mycetocyte and mycetome were coined in the belief that the symbionts were yeasts). However, the isolation procedures adopted did not exclude the possibility of contamination by yeasts from the insect surface or gut.

In virtually all mycetocyte symbioses that have been investigated critically, the symbionts have the morphological features of prokaryotes. Structural and serological data indicate that the symbionts of bloodsucking insects are rickettsias (Dasch *et al.*, 1984) and Weiss and Dasch (1981) consider that 'there is little to distinguish' them from rickettsias of the genus *Wolbachia*. The symbionts in nonbloodsucking insects vary widely in morphology and DNA base composition, suggesting that they are more heterogeneous. The symbionts of cockroaches (suborder Blattaria) are large rods (Fig. 9.6a) with

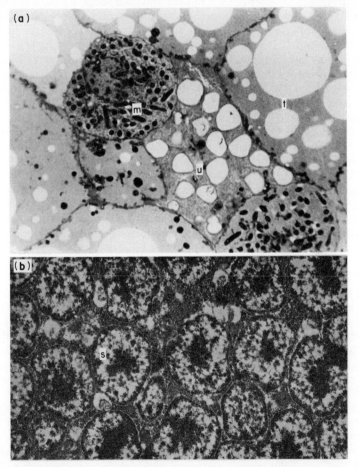

Fig. 9.6 Ultrastructural features of mycetocyte symbionts. **(a)** Rod-shaped bacteria in the cockroach *Periplaneta americana*. The mycetocytes (m) are associated with urate cells (u) and trophocytes (t) in the fat body. Magnification × 1100. (From Cochran *et al.*, 1978.) **(b)** Spherical symbionts (s) in the aphid *Megoura viciae*. Magnification × 1500. *Photograph* C. Brough.

the wall structure of Gram-negative bacteria and DNA comprising 26–28 mol % guanosine + cytosine (G + C content) (Weiss and Dasch, 1981); they have been designated as a single species *Blattabacterium cuenoti* of uncertain taxonomic position. The symbionts in many other nonblood-sucking insects, for example, most aphids (Fig. 9.6b) and the weevil *Sitophilus*, have greatly reduced cell walls and are spherical or irregular in shape. However, this uniformity in structure is not an indication of taxonomic affinity. The G + C content of symbionts in the pea aphid *Acyrtho-siphon pisum* is 31 mol % but that of *Sitophilus* symbionts is 49.8 or 54.5–55 mol % (Dasch *et al.*, 1984).

There are many reports of mycetocyte symbionts of differing morphology in a single insect. In some cases, one symbiont can adopt different forms. For example, the symbionts in *Euscelis* have complex life cycles and exhibit elaborate morphological specializations linked to the developmental stage of the host (Houk and Griffiths, 1980). However, in other cases, it is clear that many insects possess several different mycetocyte symbionts. Examples include the bedbug *Cimex* and tsetse fly *Glossina* (Weiss and Dasch, 1981). It has been estimated that among the homopterans, 55% of species have two symbionts and 30% possess three or more symbionts (Buchner, 1966).

Metabolically-active mycetocyte symbionts have been isolated from a number of insect hosts by dissection and maceration of mycetomes, and relatively pure preparations can be obtained by density gradient centrifugation. The isolated symbionts of the pea aphid *Acyrthosiphon pisum* are capable of DNA, RNA and protein synthesis for limited periods (Ishikawa, 1984), but they cannot divide or be maintained indefinitely in culture (Hinde, 1971). There is a widely-held view that the association with insects is physiologically obligate for all mycetocyte symbionts.

9.10.3 Metabolic interactions

Most insects which possess mycetocyte symbionts live throughout their lives on nutritionally-poor or unbalanced diets such as keratin, dried cereal grains, plant sap, blood. The symbionts are believed to contribute to the nutrition of the host, and the vigour, growth and fertility of the insect hosts declines markedly when their population of mycetocyte symbionts is reduced or eliminated by antibiotics or other treatments (Brooks, 1963; Houk and Griffiths, 1980; Koch, 1967).

The mycetocyte symbionts have been implicated in the nitrogen metabolism of the insect and in the provision of vitamins and sterols (see below). Most information has come from studies of cockroaches and aphids. These groups are particularly amenable to experimental study because they can be maintained on chemically-defined diets and methods are available to obtain aposymbiotic individuals. However, it is not known whether the associations in these insects are representative of all mycetocyte symbioses, many of which have not been studied at all.

Table 9.5 Dietary amino acid requirements of the aphid *Myzus persicae*. The number of mycetocyte symbionts in the treated aphids was reduced (but not eliminated) by maintaining the mother aphids on a diet containing the antibiotic chlortetracycline. The offspring were fed on artificial diets from birth and after 8 days their weights were determined. All aphids examined were apterous (i.e., wingless). Omission of non-essential amino acids caused negligible reduction in weight of both classes of aphid (data not shown), indicating that the antibiotic treatment did not interfere with the aphids' ability to synthesize amino acids. Data from Mittler (1971).

Essential amino acid omitted from diet	Mean weight of aphids (percentage of mean weight on complete diet)*	
	Control aphids	Antibiotic treated aphids
None (complete diet)	100	100
Arginine	93	67
Histidine	70	55
Isoleucine	75	53
Leucine	94	39
Lysine	62	49
Methionine	33	41
Phenylalanine	94	68
Threonine	83	52
Tryptophan	101	71
Valine	115	49

* The mean weight of antibiotic-treated aphids on the complete diet was 50% of that of the controls. Therefore, where percentage values are similar for the two classes of aphid on the test diets, the *absolute* weight of the treated aphids was approximately half that of the control aphids.

9.10.3.1 Provision of amino acids

Unlike most animals, aphids are not dependent on a dietary supply of many of the essential amino acids. For example, the growth of the aphid *Myzus persicae* is appreciably reduced by the omission of only lysine or methionine (Table 9.5). The other essential amino acids are probably provided by the mycetocyte symbionts because when the symbionts are depleted by antibiotic treatment, omission of any of the essential amino acids from the diet leads to retarded weight gain of the insect.

Amino acid synthesis has been examined directly by using the radio-tracer ^{35}S-sulphate, which can be incorporated into sulphur-amino acids (cysteine and methionine) by prokaryotes but not animals. When ^{35}S-sulphate is injected into untreated individuals of the cockroach *Blatella germanica* (Henry, 1962) or aphid *Neomyzus circumflexus* (Ehrhardt, 1968), radioactivity is subsequently recovered from sulphur-amino acids in various regions of the insect body. By contrast, aposymbiotic individuals do not metabolize ^{35}S-sulphate to amino acids, indicating that the mycetocyte symbionts may synthesize and provide sulphur-amino acids to the host.

9.10.3.2 Conservation of nitrogen

The diet of most insects which possess mycetocyte symbionts is nitrogen-poor. Two mechanisms have been proposed by which symbionts might help to conserve nitrogen within the association: nitrogen fixation and recycling of host nigrogenous waste. However, nitrogen fixation has not been detected in any mycetocyte symbionts by the modern techniques of ^{15}N incorporation or acetylene reduction (4.1.2), and the several early reports that the symbionts fix nitrogen are now considered to be mistaken.

Evidence for nitrogen recycling is fragmentary. Most is known about the association in cockroaches, especially *Periplaneta americana*. This species may contain substantial amounts of uric acid in specialized 'urate cells' of the fat body but uric acid is never excreted. The uric acid content per unit body weight of *P. americana* varies with the nitrogen content of the diet, more than doubling in insects maintained on high nitrogen foods and declining to barely detectable levels on foods poor in nitrogen (Mullins and Cochran, 1975). The urate cells are closely associated with the mycetocytes (Fig. 9.6a). It has been proposed that the mycetocyte symbionts utilize the uric acid reserves under conditions of nitrogen shortage and release nitrogen, perhaps as amino acids (see 9.10.3.1) to the host. This proposal is strengthened by the finding that aposymbiotic cockroaches accumulate more uric acid than untreated individuals (Malke and Schwartz, 1966).

9.10.3.3 Vitamin synthesis

The mycetocyte symbionts of several insect groups may provide vitamins of the B complex to the host. Some or all of these micronutrients are dietary requirements of aposymbiotic but not symbiotic individuals of the louse *Pediculus capitata* (Koch, 1967), coccid *Pseudococcus citri* (Koch, 1967), tsetse fly *Glossina* (Nogge, 1976) and the weevil *Sitophilus* (Wicker and Nardon, 1983). The synthesis of micronutrients other than B vitamins has not been investigated.

9.10.3.4 Sterol synthesis

For some years, it has been believed that the mycetocyte symbionts of aphids synthesize sterols because aphids, unlike most insects, apparently do not require exogenous sterols for sustained growth and reproduction. Although several metabolic studies suggest that the symbionts of the pea aphid *Acyrthosiphon pisum* synthesize sterols and release them to insect tissues (Houk and Griffiths, 1980), more recent data suggest that aphids are dependent on exogenous sterol sources (Campbell and Nes, 1983).

9.10.3.5 Interactions at the molecular level

Recent biochemical studies on the pea aphid *Acyrthosiphon pisum* (Ishikawa, 1984) indicate a further level in the interactions between insect and symbiont. Freshly isolated symbionts synthesize a range of proteins that are not produced in the intact association but the single major protein, 'symbionin', synthesized by the symbionts *in vivo*, is not produced by the isolated symbionts. This suggests that the host has some control over symbiont metabolism. Studies using antibiotics and other metabolic inhibitors suggest that this protein may be coded by the host genome but synthesized by the symbiont. Perhaps the mRNA for symbionin is transported from the mycetocyte nucleus to the symbionts, on whose ribosomes it is translated. The function of symbionin is unknown.

9.10.4 Transmission of the symbionts

In all insect groups that have been investigated, the mycetocyte symbionts are transmitted directly to the offspring by passage from the mycetocytes to the developing eggs or embryos in the insect ovary. This process is known as transovarial transmission. In some insects, for example, *Euscelis* and *Sitophilus*, the symbionts are transformed from a 'vegetative' phase to the 'infective' phase prior to transmission (Buchner, 1966). Passage of symbionts to the male gonads has not been observed; indeed, the symbionts in the males of many species degenerate before the insect reaches reproductive maturity (Buchner, 1966).

Symbionts may reach the ovaries by migration of mycetocytes, as in cockroaches (Brooks, 1970) or by their release from mycetocytes and passage through the haemolymph, as in the louse *Pediculus* (Eberle and McLean, 1983). The mode of entry of symbionts to the egg cytoplasm is not understood in detail but it is often associated with the passage of nutrients from trophocytes (specialized nutritive cells in the ovaries of many insect groups) (Brooks, 1963). In some viviparous insects, such as certain morphs of aphids, transmission is delayed until the blastula stage of embryogenesis, when symbionts are taken up through the blastopore of the embryo (Houk and Griffiths, 1980).

The incorporation of mycetocytes into egg or embryo is of significance to the differentiation of some insects. For example, if the symbionts are experimentally removed from the eggs of the leafhopper *Euscelis plebejus*, the resultant embryos fail to develop abdomens (Schwemmler, 1974). By contrast, not all eggs produced by the coccid *Stictococcus* under natural conditions contain symbionts. Those eggs which lack symbionts develop into males and those which contain symbionts become females (Buchner, 1966).

9.11 Chemoautotrophic symbionts of marine animals including those of deep sea hydrothermal vents

9.11.1 Chemoautotrophic bacteria

Chemoautotrophs are prokaryotes that can obtain all their energy requirements by the oxidation of inorganic compounds such as reduced sulphur, nitrogen or iron compounds, or molecular hydrogen, and can utilize carbon dioxide as the sole source of carbon. They are therefore independent of both light and organic carbon. They are always found in reducing environments, which are often poor in organic carbon or otherwise extreme (e.g., low pH, high temperature).

9.11.2　Symbiosis with sulphide-oxidising chemoautotrophs

Symbiosis with chemoautotrophs was first reported in 1980 in organisms inhabiting a most unusual habitat, the sulphide-rich deep sea hydrothermal vent of the Galapagos Rift and East Pacific Rise (Jannasch and Taylor, 1984). In these zones of sea floor spreading, sea water seeps into the earth's crust and is heated by hot rocks deep in the crust. The sea water absorbs mineral salts and methane from these rocks and its constituent sulphate is reduced to sulphide. The chemically modified 'vent' water, containing a high concentration of sulphide, is ejected from the ocean floor. In the region of mixing with the ambient sea water, there is a remarkable community of organisms, with sulphide-oxidizing chemoautotrophs as the principal primary producers (Karl *et al.*, 1980).

Abundant and conspicuous components of the vent fauna are the giant vestimentiferan pogonophorans, for example *Riftia pachyptila* (Fig. 9.7a). Like all other pogonophorans, these animals lack a mouth and gut, yet their large size (up to 2 m in length and 0.04 m in diameter) suggests that they cannot be sustained by the uptake of dissolved organic material via the epidermis. The trunk of these animals is filled with brown spongy tissue, the trophosome, which contains intracellular bacteria. The bacteria comprise two forms: short rods and the more abundant spherical cells which display some affinities to sulphide-oxidizing bacteria of the genus *Thiobacillus* (Jannasch and Taylor, 1984). Sequence analysis of 5S rRNA suggests the symbionts are members of the Enterobacteriaceae (Stahl *et al.*, 1984). Several direct lines of evidence also indicate that the bacterial symbionts oxidize sulphide and utilize the energy thereby derived to fix carbon into organic compounds. The trophosome contains two enzymes of the Calvin Benson cycle of carbon dioxide fixation and three enzymes associated with sulphide oxidation (Felbeck *et al.*, 1981); crystals of elemental sulphur (the product of sulphide oxidation) are abundant (Jones, 1981). Movement of organic carbon compounds from the symbionts to the host has not been demonstrated but the ratio of the two stable isotopes of carbon (^{13}C:^{12}C) in the animal tissues suggests that the carbon is derived from chemoautotrophic fixation and not dissolved organic matter in the sea water (Rau, 1981).

Intracellular bacteria with enzymes of carbon dioxide fixation and sulphide oxidation also occur in bivalve molluscs associated with hydrothermal vents (e.g., *Calyptogena* species) and other sulphide-rich habitats (e.g., *Solemya* species) (Cavanaugh, 1983), as well as in some habitats which have low concentrations of free sulphide (e.g. *Myrtea spinifera* and *Lucinoma borealis*) (Dando *et al.*, 1985; Dando *et al.*, 1986). In contrast to most bivalves, the gut of these animals is reduced or altogether lacking. For example, *Solemya reidi* which is abundant in waters containing 1–25 mM

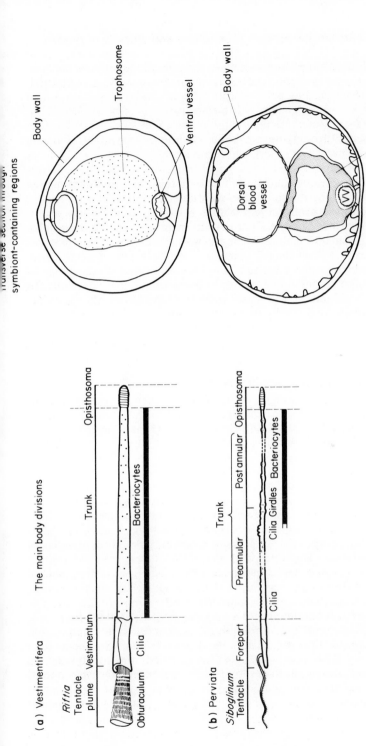

Fig. 9.7 The Pogonophora (9.11.2). The phylum Pogonophora is probably allied to the Annelida and comprises 2 subphyla: the large Vestimentifera **(a)**, which are abundant near deep sea hydrothermal vents and are up to 2 m in length and the small Perviata **(b)**, found in shallower waters and usually not more than a few centimetres in length. All pogonophorans lack a digestive tract and contain chemoautotrophic bacteria in the trunk region (stippling). In vestimentiferans, the tissue containing the symbionts (trophosome) almost fills the trunk, whereas in perviates, it forms a narrow layer (the bacterial cylinder) lining a central fluid lumen. The tissue containing the bacteria is well-supplied with blood vessels, providing carbon dioxide and oxygen to the symbionts (from Jones, 1981 and Southward, 1982).

Transverse section through symbiont-containing regions

Body wall

Trophosome

Ventral vessel

Body wall

Dorsal blood vessel

Bacterium containing tissues

The main body divisions

(a) Vestimentifera

Riftia

Tentacle plume   Vestimentum   Trunk   Opisthosoma

Obturaculum   Cilia   Bacteriocytes

(b) Perviata

Siboglinum

Tentacle   Forepart   Preannular   Post annular   Opisthosoma

Trunk

Cilia   Cilia Girdles   Bacteriocytes

hydrogen sulphide in zones of sewage and pulp mill effluent outlets, has been the subject of extensive study. The gill tissue of this species is packed with Gram-negative bacteria and, unlike the gill tissue of the *Mytilus edulis*, which is symbiont-free, it rapidly fixes ^{14}C-bicarbonate into organic acids and oxidizes sulphide to elemental sulphur and sulphate (Felbeck, 1983). The host is believed to benefit from these metabolic activities of its symbiotic bacteria in two ways: the provision of organic carbon compounds and removal of toxic hydrogen sulphide.

Perviate pogonophorans inhabit sediments on the continental slope and in fjords. Like the vestimentiferan species they possess intracellular bacteria in the trunk region (Southward, 1982) (Fig. 9.7b). The tissues containing the bacteria have enzymes of the Calvin Benson cycle and exhibit appreciable levels of carbon dioxide fixation. This explains why the ratio of the stable carbon isotopes ^{13}C:^{12}C in the pogonophoran tissues is very different from that of other invertebrates in the same habitat (Southward *et al.*, 1981). As with vestimentiferan pogonophorans and various bivalve molluscs (9.11.2), the bacterial symbionts in several perviate pogonophorans obtain energy for carbon dioxide fixation by oxidation of sulphide (Southward *et al.*, 1986).

9.12 Bioluminescence symbioses

9.12.1 Introduction to bioluminescence (Hastings *et al.*, 1985)

Bioluminescence is the production of light by living organisms. It occurs in certain bacteria, protists, fungi and animals. In bacteria and protists, the whole organism is luminescent but in the more complex organisms, light emission is restricted to specific tissues called light organs. Light is produced when a particular compound, luciferin, is oxidized, a reaction catalysed by the enzyme luciferase. The terms luciferin and luciferase are generic; their identities vary between different groups of organisms. For example, at least two distinct mechanisms have evolved in the animal kingdom and these differ fundamentally from that in bacteria (see 9.12.2) (Hastings, 1978).

Among animals, bioluminescence may serve several different functions, including illumination of the surroundings, intra-specific communication, attraction of prey (or of hosts, in the case of parasitic animals) and distraction of predators. Bioluminescence has been reported in many invertebrate groups, non-vertebrate chordates and fish, but no other vertebrates. Luminescent animals are abundant in the marine environment. At depths greater than 700 m, it has been estimated that more than 90% of species are capable of light production. They are less common in terrestrial habitats and rare in freshwaters. The luminescence in most species is intrinsic, in that it is produced by the animal, but in a significant minority of marine animals the light is generated by bacterial symbionts within the light organs.

9.12.2   Identification of bioluminescence symbiosis

Bioluminescence symbioses occur in a number of families of teleost fish, some squids of the families Loliginidae and Sepiolidae and pelagic tunicates (a group of lower chordates) of the class Thaliacea (Table 9.6).

The bacteria associated with the light organs of some hosts can readily be isolated and they are luminescent in pure culture (Hastings and Nealson, 1981). This is substantial evidence that they are the source of light in the light organ, although there is no published report of re-establishment of the association between the bacterium-free host and isolated symbiont. The symbionts have been identified as members of the genera *Vibrio* (= *Beneckea*) or *Photobacterium* (Table 9.6).

It has not proved possible to isolate luminous bacteria from certain hosts such as anomalopid fish (Haneda and Tsuji, 1971) and tunicates (Mackie and Bone, 1978), whose light organs contain bacteria or bacterium-like structures. For such cases, an alternative approach is needed to demonstrate bioluminescence symbiosis. The method that has been adopted by several investigators utilizes the fundamental chemical difference between the luciferin-luciferase of animals and bacteria. In all known luminescent bacteria, the luciferin comprises two compounds, reduced flavin mononucleotide ($FMNH_2$) and a long chain aliphatic aldehyde (RCHO). Light is produced by their oxidation, with the overall stoichiometry:

$$FMNH_2 + RCHO + O_2 \xrightarrow{\text{luciferase}} FMN + RCOOH + H_2O + \text{light}$$

Bacterial luciferase can be assayed by incubating a cell-free extract of light organs with $FMNH_2$ and the ten-carbon aldehyde, dodecanal, with light production measured by a photometer (Leisman *et al.*, 1980). The luminescence of symbionts from different sources vary in their kinetic properties; those of some bacteria decay at a rate 5–10 times faster than in other bacteria (the absolute decay rate varies with temperature and other factors) (Fig. 9.8). This difference has been used to identify the bacterial symbiont to the level of genus: fact decay in *Photobacterium* and slow decay in *Vibrio* (Leisman *et al.*, 1980; Hastings and Nealson, 1981). However, there is evidence that some *Vibrio* species display fast decay kinetics (Fig. 9.8) and therefore that luciferase kinetics are not a reliable taxonomic character (Baumann *et al.*, 1980).

Table 9.6 Associations between marine animals and bioluminescent bacteria. (Data from Hastings and Nealson, 1981; Leisman et al., 1980).

Symbiont	Host	Position of symbiont	Habitat (of fish)	Luciferase decay kinetics
A: Fish				
Photobacterium phosphoreum	Macrouridae	Ventral	Deep, cold	Fast
	Merluccidae	Rectal	'' ''	''
	Moridae	''	'' ''	''
	Opisthoproctidae	''	'' ''	''
	Trachichthydae	''	'' ''	''
Photobacterium leiognathi	Leiognathidae	Circumoesophageal	Shallow, tropical	''
	Apogonidae	Intestinal	'' ''	''
Vibrio fischeri	Monocentridae	Submandibular	Shallow, temperate	''
Not yet cultured	Anomalopidae	Suborbital	Shallow, tropical	Slow
	Ceratiodiae	Anterior projection	Deep, cold	Fast
B: Squid				
Vibrio fischeri	Euprymna (Sepiolidae)	Mantle cavity		Fast
Not yet cultured	Heteroteuthis ('' '')	'' ''		''
C: Thaliacean tunicates				
Not yet cultured	Pyrosoma (Pyrosomidae)			''

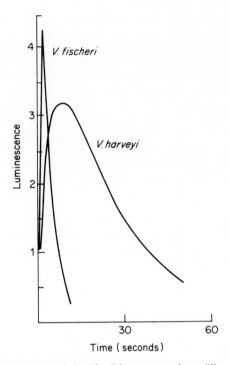

Fig. 9.8 Luminescence characteristics of cell free extracts from different luminescent bacteria. In the assay illustrated the luminescence of *V. fischeri* declines within 2–3 s and that of *V. harveyi* at 30 s after initiation of the reaction. The rate of decay (decline) in luminescence follows first order kinetics and the decay constant is expressed as reciprocal of time. Thus, the decay constant for *V. fischeri* was 0.35 s^{-1} (fast decay) and of *V. harveyi* was 0.03 s^{-1} (slow decay). (Data of Leisman *et al.*, 1980.)

9.12.3 Bioluminescence symbiosis in fish

The luminescent symbionts of fish are extracellular and housed in canals or tubules of the light organ. This organ is well-vascularized, presumably for the supply of nutrients and oxygen to the symbionts, and is open to the external surface or gut lumen of the host. The bacteria are maintained at high density (10^9–10^{10} cells ml^{-1} organ fluid). This feature is believed to be important for the continued production of luciferase and luminescence by the bacteria. Luciferase synthesis is induced when a specific compound ('autoinducer') released by the bacteria into the medium reaches a certain concentration (Hastings, 1978) and this critical concentration is attained in healthy dense cultures but not dilute cultures of the bacteria. Thus, the light organs of fish which are dependent on bacterial symbionts produce light continuously. The host controls emission of light from its body by means of mechanical shutters, reflectors or chromatophores.

The position of the light organ varies between different groups of fish (Table 9.6) and in many cases can be related to the function of the luminescence. For example, in angler fish (Ceratiodiae), the light organ is at the tip of a projection from the head, where it acts as 'bait' attracting would-be predators, which are then consumed. The light organs associated with the digestive tract of many mid-water fish match the background (the down-welling light from the surface) and so make the fish invisible to potential predators below them. The light organs on the head of monocentrids and anomalopids are subject to rapid on-off control by the host and are used in intra-specific communication.

The morphology and luciferase-kinetics of the bacterial symbionts suggest that the associations with fish are highly specific. The population of bacteria in any one host is a homogeneous culture and the symbionts of different individuals of one host species are indistinguishable (Hastings and Nealson, 1981). In most fishes, the symbionts are Gram-negative, flagellate rods that contain luciferase with fast decay kinetics and can readily be isolated into culture. A total of three species have been identified: *Photobacterium phosphoreum, P. leiognathi* and *Vibrio fishcheri* (Table 9.6). The symbionts of anomalopids have not been identified and differ from other luminous bacteria in their spherical shape, thin cell wall, slow decay kinetics of luminescence and inability to grow in culture (Haneda and Tsuji, 1971) (Table 9.6).

P. phosphoreum is very sensitive to high temperature in culture, so it is not surprising to find it is the usual symbiont of fish in deep waters. By contrast, *V. fischeri* and *P. leiognathi*, which exhibit greater thermal tolerance, are found in fish in warm and shallow waters (Table 9.6).

Although the three bacterial species in luminescence symbioses are aerobic, they vary in their response to oxygen tension in culture. The intensity of light produced by cultures of *P. leiognathi* increases with oxygen level but that of *V. fischeri* and *P. phosphoreum* is maximal at relatively low oxygen tension and diminishes with increasing levels.

The canals of the light organs housing *P. phosphoreum* and *V. fischeri* are bounded by cells rich in mitochondria but those containing *P. leiognathi* are not. Nealson (1979) has developed a model of the mechanisms by which the population size and luminescence of, firstly, *P. phosphoreum* and *V. fischeri* and, secondly, *P. leiognathi* may be regulated (Fig. 9.9). In symbioses with *P. phosphoreum* or *V. fischeri*, it is proposed that nutrients, especially glucose, are freely available to the bacteria, which metabolize the glucose to pyruvate (unlike *P. leiognathi* they produce substantial amounts of pyruvate from glucose in culture). The pyruvate is respired by the dense array of mitochondria in the wall of the light organ, so decreasing the oxygen concentration in the immediate vicinity of the symbionts. This causes an increase in luminescence and decrease in growth rate. By contrast, it is proposed that oxygen tension in the light organs containing *P. leiognathi* is high, so as to maximize light production by the symbionts. The bacterial population may be controlled either by nutrient limitation or by the regular expulsion of excess symbionts into the gut, where they are digested (by con-

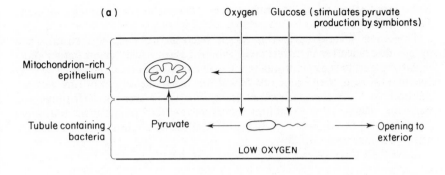

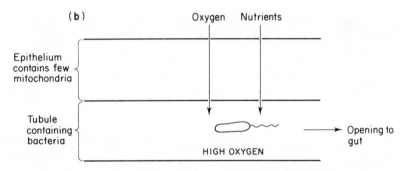

Fig. 9.9 Models for the control of light production and growth of the bacterial symbionts in light organs of fish. See text for further details (data from Nealson, 1979).
(a) *P. phosphoreum* and *V. fischeri*: Competition between mitochondria and symbionts for oxygen reduces oxygen content in the vicinity of the symbionts and enhances luminescence. **(b)** *P. leiognathi*: High oxygen content in the tubule enhances luminescence.

trast, the light organs of *P. phosphoreum* and *V. fischeri* do not open into the gut). However, the oxygen tension in the light organs of fish is unknown and this model remains untested.

9.12.4 Bioluminescence symbiosis in squids

Compared to that in fish, relatively little is known about bioluminescence symbiosis in squids (cephalopods of the order Decapoda). In those symbioses that have been well-documented, the bacteria are maintained in paired light organs between the inksac and anus in the mantle cavity (Herring, 1977). It is not known whether the symbionts are intracellular or extracellular.

In some squids, the light is visible through the mantle wall of the animal, but in most it becomes apparent only when luminescence is discharged into the surrounding water. Luminescence is thus believed to function to distract or frighten other organisms in the dark (where the ink produced by some squid species is ineffective) (Herring, 1977).

There are several early reports of bacteria isolated into culture and assigned to a range of different genera (Buchner, 1966), but whether these isolates are truly the symbionts or surface contaminants is unclear. The only bacterial symbiont of squids to have been isolated into culture by modern methods is *V. fischeri*, obtained from *Euprymna scalopes* (Hastings and Nealson, 1981). The symbiont of *Heteroteuthis hawaiiensis* (although identified by the presence of bacterial luciferase) could not be cultured *in vitro* (Leisman *et al.*, 1980).

9.12.5   Bioluminescence symbiosis in tunicates of the class Thaliacea

There has been much dispute as to whether the luminescence in this group of tunicates is intrinsic or bacterial in origin. Although the light organs of several species are known to contain a dense population of intracellular bacteria, their involvement in luminescence has been discounted by some authors for two reasons. First, the bacteria bear no morphological resemblance to other luminous bacteria. They are elongate thin-walled cells (Mackie and Bone, 1978) and, according to the early account of Buchner (1966), are spore-producing forms. Secondly, light is not produced continuously as in the symbioses in fish and squids, but generated intermittently under precise control of the host. For example, the light organs of *Pyrosoma* produce short flashes of light only in response to photic or mechanical stimuli. Despite these characteristics, it is now very probable that the bioluminescence in *Pyrosoma* is a property of the bacterial symbiont because, although the symbionts cannot be cultured *in vitro*, cell-free extracts of the light organs contain bacterial luciferase (Table 9.6). The luciferase of other bioluminescent tunicates has not been investigated.

The ability of *Pyrosoma* to control light generation by its symbionts suggests that host and symbiont are more closely integrated in this association than in the bioluminescence symbioses in fish and squids. This difference has been correlated with the intracellular position of the symbionts in *Pyrosoma* (Mackie and Bone, 1978). The mechanism of control is unknown, although it has been suggested that the immediate trigger of luminescence may be increased levels of free calcium ions in the light organ.

9.12.6   Acquisition of symbionts

The fish and squid hosts acquire their luminescent symbionts by infection *de novo* at each generation. Luminescent bacteria, including species capable of symbiosis such as *V. fischeri*, are widespread in the marine environment (Ruby *et al.*, 1980) and these forms probably represent the main source of infection. However there is evidence for direct transmission of the symbionts in *Pyrosoma* (Buchner, 1966).

10
Symbiosis and evolution

10.1 Introduction

This chapter considers two interrelated topics: the origin and evolutionary history of symbioses described in this book (10.2), and the importance of symbiosis in the evolution of living organisms in general (10.3) and of eukaryotes in particular (10.4). These subjects have stimulated much study and speculation and the reader is referred to Boucher (1985) for a more detailed coverage than is presented here.

10.2 The origin and evolution of modern symbioses

10.2.1 Evidence from the fossil record

Very few fossilized structures indicative of symbiosis have been identified. Lichen-like associations have been found in strata of the miocene epoch, and possibly also from the Mesozoic era (Smith, 1927). Skeletons of scleractinian corals are well-represented in the record from the Mesozoic to present, but it is unknown whether these fossilized forms possessed dinoflagellate symbionts (3.2). The root-like structures of *Rhynia* and *Asteroxylon*, early land plants of the Silurian and Devonian periods (4.5–3.5×10^8 years ago), are infected with the fossil fungus *Palaeomyces* in a manner resembling modern vesicular-arbuscular mycorrhizas (Fig. 10.1 and see Fig. 7.2e). Similar associations are known in the roots, and occasionally stems, of pteropsids and other terrestrial plants of the Carboniferous period (3.5–2.8×10^8 years ago). Pirozynski and Malloch (1975) have advanced the theory that these fungi enhanced the ability of the early plants to acquire phosphorus and other minerals (see 7.5), and thereby played an essential role in the colonization of land by plants.

The paucity of information from the fossil record has led some to studies of extant associations for evidence of their origin and evolutionary history.

10.2.2 Evidence from extant associations

Some of the associations described in this book may have evolved from parasitic relationships, through changes in the interactions between host and an

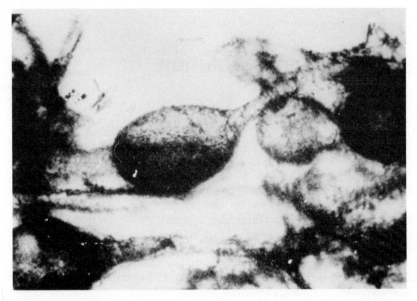

Fig. 10.1   Vesicles of the fungus *Palaeomyces asteroxyli* inside the inner cortex of the creeping organ of Devonian lycopsid, *Asteroxylon* (Kidston and Lang, 1921).

overtly parasitic symbiont. One possible example refers to the orchid mycorrhizas, the fungal symbionts of which include species of *Armillaria* and *Rhizoctonia*, which are also pathogens of other plants (7.2.4 and Table 7.2). A persuasive model of the evolution of ectomycorrhizal fungi from parasites has also been developed (Cooke and Whipps, 1980; Lewis, 1973). Other symbioses may have arisen from casual associations. For example, the luminescence symbioses between species of *Vibrio* and *Photobacterium* and various marine fish (9.12) probably evolved from a transient relationship with the gut or skin of the host, as is commonly found among nonsymbiotic *Vibrio* and *Photobacterium* (Ruby and Morin, 1979).

In many associations arguments can be presented for either of these modes of evolution. In lichens, for example, the tendency of the fungus to penetrate the cells of its algal symbionts, especially during laboratory synthesis experiments, has led Ahmadjian and Jacobs (1983) to propose that lichen fungi have a parasitic origin. By contrast, detailed studies by Quispel (1943) on the loose associations on tree trunks between crusts of unicellular algae and the hyphae of lichen-like fungi suggest a casual origin.

Changes in the structural relationship between host and symbiont may have played a crucial role in the evolution of certain symbioses. Thus, the mycetocyte symbioses of insects (9.10) may have arisen from gut symbioses by the gradual separation and detachment from the gut lumen of gut epithelial cells and their enclosed symbionts. The principal evidence comes from anobiid beetles, which contain yeast cells in outpocketings of the midgut (8.4.1). Koch (1967) has arranged a series in which the symbionts become

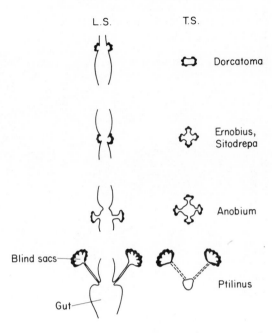

Fig. 10.2 Diagrammatic representation of yeast-containing blind sacs of anobiid beetles, showing trend of increasing separation from gut. After Koch (1967).

increasingly separated from the gut lumen (Fig. 10.2). Correlated with the change in position of the sacs is an increased percentage of intracellular symbionts. Thus, in *Dorcatoma* species the yeast cells are extracellular, but in *Ptilinus* species, 95–100% of the symbionts are within the host cells which line the blind sacs.

10.2.3 Conditions which predispose the evolution of symbiosis

Many symbioses are found in nutrient-poor conditions or in hosts which depend on a nutrient-poor diet. This is particularly well-illustrated by the distribution of microbial symbionts among insects. About 10% of the 700 000 known insect species possess symbionts and the majority of these live on grossly inadequate diets (Table 10.1). The symbionts of many haematophagous insects provide B vitamins, which are deficient in blood; those of insects dependent on nitrogen-poor plant products (e.g. wood) may provide essential amino acids, recycle host waste nitrogen or fix nitrogen; and symbionts of insects which feed on plant polysaccharides degrade the ingested material to a form which can be utilized by the host. An apparent exception to this generality refers to certain blood-sucking dipterans which

Table 10.1 Survey of symbiosis among insects in relation to diet.

Diet	Order	Example	Prokaryotes	Protozoa	Fungi	Endosymbiotic mycetocytes	Endosymbiotic gut	Ectosymbiotic[1]
Vertebrate blood	Diptera	Glossina (tsetse fly)	+			+ (Midgut epithelium)		
	Hemiptera	Cimicids (bed bugs)	+			+ (Abdomen)		
		Triatoma, Rhodnius (kissing bugs)	+				+ (Midgut)	
	Anoplura (sucking lice)	Many species	+			+ (Midgut epithelium or abdomen)		
Plant sap	Hemiptera	Most homopterans (including leafhoppers, aphids, psyllids)	+			+ (Abdomen)		
		Many scutellerids	+				+ (Caeca)	
		Many lygaeids	+			+ (Abdomen)		
Cellulose-rich plant products (e.g. wood, stored grain)	Isoptera[2]	Higher termites – Macrotermitinids	+		+			+
		Other higher termites	+				+ (Hindgut)	
		Lower termites	+	+			+ (Hindgut)	

Header grouping: **Insect host** (Diet, Order, Example); **Symbionts** (Prokaryotes, Protozoa, Fungi); **Location of symbionts** (Endosymbiotic: mycetocytes, gut; Ectosymbiotic[1]).

	Diptera	*Tipula* (crane fly)	+		+ (Hindgut)
	Hymenoptera	Attinine ants		+	+
		Siricid wasps		+	+
	Coleoptera	Curculionids (e.g. *Apion*, *Sitophilus*)	+		+ (Malpighian tubules or gut epithelium)
		Anobiids (e.g. *Anobium*, *Sitodrepa*)		+	+ (Caeca)
		Ambrosia beetles (members of families Scolytidae and Platypodidae)		+	+
Complex diets	Orthoptera	Cockroaches	+	+	+ (Fat body)
	Diptera	Tephritids e.g. *Dacus*	+		+ (Hindgut) + (Caeca, foregut or hindgut)
	Hymenoptera	Many formicine ants	+		+ (Midgut epithelium)

¹ The ectosymbionts are filamentous fungi usually maintained in the immediate environment of the insects (e.g., in the nests of macrotermidinids and tunnels in wood excavated by ambrosia beetles) but also associated on or near the surface of the insects at particular parts of the host life cycle (e.g., during migration of young ambrosia beetles to a new site). In general, the ectosymbioses are of moderate specificity (see Table 11.1) and obligate for both partners. For further discussion, see review by Batra, 1979.
² See 8.4.

Table 10.2 Distribution of symbiosis among blood-sucking dipterans.

Larval food source		Insect genus	Symbionts
Blood (i.e. insect is viviparous)	Nutritionally unbalanced	Glossina	+
		Melophagus	+
		Nycteribia	+
		Eucampsipoda	+
		Nycteribosca	+
Plant sap		Dasyhelea	+
Decaying vegetation	Nutritionally balanced	Stomoxys	–
		Lutzomyia	–
		Phlebotomus	–
Carnivorous		Tabanus	–
		Chrysops	–

do not possess symbionts (Table 10.2). However, the larvae of these species feed on alternative nutrient-sufficient food sources, whereas species containing symbionts are dependent on blood through the life cycle or utilize an alternative nutritionally unbalanced diet, such as plant sap, during the larval phase.

Other associations found in nutrient-poor conditions include many lichens and mycorrhizas and the various symbioses between marine algae and protists or invertebrates in tropical oceans. It is assumed that under conditions of nutrient stress, the host derives considerable benefit from the nutritional input from the symbionts. Under nutrient-rich conditions, such inputs would be of little significance and the cost to the host of maintaining symbionts could become appreciable.

However, the correlation between the distribution of symbioses and nutrient-poor conditions is not absolute. Many organisms tolerate nutritional stress without symbiosis, e.g. some lepidopteran insects (which feed on structural plant material as larvae, and nectar as adults), and certain herbivorous vertebrates (8.3.1). Thus, the evolution of symbiosis can be considered as just one of several alternative strategies which can be adopted in nutrient-poor habitats. Furthermore, a number of associations occur in apparently nutrient-rich habitats. For example, lichen species in woodlands, moist grasslands and seashores are unlikely to encounter nutrient shortage; and associations between *Chlorella* and invertebrates or protists occur in nutrient-rich ponds and streams rather than in oligotrophic waters.

10.3 Evolutionary potential of symbiosis

Symbiosis can be considered to have evolutionary potential in that it enables an organism to 'acquire' novel characteristics in the form of properties of its partner. For example, heterotrophic hosts containing photosynthetic symbionts 'acquire' the capacity for CO_2 fixation, eukaryotes containing nitrogen-fixing symbionts 'acquire' the ability to utilize atmospheric nitrogen and herbivorous vertebrates 'acquire' cellulolytic activity through their gut symbionts. Symbiosis has been compared with other processes which produce novel combinations of characteristics, such as sex in eukaryotes (Margulis, 1980) and direct gene transfer by such vectors as viruses and plasmids (Richmond, 1979). Nevertheless, most biologists consider that the evolutionary importance of symbiosis has been trivial compared to the other mechanisms by which novel and heritable characteristics are produced.

The outstanding exception is the growing consensus that symbiosis was of crucial importance in the evolution of eukaryotes, and in particular that mitochondria, plastids and possibly other organelles have evolved from microbial symbionts. Early investigators noted similarities between these organelles and microorganisms at the level of the light microscope, but only recently have these ideas been revived and refined, largely through the writings of Margulis (1970, 1981). A considerable body of morphological and biochemical data on the subject is now available and, since the hypothesis has had a profound influence on cell biology, it will be explored in detail in the next section.

10.4 Evolution of the eukaryotic cell

10.4.1 Introduction

It is generally agreed that eukaryotes have evolved from some prokaryote-like ancestor, largely because eukaryotes share certain key biochemical features with modern prokaryotes such as possession of ATP and nucleic acids, and because eukaryotes are structurally more complex (see 1.5).

Although the fossil record does not pinpoint precisely when eukaryotes evolved, the earliest undoubted fossil prokaryotes occur at 3.5×10^9 years ago, and the first undoubted eukaryotes (multicellular algae) at about 0.9–0.8×10^9 years ago. The cell size of microfossils remained constant and typical for prokaryotes from their earliest appearance until about 1.6×10^9 years ago, after which the size of some of them began to increase, reaching 40–60 μm diameter about 1.4–1.2×10^9 years ago. Some interpret these fossils as protoeukaryotes or eukaryotes.

Theories of the evolutionary origin of eukaryotes can be grouped under two headings.

a) *Autogenous theories*, which hold that all structures and functions of eukaryotes evolved gradually from a single stock of prokaryotes. A common feature of these theories is the proposed infolding of regions of the cell membrane to form internal vesicles, which subsequently evolved into the various organelles.

b) *Symbiotic theories*, which consider that certain eukaryotic organelles evolved from prokaryotic organisms that entered into symbiosis with the immediate ancestor of eukaryotes, the 'protoeukaryote'. Thus, the different components of the eukaryotic cell are held to have had a long independent evolutionary history before coming together in the eukaryotic cell.

Modern symbiotic theories are based on a scheme, known as the *serial endosymbiosis theory* (SET), devised by Margulis (1970) (see Fig. 10.3). Specifically, three consecutive symbioses are proposed, in which the protoeukaryote became host: first, to aerobic bacteria, which evolved into mitochondria; second to spirochaetes, which evolved into cilia and flagella and from which other microtubule-containing structures arose; and, third, to cyanobacteria, which became the plastids of algae and plants.

10.4.2   The origin of mitochondria

The structural organization of mitochondria is consistent with their evolution from bacterial symbionts. Their inner membrane, which bears the electron transport chain, is considered to be homologous to the cell membrane of aerobic bacteria, and the outer membrane to be of host origin, equivalent to the vacuolar membrane surrounding many intracellular symbionts.

Consistent with a symbiotic origin, mitochondria are self-replicating, contain DNA and are never synthesized *de novo* within cells. However, they contain only a small fraction of the DNA required for their own biogenesis, sufficient only to code for the synthesis of a few protein molecules of the respiratory complexes and some mitochondrial tRNA and rRNA molecules. Most mitochondrial proteins, including many required for the operation of the mitochondrial genetic system (e.g. DNA and RNA polymerases, ribosomal proteins) are coded by nuclear genes and synthesized on cytoplasmic ribosomes. The symbiotic theory accounts for the low mitochondrial DNA content by assuming a substantial loss and transfer to the nucleus of genetic information. The movement of DNA between different genomes within the eukaryotic cell is well-documented. Of particular relevance is the finding that subunit 9 of the F_o component of the mitochondrial ATPase is coded by mitochondrial DNA in the yeast *Saccharomyces cerevisiae* and by nuclear DNA in the filamentous fungus *Neurospora* (Borst and Grivel, 1978). It is not known which condition is ancestral, although the comparatively close phylogenetic relationship between the two fungi suggests the transposition occurred relatively recently.

Most autogenous theories cannot account for the presence of DNA in mitochondria. However, Raff and Mahler (1975) suggested that when part of the protoeukaryote's cell membrane infolded, to form the mitochondrial membranes, the resultant vesicle incorporated a plasmid bearing the minimum information necessary for its sustained functioning.

The mitochondrial genetic system displays a number of features in common with eubacteria and different from the eukaryotic nucleocytoplasm. For example, mitochondrial DNA is not associated with histone

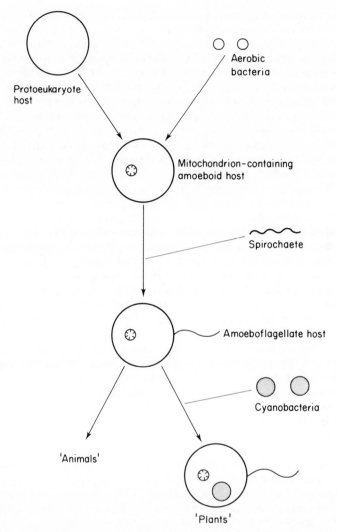

Fig. 10.3 Serial endosymbiosis theory (SET) of the evolution of the eukaryotic cell as suggested by Margulis (1970). It is envisaged that the protoeukaryote (i.e., immediate ancestor of eukaryotes) gave rise to the nucleus and cytoplasm, including the 'endomembrane' organelles (e.g., endoplasmic reticulum, Golgi apparatus, microbodies, vesicles), while symbiotic bacteria, spirochaetes and cyanobacteria evolved into mitochondria, microtubule-containing structures and plastids, respectively.

proteins; the size of mitochondrial ribosomes is closer to those of eubacteria than those of eukaryotic cell cytoplasm; protein synthesis in mitochondria is abolished by specific inhibitors of the bacterial system (e.g. chloramphenicol, streptomycin) but not of the eukaryotic cytoplasmic system (e.g. cycloheximide); and the polypeptide chain initiator in the eukaryotic cytoplasm is methionine-tRNA^{met}, but in mitochondria and eubacteria is formyl-methionine-tRNA^{met}.

These characteristics have been cited as evidence in favour of the symbiotic theory of the origin of mitochondria, but all components of the eukaryotic cell have presumably evolved from prokaryotes (10.4.1) and it could be argued that mitochondria have arisen autogenously but have undergone less evolutionary change than the nucleocytoplasm and so retained more prokaryotic features. The situation has been complicated by recent data which indicate similarities between the genetic organization of mitochondria and the nucleus and also certain unique features of the mitochondrial system. Thus, split genes (i.e. genes in which the expressed regions are interrupted by one to several intervening sequences) have been identified in the nuclear genome of many eukaryotes and the mitochondrial genome of yeast but not, to date, in eubacteria (Locker *et al.*, 1981). The genetic code of mitochondria differs from that in the eukaryotic nucleus and eubacteria in several respects and varies between mitochondria of different eukaryotes. For example, *UGA* is a termination signal in bacteria and the eukaryotic cytoplasm, but it is the codon for tryptophan in mammalian and yeast mitochondria; *AUA* codes for methionine in mammalian mitochondria but for isoleucine in eubacteria, eukaryotic cytoplasm and yeast mitochondria. These conflicting data confirm the view of some authors (Gray and Doolittle, 1982) that consideration of 'eubacterium-like' or 'eukaryote-like' traits in mitochondria is of little value in deciding the validity of autogenous and symbiotic theories.

Supporters of the symbiotic theories can point to extant prokaryotes which so closely resemble mitochondria in metabolic characteristics that they can serve as a model for the putative bacterial ancestor. The aerobic bacterium *Paracoccus denitrificans* is very similar to mitochondria in the components of its respiratory chain, sensitivity to metabolic inhibitors and stoichiometry of oxidative phosphorylation (the H^+:O ratio) (John and Whatley, 1975). Whatley *et al.* (1979) stated that 'no significant feature of the mammalian respiratory chain has ever been shown to be absent from *Paracoccus*' and they suggest that 'the evolutionary transition from an aerobic bacterium resembling *Paracoccus* to a mitochondrion, as envisaged by the symbiotic theory, would be biochemically a simple one'. *Paracoccus* has been assigned to the family Rhodospirillaceae (Gray and Doolittle, 1982) and it is pertinent that protein and nucleic acid sequence studies indicate a closer relationship of mitochondria to the Rhodospirillaceae than to the eukaryotic nucleocytoplasm (Dayhoff and Schwartz, 1981). Since it is very unlikely that the eukaryotic nucleocytoplasm arose from a Rhodospirillacean-like ancestor (see 10.4.5), these data represent valuable circumstantial evidence in favour of the symbiotic origin of mitochondria.

Most discussions assume that the mitochondria of all eukaryotes are homologous and therefore all variation in mitochondrial form has evolved secondarily in the different eukaryotic lineages, However, it is possible that mitochondria are polyphyletic (Stewart and Mattox, 1984). Specifically, aerobic protists can be assigned to one of at least two groups on the basis of the morphology of the mitochondrial cristae, one group with tubular and the second with lamellar (flattened) cristae. The two types of mitochondria may have arisen from distinct endosymbionts, both related to the Rhodospirillaceae. Preliminary molecular data are consistent with this proposal.

Some protists, notably trichomonads and certain holotrichs, may have acquired anaerobic prokaryotic symbionts, either instead of the aerobic symbionts which gave rise to mitochondria or after the secondary loss of mitochondria. These protist groups possess *hydrogenosomes* (9.3), membrane-bound organelles within which pyruvate (the end product of glycolysis) is oxidized to acetate with the production of ATP by substrate level phosphorylation and release of hydrogen (Muller, 1980). This metabolic pathway resembles the anaerobic metabolism of clostridia, a group of obligately anaerobic bacteria, and is unknown among aerobic eukaryotes. Further evidence for the symbiotic origin of hydrogenosomes comes from the demonstration of hydrogenosomal DNA in one trichomonad, *Tritrichomonas foetus* (Muller, 1980).

10.4.3 The origin of microtubules

Microtubules are hollow, tubular structures composed of a helical lattice of a single subunit, the globular protein tubulin, arranged as dimers of two related polypeptides, α-tubulin and β-tubulin. They are an important component of the cytoskeleton, contributing to a range of subcellular structures (e.g. the mitotic spindle and flagellum). Although microtubules are capable of self assembly, *in vitro*, in the absence of any macromolecules, most microtubules in the intact cell originate from specialized self-replicating sites called microtubule organizing centres (MTOCs) (Pickett-Heaps, 1974). Many MTOCs are not identifiable at the electron microscope level and may be represented by a localized concentration of a critical compound, but other MTOCs are highly organized organelles (e.g. the kinetosomes).

According to the symbiotic theory proposed by Margulis, the cilia, flagella and other microtubule-containing structures arose from spirochaetes which became associated with the protoeukaryote (Fig. 10.3). Spirochaetes are helically-shaped, motile prokaryotes whose movements are powered by two to many periplasmic axial filaments. The axial filaments are homologous with the flagella of other bacteria and bear no relation to eukaryotic flagella in either composition or mechanism of action.

Margulis and coworkers (1979 and 1981) envisaged four stages in the evolution of eukaryotic flagella (Fig. 10.4). Initially, free-living spirochaetes became casually associated with the surface of the protoeukaryote (stage 1) but, as the relationship became more specific and permanent, specialized attachment sites evolved (stage 2). The spirochaetes probably conferred motility on the host and may have derived nutrients from the host. Subsequently (stage 3), the spirochaetes became enclosed within the host cytoplasm. Many spirochaete structures, including the axial filaments, cell membrane and outer layers, were presumably redundant in the intracellular habitat and were lost. However, the attachment sites of the surface associa-

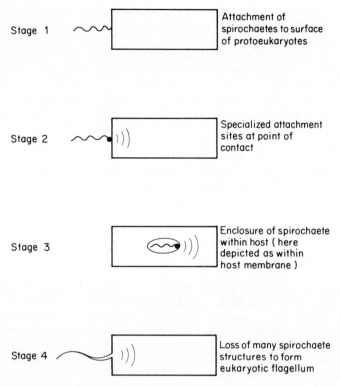

Fig. 10.4   Stages in the evolution of the eukaryotic flagellum from symbiotic spirochaetes, as envisaged by Margulis (1981).

tion were retained and evolved into the kinetosomes and flagellar root systems from which the microtubules of the eukaryotic flagellum are elaborated. The spirochaete DNA that coded for this microtubule-based motility system was transferred to the host genome and the remainder of the symbiont DNA was lost. This relationship (stage 4) is essentially the condition of the eukaryotic flagellum. The kinetosomes and flagellar root systems subsequently gave rise to other MTOCs and microtubule-containing structures within the eukaryotic cell.

If this theory is correct, then the putative spirochaete ancestor, but not the prokaryote group from which the protoeukaryote arose, should possess tubulin. The incidence of tubulin among extant prokaryotes has not been surveyed comprehensively, but it is believed to be absent from most groups. However, Margulis *et al.* (1978) observed longitudinally-oriented cytoplasmic filaments of similar diameter to microtubules in spirochaetes of the family Pillotaceae. Antibody raised to eukaryotic tubulin binds to these spirochaetes and cell-free extracts of *Pillotina* contain a soluble protein which comigrates with eukaryotic tubulin by gel electrophoresis. Other spirochaetes which lack the characteristic cytoplasmic filaments of the Pillotaceae were negative for both tests for tubulin. However these conclusions need to be confirmed by more precise methods, such as the isolation and purification of tubulin-like protein and identification of tubulin genes in the Pillotaceae.

Associations analogous to stages 1 and 2 in Fig. 10.4 are the 'motility symbioses' between various motile prokaryotes, particularly spirochaetes, and protozoa inhabiting the hindgut of termites (9.2). The site of attachment between the partners may be highly specialized, in some cases including structures that bear a remarkable resemblance to flagellar roots (Fig. 9.2). Intracellular spirochaetes also occur in these protozoa (Margulis *et al.*, 1979), a condition analogous to stage 3 in Fig. 10.4.

While symbiotic theories postulate that the flagellum evolved first and then gave rise to microtubules, autogenous theories take an opposite standpoint. Microtubules are held to have evolved first, either in the cytoplasm of the protoeukaryote where it served a skeletal function (Cavalier-Smith, 1975) or in the nuclear region providing an effective framework for the orderly segregation of DNA (Pickett-Heaps, 1974). More complex structures, such as the flagellum, evolved later from the microtubule. Unfortunately for the autogenous theories, there are no living organisms representing intermediate stages in the evolution of flagella and other complex microtubular organelles. On the other hand, the presence of microtubules and often a mitotic spindle but not flagella in rhodophytes can readily be explained by the autogenous theories. Symbiotic theories have to postulate that rhodophytes have lost the flagella secondarily (Margulis, 1981), although no plausible selection pressure for such an event in this entirely aquatic group has been proposed.

10.4.4 The origin of plastids

Plastids, like mitochondria, are self-reproducing, semi-autonomous organelles that contain DNA and a translation system separate from the nucleocytoplasm. The plastid genome is $0.8–1.3 \times 10^8$ daltons in size (slightly larger than the average mitochondrial genome) and codes for some plastid-specific rRNAs and tRNAs and a small proportion of plastid proteins. The plastid genetic system also resembles those of mitochondria and eubacteria in the small size of its ribosomes and inhibitor sensitivity of protein synthesis. Extensive sequence studies of chloroplast proteins and rRNA molecules provide strong evidence for a symbiotic origin of plastids. They show greater homology with cyanobacteria than with the eukaryotic nucleocytoplasm (Schwartz and Dayhoff, 1981).

SET originally proposed that the plastids of all photosynthetic eukaryotes arose from a single association between cyanobacteria and the early eukaryotic cell (Fig. 10.3), but this is probably an oversimplification. Not only do plastids vary widely in structure, but also three different groups of photosynthetic eukaryotes can be recognized on the basis of their choroplast pigments: the *rhodophytes*, which contain chlorophyll *a* and phycobilins; the *chlorophytes and higher plants*, which have chlorophyll *a* and chlorophyll *b*;

and the ***chromophytes***, with chlorophyll *a* and chlorophyll *c*. It has been suggested (Gibbs, 1981; Whatley *et al.*, 1979) that the plastids of each of these groups arose from a distinct ancestral prokaryotic symbiont. Those of the rhodophytes may be derived from a cyanobacterium-like ancestor, and those of the chlorophytes and higher plants may be derived from a prokaryote similar to the prochlorophytes (Table 5.1 and see section 5.4), which possess chlorophyll *b* and stacked thylakoids. No prokaryote containing chlorophyll *c* is known.

The plastids of rhodophytes, most chlorophytes and all plants are bounded by two membranes. By the symbiotic theory, the inner membrane represents the cell membrane of the prokaryotic symbiont and the outer membrane is the vacuolar membrane of the protoeukaryote host (Fig. 10.3). However, the plastids of the chromophytes and euglenoids have three or four bounding membranes. It has been suggested that such organisms are derived from an association between a non-photosynthetic eukaryotic host and photosynthetic *eukaryotic* symbiont (Gibbs, 1981; Whatley *et al.*, 1979). This hypothesis is particularly well-illustrated by the cryptomonads, a group of chromophytes. The proposed origin of the four membranes investing the plastid is indicated in Fig. 10.5. The periplastid space represents the nucelocytoplasm of the eukaryotic symbiont (host 1 in Fig. 10.5) and contains starch, cytoplasmic ribosomes and a 'nucleomorph', which may be a highly reduced eukaryotic nucleus (Morrall and Greenwood, 1982). The outermost of the three membranes of plastids of dinoflagellates and euglenoids may represent the cell membrane of the eukaryotic symbiont (host 1 in Fig. 10.5), the vacuolar membrane of the second host having been lost (Gibbs, 1981). Alternatively, isolated plastids from the photosynthetic eukaryote (host 1) may have been acquired by the secondary host (host 2) and retained within a vacuolar membrane which is now represented by the outermost plastid membrane (Whatley *et al.*, 1979).

The common occurrence of intracellular photosynthetic symbionts in a wide range of modern non-photosynthetic eukaryotic hosts (chapters 2, 3 and 5) adds to the plausibility of the theory that plastids of different groups arose from a variety of prokaryotes and eukaryotes. These associations also illustrate how plastids may have evolved from symbionts by the gradual loss of redundant structures and genetic information. Some symbionts, (e.g. *Chlorella*) may be roughly analogous to an early stage in the development of plastids. Although the growth and division of these algae are closely controlled by the host in symbiosis, they are genetically autonomous and not physiologically dependent on the association. Their DNA content is similar to nonsymbiotic relatives and they can be maintained apart from their hosts. Other photosynthetic symbionts bear a much closer resemblance to plastids. The symbiont of *Cyanophora paradoxa* strongly resembles free-living cyanobacteria in ultrastructure and possession of a peptidoglycan wall but has a genome size (1.2×10^8 daltons) similar to that of plastids (see 5.3.5.1). In the ciliate *Mesodinium rubrum* (3.4.2), the symbiont is drastically reduced in structure, the cell wall is entirely lacking,

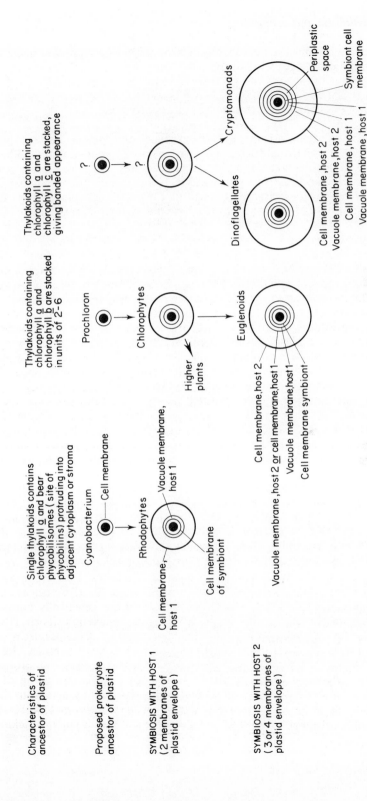

Fig. 10.5 Possible origin of plastids of photosynthetic eukaryotes (Whatley and Whatley, 1984).

and in some isolates the nucleus has become physically separated from the plastids and other organelles of the symbiont.

10.4.5   The nature of the protoeukaryote host

Essential to the symbiotic theory is the existence of a 'protoeukaryote' host (see Fig. 10.3) which could acquire the various prokaryote symbionts. There are no well-documented examples of prokaryotes containing other pro-karyotes as intracellular symbionts and therefore discussion of the possible nature of the protoeukaryote host will be even more speculative than the previous consideration of the nature of the putative symbionts.

Margulis (1970) proposed that the protoeukaryote was an anaerobic, walled prokaryote, not unlike some extant eubacteria. She envisaged the initial symbiont gained access to this host cell by a mechanism similar to that adopted by *Bdellovibrio*, a small, Gram-negative bacterium which attacks a number of other bacteria (Stolp, 1979). By a combination of mechanical and enzymatic methods, a single bdellovibrio bores its way through the host cell wall and comes to lie in the space between the cell wall and cell membrane. Here, it reproduces, its growth and division fuelled by nutrients extracted from the host cytoplasm through the intact cell membrance. After about 4 hours, the *Bdellovibrio* progeny are liberated from the killed host. Margulis (1970) proposed that, once the first symbiont (the mitochondrial ancestor) became established, the host developed the capacity for phagocytosis and this was how later symbionts were acquired.

However, this is not a satisfactory model for the entry of a symbiont into the 'protoeukaryote', since *Bdellovibrio* does not enter the host cytoplasm, and does not maintain a stable relationship with it. An alternative view is that the ancestor was a wall-less prokaryote that acquired all the symbionts by phagocytosis. This proposal would explain the absence of peptidoglycans (a common component of prokaryote cell walls) in eukaryotes. Proponents of autogenous theories (e.g. Raff and Mahler, 1975; Cavalier-Smith, 1975) also considered that the protoeukaryote had this characteristic because only mem-branes capable of phagocytosis would be able to produce organelles by the infolding and pinching off of intracellular vesicles. Phagocytically-com-petent cells would be expected to have the following characteristics:

a) greater fluidity or flexibility of the cell membrane than exhibited by most prokaryotes; sterols, such as cholesterol, confer this property on eukaryotic cell membranes,
b) possession of contractile cytoplasmic filaments which can draw the infolding cell membrane inwards; phagocytosis in eukaryotic cells is mediated by a network of actomyosin filaments,
c) high energy-yielding metabolism, such as aerobiosis; the intrinsically aerobic biochemistry of the eukaryotic cytoplasm has been cited as evidence that the protoeukaryote was at least partially aerobic. Duve (1969) has suggested that, although the protoeukaryote lacked mitochondria and there-fore oxidative phosphorylation, it was capable of microbody-mediated

aerobic respiration. Microbodies are present in all groups of eukaryotes. They contain metabolic pathways which utilize oxygen with net energy production, although microbody-mediated respiration would be less efficient than mitochondrial respiration.

Many of the characteristics of the putative protoeukaryote ancestor are exhibited by archaebacteria (see Chapter 1) and, in particular, by *Thermoplasma acidophilum* (Searcy *et al.*, 1978 and 1981). This organism is an acidothermophile, with optimal growth conditions of pH 1–2 and 59°C (it was originally isolated from a burning rubbish tip). It has no cell wall; it respires aerobically via enzymes that resemble those in eukaryote microbodies (inhibitor and spectrophotometric studies confirm the absence of oxidative phosphorylation and cytochromes characteristic of mitochondria); and it possesses contractile cytoplasmic filaments of 6 nm diameter. It is not clear whether these filaments contain a protein homologous to eukaryotic actin. Cytoplasmic proteins with the electophoretic mobility of actin have been identified but, unlike actin, the filaments do not bind meromyosin. *T. acidophilum* is a small cell and not capable of phagocytosis but another acidophilic archaebacterium *Sulfolobus acidocaldarius* is reported to 'wrap around insoluble particles at least to a limited extent' (Searcy *et al.*, 1978).

Although archaebacteria resemble eubacteria in gross characteristics, they exhibit many biochemical features more akin to eukaryotes. For example, translation is initiated by non-formylated methionine in archaebacteria and eukaryotes, but by formylated methionine in eubacteria (Woese *et al.*, 1978). Genes containing intervening, non-translated regions have been identified in eukaryotes and the archaebacterium *Halococcus morrhuae* (Luehrsen *et al.*, 1981) but not in any eubacterium. Although sterol synthesis (a characteristic of eukaryotes) has not been demonstrated among archaebacteria, thermophilic species, including *T. acidophilum*, can synthesize polyisoprenoids, the immediate precursors of sterols (Searcy *et al.*, 1978). *T. acidophilum* also possesses, associated with its DNA, a basic protein of similar amino acid composition to eukaryotic histones.

An important consideration is the time, relative to the acquisition of various hypothetical symbionts, the host genetic material became separated from the cytoplasm by the development of the membrane-bound nucleus. (Eukaryotes have other features which distinguish them from prokaryotes (see chapter 1), but these are not essential to the definition of the eukaryotic condition.) The eukaryotic nucleus probably evolved autogenously by the invagination and endocytosis of a portion of the cell membrane to form a vesicle surrounding the DNA (Whatley and Whatley, 1984). An intracellular motility system is generally regarded as necessary for the division of the nucleus and segregation of DNA. Many authors (e.g. Cavalier-Smith, 1975; Pickett-Heaps, 1974) assumed that this was provided by microtubules, as in the mitotic spindle of most extant eukaryotes. Therefore, by SET, the eukaryotic condition was not reached before the integration of the spirochaete symbionts into the host (Margulis, 1970). An alternative view (Heath, 1980; Roos, 1984) is that *actin* provided the framework for the effective functioning of the early eukaryotic nucleus and the involvement of microtubules was secondary. Thus, the possession of actin filaments and a cell membrane capable of phagocytosis are required for both the autogenous development of the eukaryote nucleus and acquisition of symbionts by phagocytosis. It is therefore conceivable that the eukaryotic condition developed prior to the evolution of mitochondria. The 'giant amoeba' *Pelomyxa palustris* may represent this stage in the evolution of early eukaryotes (Whatley *et al.*, 1979). This wall-less, microaerophilic organism has eukaryotic nuclei, which apparently divide in the absence of microtubules, and also contains aerobic bacteria, which may serve an analogous function to the mitochondria in most eukaryotes (see 9.4).

10.4.6   Evaluation of the symbiotic theories and some implications

It is unlikely that the evolutionary origin of eukaryotes will ever be known for certain. However, the structural and biochemical evidence for the symbiotic origin of mitochondria and plastids is difficult to refute. The case for the evolution of the eukaryotic flagellum and other microtubule-containing structures from spirochaetes is considerably weaker, and the validity of this aspect of SET cannot be resolved until more information on the biology of spirochaetes and MTOCs becomes available. For example, it is not established unequivocally whether any spirochaetes contain tubulin and the function and nature of RNA in MTOCs is unknown.

The suggestion that eukaryotes may have evolved from stock allied to archaebacteria is of particular interest in the light of the evidence that archaebacterial and eubacterial lines may have diverged at an early stage of prokaryote evolution (Woese *et al.*, 1978). By symbiotic theories, it follows that eukaryotes possess characteristics of two very different prokaryotic lineages: nucleocytoplasm of archeabacterium-like stock and certain organelles from various groups of eubacteria. The implication that the eukaryotic cell represents a multiple of diverse prokaryotic cells requires considerable revision to the traditional concept of the cell as the fundamental unit of life.

11
Conclusions: comparisons of the characteristics of symbiosis

11.1 Introduction

This chapter compares the range of symbioses considered in chapters 2–9, and discusses both the features they have in common and some of the important differences between them. The comparison is based on the characteristics used to describe symbioses in Chapter 1 (and summarized in Table 1.1).

11.2 Relative size of the partners: the distinction between host and symbiont

The convention adopted in this book of a strict distinction between host and symbiont is rarely followed by other authors, who commonly refer to both partners as symbionts. This latter convention could be taken to imply that the partners gain equal or mutual benefit from a symbiosis, but as Section 11.10 below will show, the evidence is frequently inadequate to sustain this view. Distinction between host and symbiont also facilitates and clarifies comparisons of some of the other characteristics of symbiosis.

11.3 Relative position of the partners

11.3.1 At the level of the host organism

The symbionts are always confined to specific regions of the host. For example, photosynthetic symbionts are positioned so that they have access to light (e.g., Figs. 2.1 and 6.2), the gut symbionts of vertebrates are restricted to the gut lumen and do not occur in the surrounding tissues (8.1), and neither bacterial nor fungal symbionts of plant roots extend beyond the root cortex and into the stele (4.2.3 and 7.2). There are numerous examples of specialized host organs which house symbionts, such as the light organs of fish (9.12.3) and the cavities containing cyanobacterial symbionts in liverworts and *Azolla* (5.3.4.1). However, despite a wealth of descriptive data, there have been no studies of the mechanisms by which the location of symbionts is determined.

11.3.2   At the level of the host tissues and cells

Most symbionts in fully established associations can be assigned to a single position relative to the host in the series illustrated in Fig. 1.1. Mycorrhizal fungi are a notable exception since the ectosymbiotic mycelium at the root surface is connected to an endosymbiotic mycelium within the root tissues (Fig. 7.1). A few associations have both extracellular and intracellular symbionts. Examples include yeasts in the gut of some anobiid beetles (8.4.1), some bacteria in marine sponges (9.8), and rhizobia in indeterminate nodules on legume roots (4.2.5.1). Extracellular rhizobia in the persistent infection threads act as a reservoir for intracellular infection of host cells, and differ from the intracellular bacteroids both in their morphology and in their inability to fix nitrogen. The characteristics of extracellular and intracellular symbionts within the same host have not been compared in other associations.

In general, the degree of host influence over a symbiont seems to be correlated with the closeness of the spatial relationship between the partners, increasing in the series from ectosymbionts to extracellular endosymbionts to intracellular endosymbionts. However, there are a few exceptions to this. For example, the same type of dinoflagellate symbiont is extracellular in the haemal sinuses of tridacnid molluscs (3.2.8), but intracellular in marine coelenterates; the symbionts in both locations respond in the same way to 'factors' prepared from host tissues (3.2.8).

Intracellular symbionts are usually located in the cytoplasm, or less commonly in the endomembrane system (including the endoplasmic reticulum and Golgi apparatus) but have not been reported within plastids or mitochondria. Nearly all intracellular symbionts are enclosed in vacuoles bounded by host membranes; these are probably derived from the portions of host cell membrane which enveloped the symbionts when they originally entered the cell (usually by phagocytosis). Although this vacuolar membrane undoubtedly plays an important role in host-symbiont interactions, nothing is known of its properties beyond the observation that in *Paramecium bursaria*, the density of intramembranous particles was different from that in the membranes of digestive vacuoles (Meier *et al.*, 1984).

The 'cryptic' symbionts of certain dinoflagellates and the ciliate *Mesodinium rubrum* are most unusual in that their cytoplasm is separated from that of the host by only a single membrane (3.4.2). These symbionts may have been acquired by phagocytosis but the vacuolar membrane was subsequently lost. Alternatively, like certain parasitic protists (Moulder, 1979), they may have penetrated the host cell membrane actively by mechanical or enzymatic means. By either of these explanations, the bounding membrane is of symbiont origin. A third possibility is that the symbionts have been acquired by a specialized form of endocytosis called myzocytosis exhibited by certain dinoflagellates in which the cell membrane of the engulfed cell is not taken up (Schnepf and Deichgraber, 1984). By this last interpretation, the bounding membrane is of host and not symbiont origin.

Intracellular symbionts are very rare or absent in three major groups, pro-karyotes, fungi and vertebrates. Their virtual absence from prokaryotes and fungi is probably correlated with the inability of these groups to ingest particles by phagocytosis (see Table 1.3), the means by which intracellular symbionts are acquired. Although many groups of vertebrates have endo-symbionts (e.g., gut symbionts particularly in birds and mammals (8.2, 8.3), luminescent symbionts in certain teleost fish (9.12)), the symbionts do not gain access to the cells or body cavity of the host. This is probably related to the efficient immune system of vertebrates, which uniquely includes immunoglobulins and circulating lymphocytes.

11.4 Necessity of symbiosis to the organisms involved

The necessity of symbiosis to an organism has traditionally been described in terms of being either obligate (necessary) or facultative (not necessary) (1.3.3). In practice, the dichotomy of this approach does not permit adequate comparison between different associations. For example, it does not reflect the wide variation in the length of time for which different symbionts can lead a free-living existence in nature in the absence of hosts. Thus, the rhizobial symbionts of legumes can live for very long periods (measured in tens of years) in soils from which host plants have disappeared, but they are usually not recorded from soils in which host plants have never grown (4.2.1.3). Free-living colonies of the *Trebouxia* symbionts of lichens are occasionally found in nature (6.1), but usually growing in the vicinity of *Trebouxia*-containing lichens (6.5.1) and the consensus of opinion is that the period of their inde-pendent existence is likely to be relatively short, i.e., measured in months or possibly a few years. The dinoflagellate symbiont *Symbiodinium micro-adriaticum* occurs in a non-motile form within cells of its marine invertebrate hosts. Motile, free-swimming forms are found in the vicinity of hosts (3.2.7.1), but the duration of this free-living phase is likely to be very short. Similarly, some ectomycorrhizal and vesicular–arbuscular fungi, apart from surviving as resting spores, are believed also to be capable of brief periods of saprophytic existence in the soil (7.2).

It would be better to regard the characteristic of necessity as a continuum (cf. Starr, 1975) of greater or lesser necessity. Thus, symbiosis is of greater necessity to *Trebouxia* than to rhizobium but probably of lesser necessity than to mycorrhizal fungi and *Symbiodinium*. The partners of any one association may not be on the same point along this continuum. For example, symbiosis is of greater necessity for vesicular-arbuscular mycorrhizal fungi than for many of their plant hosts.

This raises the question of whether there are symbionts which are at one extreme of this continuum and are truly facultative. Rhizobia and *Frankia* might be considered in this category, but their absence from soils which have never borne hosts suggests that they might exhibit a very small degree of dependence. The luminescent symbionts of deep-sea fish belong to the widespread genera *Vibrio* and *Photobacterium*. These may well prove to be additional examples of more-or-less completely facultative symbionts, but there is a need for definitive demonstrations that the same strain which is symbiotic is also permanently free-living in regions of the ocean away from hosts.

Some authors have suggested that necessity evolves slowly and the degree of dependence upon a partner is an indicator of the age and intimacy of the association (e.g., Buchner, 1966). This is not universally valid. For example, strain D of the protist *Amoeba proteus* became dependent upon its X-bacteria symbionts within 200 generations of initial infection (9.6). On the other hand, as discussed in 11.6, a high degree of dependence may never evolve in partners of associations which, for various reasons, are unlikely to be perpetuated by direct transmission even though the symbioses are probably of great antiquity.

11.5   Duration and stability

This book has adopted the view that only those associations for which contact between the partners persists 'for an appreciable length of time' should be considered as symbioses (1.3.4). Although apparently imprecise, this criterion has in fact posed very few problems. This is because in nearly all associations, one or more of the interactions (e.g., nutritional) is of continuing rather than temporary significance to at least one of the partners. Amongst the very few ambiguous cases are the relationships between aeolid nudibranch molluscs and *Symbiodinium microadriaticum* (3.5.1), but this may be resolved by further study.

The persistence of a symbiosis depends on the balanced growth of the partners. There is remarkably little variation in the proportion of symbiont to host between the various types of symbiosis, the biomass ratio (symbiont:host) in many cases lying within the range 1:10 and 1:100 (e.g., 2.3, 3.2, 6.2.2). The few exceptions to this generalization include the bacterial symbionts of sponges (9.6) and cyanobacterial symbionts of homiomerous lichens (6.2.2), each of which contribute up to 30–50% of the total biomass of the association.

The host is believed to play a central role in determining the biomass ratio, and three regulatory mechanisms have been proposed: expulsion of excess symbionts; destruction (often by digestive attack) of excess symbionts; and limitation of symbiont growth and cell division.

In general, expulsion is of only minor importance, although it has been suggested as a regulatory mechanism for the bioluminescent symbiont *Photobacterium leiognathi* in fish (9.12.3) and for algal symbionts of some invertebrates (3.2.6).

Regular breakdown of symbionts occurs in some associations such as rhizobium bacteroids in senescing regions of nodules (4.2.3) and cyanobacterial symbionts in some plants (5.3.4.2), but active host involvement (as opposed to autolysis) has not been demonstrated. Although foregut symbionts of ruminants are normally digested (8.2.2.1), this is primarily of nutritional significance and is believed to play only an incidental role in regulation. Likewise, the periodic disintegration of the haustoria-like projections of mycorrhizal fungi (7.3.1.2) may be concerned primarily with nutritional interactions. The view that host-mediated destruction of symbionts is not an important regulatory mechanism is further supported by the several intracellular symbionts which are known to suppress host digestive attack (see 2.2.4).

Limitation of symbiont growth and cell-division is therefore likely to be the most important regulatory mechanism, and it is borne out by the very low division rates of many symbionts. It would be an efficient mechanism since energy and nutrients utilized by symbionts for growth are not 'wasted' by subsequent expulsion or destruction. It is generally assumed that the growth of intracellular symbionts is limited by the restricted availability of specific nutrients from the host cell, but mechanisms by which this mode of regulation might occur are only beginning to be elucidated (e.g., 2.2.3). It seems less likely that restricted nutrient supply explains the regulation of lichen symbionts, or the spread of mycorrhizal fungi in host roots. Physical limitation and surface interactions between host and symbiont may be of greater importance, but there have been very few investigations of the problem.

11.6 Perpetuation of symbiosis

The likelihood that a host derives its symbionts directly from another host rather than from the surrounding environment depends partly on the kingdom to which the host belongs. Direct transmission is the norm among protist hosts, but most symbionts of plants (e.g., mycorrhizal fungi, rhizobia) originate from the environment. Among fungal and animal hosts, the situation is variable. In lichens, symbionts are directly transmitted in the species which reproduce by asexual propagules, but reinfection from the environment must occur for those which reproduce only sexually (6.5.1). Animals range from hosts in which there is direct transmission in the egg cytoplasm (as with the prokaryote symbionts of insect mycetocytes (9.10.4) and some marine sponges (9.8)), to those in which the source of symbionts are free-living populations, as in bioluminescent symbionts of fish (9.12). Behaviour of the animal hosts is often important. For example, the protozoan symbionts in the foregut of ruminants are transmitted when adults lick the young (8.2.2.8), and hindgut symbionts of both termites and some small mammals are transmitted by coprophagy (8.3.3.4, 8.4); the gut symbionts of many insects are smeared on to eggs and then eaten by newly hatched larvae (Koch, 1967).

Direct transmission virtually assures infection of the next host generation and, at first sight, appears superior to a reliance on symbionts derived from the environment. However, direct transmission has the major disadvantage that it severely restricts the variety of symbionts available to the host. This may be especially important to higher plants where different soil conditions may favour associations with different strains or species of root symbionts. Many higher plants exhibit a low degree of dependence on symbiosis, and there is some evidence that acquisition of symbionts at an early stage in seedling development may impose costs which result in temporarily retarded rather than enhanced growth (7.4.2). An additional disadvantage of direct transmission might be that symbionts which evolve features detrimental to the host cannot readily be discarded.

Some symbionts with a high degree of dependence on the host tolerate short free-living phases which may occur during perpetuation of the symbiosis in a very specialized condition. Examples include the encysted forms of protozoan gut symbionts of the woodroach *Cryptocercus* (8.4.3.2) and the bacterial gut symbionts of ruminants in water droplets (8.2.2.8). Mycorrhizal fungi present a special case in that mycelial strands can spread out from mycorrhizal organs through the soil to infect new roots. Many of these fungi can also survive prolonged periods away from hosts as resting spores in the soil.

Where symbionts are acquired from the surrounding environment, their availability in the vicinity of hosts may be enhanced by various means, such as the enhanced division of rhizobia in the rhizosphere of legumes (4.2.5.1), the accumulation of *Tetraselmis* around egg capsules of *Convoluta roscoffensis*, and the apparently directional growth of hyphae of mycorrhizal fungi in the soil, when in close proximity to root surfaces (7.2.1).

Lichens (6.5.1), and also some hermatypic corals (see Table 3.6) are remarkable in that some host species acquire symbionts by direct transmission, while other species in the same genus and in similar habitats acquire symbionts from the environment. Further study of these would be of considerable interest to determine the relative effectiveness of the two modes of perpetuation. For example, the prediction could be tested that the specificity of the host for symbionts is higher in associations perpetuated by direct transmission.

11.7 Specificity and recognition

The degree of specificity of the partners for each other varies widely between the different associations, but within each type of symbiosis, the specificity of the host for its symbiont is higher than that of the symbiont for its host (Table 11.1).

Two approaches have been used to investigate specificity. In the first, 'experimental' approach, isolated hosts or symbionts are offered a number of potential partners under laboratory or greenhouse conditions, and the specificity is determined from the range of organisms with which they form a viable symbiosis. In the second, or 'ecological' approach, specificity is estimated from the range of partners associated with a given organism in nature. A higher degree of specificity is nearly always found by the ecological than by the experimental approach. Thus, a narrower range of ectomycorrhizal fungi associate with a given tree species in nature than

Table 11.1 Survey of the Specificity of Associations*. Specificity can be divided into 5 categories, from very high to very low, determined by the degree of difference between the taxa with which an organism can associate (Table 1.2). Although the available data are not very precise, because the information on the taxonomy of the organisms varies greatly, a clear trend emerges that the host is more specific for its symbionts than the symbiont for its hosts.

Level of Specificity (see Table 1.2)	Chlorella and freshwater hosts		Symbiodinum and marine hosts		Rhizobia and legumes		Cyanobacteria		Lichens		Ectomycorrhizas		VA mycorrhizas		Bioluminescence symbioses	
	H†	S‡	H	S	H	S	H	S	H	S	H	S	H	S	H	S
Very high					✓											
High			✓		✓				✓						✓	
Moderate	✓					✓	✓		✓	✓		✓	✓			
Low									✓	✓	✓	✓				
Very low		✓		✓				✓			✓	✓		✓		✓

* Gut symbioses are excluded from the table because the hosts form associations with a community of different symbionts and most of the associations in Chapter 9 have been inadequately studied for such analysis to be made.

† H – specificity of host for symbiont.
‡ S – specificity of symbiont for host.

form mycorrhizal organs with it in laboratory synthesis experiments (7.7.1). Such situations may arise partly because fewer potential partners are available in nature than under experimental conditions, and partly because relatively ineffective associations which are viable in the laboratory do not survive under field conditions.

Closely linked to the characteristic of specificity is the concept of recognition (see 1.3.6). In all symbioses which have been examined in detail, recognition can be divided into a number of stages, including initial contact, incorporation of symbionts into host tissues or cells, establishment of nutritional or other interactions, and regulated proliferation of symbionts. Discrimination against organisms which are ultimately unacceptable as symbionts may occur at various points during this process, and no single stage is of overriding importance. A complex, multi-stage recognition process may well be of selective advantage to a host because parasitic or otherwise inappropriate organisms would be unlikely to exhibit all the critical features of an acceptable symbiont. If recognition involved only a single characteristic, then inappropriate organisms might gain access to the host more easily.

Some stages of recognition involve tolerance, avoidance or suppression of host defences against invasion. However, since acquisition of suitable symbionts is often of considerable advantage to the host (see 11.10), one might expect mechanisms to evolve by which hosts *positively* select symbionts. Much attention has focused on the possibility that this might involve highly specific binding between chemical groups on the surface of the partners. Lectins are important in cell-to-cell recognition in some pathogenic and developmental interactions, and interest has naturally focused on their possible role in recognition in symbiosis (e.g., 2.2.4.2, 4.2.5.2, 6.5.3). However, even in the most well-researched case of the legume/rhizobium symbiosis (4.2.5.2), lectin-saccharide interactions are not the sole determinants of specificity, but represent a component in just one of a series of recognition stages.

11.8   Modes of interaction

The variety of interactions between partners of the associations described in this book are summarized in Table 11.2. Almost all the symbioses listed are characterized by nutritional interactions which, with few exceptions, are predominantly biotrophic. Biotrophy (1.3.7) has been the subject of more experimental investigation than any other aspect of symbiosis, and so will be considered in some detail.

11.8.1   Biotrophy

Most experimental studies of biotrophy have principally involved tracing the movement of isotopes between partners, and then attempting to infer the mechanism of transport from this largely indirect evidence. Nearly all investigations have been concerned with the transport of major nutrients (especially in associations involving photosynthetic or nitrogen-fixing organisms). Little is known about other kinds of biotrophic transport which might be important such as movement of vitamins, growth factors, trace elements and hormones. Five aspects of biotrophy have received particular experimental attention.

11.8.1.1 Identification of mobile nutrients

Identification is usually indirect, based on analysis of products released by freshly isolated symbionts (where this is feasible) and/or combined with studies of assumed pathways of accumulation in the recipient. There are only a few examples where mobile nutrients have been identified by more direct methods (the 'inhibition technique' in lichens (6.4.1.2) and the use of digitonin to demonstrate ammonia release from cyanobacteria in symbiosis (5.3.3.1, 6.4.1.2)).

All the evidence suggests that major nutrients move in the form of only one or a few low molecular weight compounds. Common examples include: simple sugars or polyols, neutral amino acids, short chain fatty acids, ammonia and phosphate.

11.8.1.2 Production of mobile nutrients

Many mobile nutrients are normal products of donor cells in the free-living state, although the amounts produced are increased in symbiosis. This occurs in nitrogen-fixing symbionts because the key enzyme of ammonia assimilation, glutamine synthetase, is repressed (4.2.4.1, 5.3.3.1) so that large amounts of ammonia become available for release. It would be interesting to determine whether analogous mechanisms lead to the production of other kinds of mobile nutrient. Carbohydrate release from lichen symbionts is associated with reduced synthesis of polysaccharides (6.4.1.3), but it is not known whether this is cause or effect.

It has been suggested for a number of symbioses that some mobile carbohydrates might be cell wall precursors which have been diverted from the normal pathway of wall synthesis (e.g., 6.4.1.3, 7.3.2). In mycorrhizas, this view is supported by the occurrence of phosphatases and carbohydrases on the fungal surface associated with the plant cells from which carbohydrates are derived. However, in lichens, the mobile carbohydrates are rarely common components of the cell wall. The frequently observed reduction of cell wall thickness in symbiosis may not necessarily indicate diversion of wall synthesis into mobile carbohydrate production. The loss of the cell wall of *Tetraselmis* on entry into symbiosis with *Convoluta* (3.3) is accompanied by a shutdown in synthesis of wall precursors. The reduction in cell walls of intracellular symbionts might be a response to the mechanical and osmotic stability of the cellular environment.

Table 11.2 Summary of interactions between host and symbionts.

Chapter	Host	Symbiont	Nutritional interactions			Other metabolic interactions	Miscellaneous interactions
			Symbiont→Host	Host→Symbiont	Comments		
2	Freshwater invertebrates and protists	Chlorella	Maltose (reports of glucose in sponges)	(i)	Host feeds holozoically		1. Some hosts may be protected against attack by predators and parasites. 2. Symbiont gains mobility.
3	Marine invertebrates and protists	Symbiodinium microadriaticum	Glycerol neutral amino acids fatty acids sterols	(i)	Most hosts feed holozoically. Symbionts may recycle N & P	Calcification stimulated by symbiont photosynthesis	
	Convoluta roscoffensis	Tetraselmis	Neutral amino acids sterols fatty acids	Uric acid (host waste product) (i)	Adult hosts do not feed holozoically		
	Foraminifera	Various algae	? 'Photosynthate'	(i)		Calcification stimulated by symbiont photosynthesis	
4	Legumes	Rhizobia	Ammonia	Photosynthate (? organic acids)	Symbiont glutamine synthetase repressed	Host and symbiont interact in synthesis of leghaemoglobin	
	Non-legumes	Frankia	Ammonia	Photosynthate (? organic acids)	? ''		
5	Cyanobacteria	Aerobic bacteria	—	—		Bacteria use O_2 from host photosynthesis, which enhances N_2 fixation in host	

	Host	Symbiont					
	Plants	Cyanobacteria	Ammonia		Symbiont glutamine synthetase repressed, yielding surplus of ammonia		
6	Lichen fungi	Cyanobacteria	Glucose, ammonia	–?	''		
	Lichen fungi	Algae	Polyols	–?		Host and symbiont interact in synthesis of secondary metabolites	Symbionts shielded from high light intensities. Symbiont water loss retarded.
7	Green plants (except orchids)	Fungi	Mineral nutrients, especially phosphorus, nitrogen & potassium	Photosynthate			Host roots protected against pathogenic attack. Host drought resistance enhanced
	Orchids and many achlorophyllous plants	Fungi	Trehalose (juvenile hosts) ? mineral nutrients	–	Interaction between adult photosynthetic orchid and symbiont little studied		?
8	Vertebrates Insects	Various prokaryotes; often protozoa and fungi	Volatile fatty acids	Symbionts utilize food ingested by host	1. Rumen symbionts regularly digested – conserves N for whole symbiosis. 2. Some termite gut symbionts fix nitrogen; some other symbionts utilize host uric acid		Host protected from some gut pathogens

Table 11.2 cont'd

Chapter	Host	Symbiont	Nutritional interactions				Other metabolic interactions	Miscellaneous interactions
			Symbiont→Host	Host→Symbiont	Comments			
9	Protozoa, e.g., *Mixotricha paradoxa*	Spirochaetes and other motile prokaryotes	–	–				Host acquires motility
	Trypanosomes, e.g., *Crithidia oncopelti*	Prokaryotes (bipolar bodies)	Haem	(i)				
	Paramecium aurelia	Prokaryotes	Folic acid, biopterin from *lambda*	(i)				'Kappa' kills sensitive paramecia and so enhances host competition for food
	Various anaerobic protozoa	Methanogenic bacteria	–	? (Some i)			Symbiont utilises host H$_2$, enhancing oxidative metabolism of host	
	Insects	Mycetocyte symbionts (prokaryotes)	Amino acids vitamins	(i)				
	Vestimentiferan pogonophora and molluscs	Sulphide-oxidising chemoauto-trophic bacteria	Organic carbon compounds	(i)				Symbionts remove toxic H$_2$S from tissues
	Teleost fish, squids, thaliacean tunicates	Luminescent bacteria (e.g., *Photobacterium*)	–	Thaliacean symbionts (i)				Host utilises symbiont luminescence in various ways, probably mostly behavioural

Notes: (i) = intracellular symbiont, therefore all nutrients derived from surrounding host cell, – = no motile nutrients identified.

11.8.1.3 Release from donor cells

The release of most nutrients is likely to be mediated by specific membrane carriers since there is little evidence of an increase in non-specific membrane permeability. Energy-dependent transport systems appear to be involved in release from *Chlorella* (2.2.2.2), lichen (6.4.1.3) and mycorrhizal symbionts (7.5.1).

Most donors release little or none of the mobile nutrient when they are grown in isolation (exceptions include release in culture of maltose by *Chlorella* symbionts and ammonia by *Bradyrhizobium japonicum*). The mechanisms by which recipients promote nutrient release are unclear. Unidentified host 'factors' have been implicated in the stimulation of photosynthate release by the dinoflagellate symbiont *Symbiodinium microadriaticum* (3.2.3.1), but a search for similar compounds in the lichen symbiosis was unsuccessful (6.4.1.3). The high density of ATPase bound to the plant membranes which surround mature arbuscules of vesicular–arbuscular mycorrhizal fungi (7.5.1) may have a role in stimulating phosphate release.

11.8.1.4 Uptake by recipients

Nutrients released from the donor diffuse to the recipient across an intervening space which may be of matrix material when one of the partners is fungal, or vacuolar space as with intracellular symbionts. Rapid uptake and assimilation of nutrients by recipients have often been suggested as a factor promoting rapid diffusion across this space. Additionally, nutrient uptake may be promoted by a large surface area of contact between the partners; examples include the interface between mycorrhizal fungi and root tissues, and that between *Convoluta roscoffensis* and its algal symbionts.

11.8.1.5 Quantitative aspects

The wealth of experimental data on biotrophy may conceal the fact that there have been very few direct and accurate estimates of the absolute amounts of nutrients a recipient obtains from a donor. This is mainly because it is difficult to study events at the interface between the partners (1.4). Although isotopes such as ^{14}C show that nutrient movement occurs, the specific activity of the isotope in the compound which moves is usually not known so that its absolute amount cannot be calculated (e.g., 2.2.2.2, 3.2.4.3, 6.4.1.1).

11.8.2 Other interactions

Few of the other interactions listed in Table 11.2 are sufficiently widespread to afford sensible comparison between different types of symbiosis. However, of particular note is the growing evidence that some symbionts may protect their hosts against infection by detrimental microorganisms, for example the gut symbionts of vertebrates (8.3.5), *Chlorella-Paramecium* symbiosis (2.2.5.2) and mycorrhizas (7.6). The observation that sea anemones with dinoflagellate symbionts have elevated levels of superoxide dismutase (3.2.3.3) draws attention to the possibility that organisms in symbiosis protect themselves against potentially toxic products of their partners.

11.9   Integration

Most associations exhibit morphological and other features different from those displayed by the partners on their own. However, it is difficult to devise any practical index which allows the degree of integration in a symbiosis to be assessed. Furthermore, integration in features such as morphology is in part the product of interactions which have received no experimental investigation. Although integration is a striking feature of symbiosis, it is a characteristic of limited value in making comparisons at our current level of understanding of the associations.

11.10   Significance of symbiosis to the well-being of the partners

Most of the symbioses described in this book are conventionally regarded as mutualistic, i.e., it is believed that both partners benefit from the association. However, 'benefit' is often difficult to identify (see 1.1) largely because, until recently, the term has not been defined in a biologically meaningful way (1.3.9). Law and Lewis (1983) introduced much greater precision by defining associations as mutualistic if the fitness of the associating organisms is greater when they are together than when they are apart.

However, equating benefit with improved fitness leads to two further problems. Firstly, there is no universally agreed definition of fitness applicable to all the kinds of organisms found in symbiosis, although most biologists would regard 'improved fitness' to cover phenomena such as the production of larger numbers of offspring or offspring of greater competitive ability. Secondly, as the detailed descriptions of symbioses in chapters 2–9 indicate, that there have been no investigations which have had the primary aim of demonstrating that symbiosis leads to improved fitness for both partners. In the strict sense, therefore, there has been no complete and rigorous experimental proof that any symbiosis is mutualistic.

On the other hand, many experiments have involved measurements of what might be considered as components or partial indices of fitness, the two commonest being improved acquisition of nutrients, and enhanced growth. These experiments clearly indicate that the fitness of most hosts may be increased by symbiosis, but that the fitness of most symbionts, with the exception of root symbionts, is reduced. For example, intracellular symbionts gain nutrients from host cells, but if the host restricts nutrient supply as a means of regulation (11.5), then it is difficult to argue that the fitness of symbionts is enhanced. Many symbionts grow more slowly in symbiosis than in culture, but while such a direct comparison may be invalid (because conditions in culture are not the same as in symbiosis), it highlights the fact symbionts often pass to the host substantial quantities of nutrients which might otherwise be allocated to their own growth.

The problem becomes particularly difficult for associations in which the partners exhibit a high degree of dependence upon each other. Since host and symbiont cannot live apart, the association must be considered mutualistic by the definition of Law and Lewis. Nevertheless, it is not at all clear that the fitness of an organism is always enhanced by dependence upon another organism. The example of the xD strain of *Amoeba proteus*, which rapidly evolved dependence upon an originally pathogenic bacterium (9.6), reinforces this doubt. Obligacy implies loss of features, and this is not necessarily 'improved fitness'.

It has been argued that very common symbionts, such as *Symbiodinium* in marine invertebrates and *Trebouxia* in lichens, have achieved a wider distribution and sometimes greater population density through symbiosis. This draws attention to a further problem that the definition of mutualistic symbiosis, with its concept of 'improvement', implies a comparison with the previous nonsymbiotic situation. However, most symbionts lack close nonsymbiotic relatives with which to make sensible comparisons. Further, as already considered, it is also questionable whether the fitness of an organism is always improved if it can no longer colonize habitats away from its host. The situation is directly comparable to the question of whether agricultural animals and crops benefit from their domestication by man and, without still further refinements of the concepts of harm and benefit, the question is essentially unanswerable.

Some authors (e.g., Odum, 1959; Read, 1970) have classified interactions between pairs of organisms in terms such as ' + / – ', ' + /0' and ' + / + ', where ' + ' can be considered to denote some index of improved fitness such as increased growth, and ' – ' denotes the opposite. Under this convention, interactions denoted ' + / – ' are parasitic, and ' + / + ' are mutualistic. This approach can be modified to describe symbioses if two additional symbols, 'h' and 's', are introduced to denote host and symbiont respectively. Parasitic symbioses would then be classified 'h – /s + ', while most associations described in this book should be considered as 'h + /s?'; the symbionts are, in general, maintained in a way that enhances host fitness, and one can argue that this entails a net reduction in fitness in some cases (e.g., most intracellular symbionts, lichen symbionts) or net enhancement in others (as in most root symbionts, which acquire substantial amounts of photosynthate from their host plants and can compete successfully with nonsymbiotic microorganisms in the surrounding soil).

The characteristic of 'significance of symbiosis to the well-being of the partners' is clearly difficult to evaluate, and it should not be considered more important than other characteristics in describing symbioses. This view confirms the original definition of symbiosis as the 'living together of dissimilarly named organisms', with no reference to harm or benefit (1.1).

References

Ahmadjian, V. (1962). Investigations on lichen synthesis. *American Journal of Botany*, **49**, 277–83.

Ahmadjian, V. (1963). The fungi of lichens. *Scientific American*, **208**, 122–31.

Ahmadjian, V. (1982). Algal/fungal symbioses. In *Progress in Phycological Research*, Vol. 1 (Round, F.E. and Chapman, V., eds) pp. 179–233. Elsevier.

Ahmadjian, V. (1987). Studies on the development of synthetic lichens. In *Progress and Problems in Lichenology in the Eighties*. (E. Peveling, A. Henssen, O.L. Lange, and C. Leuckert, eds) J. Cramer (In press.)

Ahmadjian, V. and Jacobs, J.B. (1981). Relationship between fungus and alga in the lichen *Cladonia cristatella* Tuck. *Nature*, **289**, 169–72.

Ahmadjian, V. and Jacobs, J.B. (1983). Algal-fungal relationships in lichens: recognition, synthesis and development. In *Algal Symbiosis*. (L.J. Goff, ed.) pp. 147–72. Cambridge University Press.

Ahn, T.I. and Jeon, K.W. (1984). Strain specific proteins of symbiont-containing *Amoeba proteus* detected by two-dimensional gel electrophoresis. *Journal of Protozoology*, **30**, 713–15.

Aitken, A. and Stanier, R.Y. (1979). Characterization of peptidoglycan from the cyanelles of *Cyanophora paradoxa*. *Journal of General Microbiology*, **112**, 219–23.

Akkermans, A.D.L. and van Dijk, C. (1981). Non-leguminous root nodules with actinomycetes and *Rhizobium*. In *Nitrogen fixation. Volume 1: Ecology*. (W.J. Broughton, ed.). Clarendon Press, Oxford. pp. 57–103.

Alexander, C., Alexander, I. and Hadley, G. (1984). Phosphate uptake by *Goodyera repens* in relation to mycorrhizal infection. *New Phytologist*, **97**, 401–11.

Alexander, C. and Hadley, G. (1985). Carbon movement between host and mycorrhizal endophyte during the development of the orchid *Goodyera repens*. *New Phytologist*, **101**, 657–65.

Ames, P. and Bergman, K. (1981). Competitive advantage provided by bacterial motility in the formation of nodules by *Rhizobium meliloti*. *Journal of Bacteriology*, **148**, 728–9.

Ames, R.N., Reid, C.P.P., Porter, L.K. and Cambardella, C. (1983). Hyphal uptake and transport of nitrogen from two ^{15}N-labelled sources by *Glomus mosseae*, a vesicular–arbuscular mycorrhizal fungus. *New Phytologist*, **95**, 381–96.

Ball, G.H. (1969). Organisms living on or in protozoa. In *Research in Protozoology*. III. (T-T. Chen, ed.) pp. 565–718. Pergamon Press, UK.

De Bary, A. (1879). Die Erscheinung der Symbiose. *Naturforschung Versammlung Cassel*, LI, Tagebl. p. 121.

Batra, L.R. (ed.) (1979). *Insect-Fungus Symbiosis. Nutrition, Mutualism and Commensalism*. 276 pp. John Wiley, New York.

Bauchop, T. (1977). Foregut fermentation. In: *Microbial Ecology of the Gut* (R.T.J. Clarke and T. Bauchop, eds) pp. 223-51. Academic Press, London.

Bauchop, T. (1979). Rumen anaerobic fungi of cattle and sheep. *Applied and Environmental Microbiology*, **38**, 148-58.

Baumann, P., Baumann, L., Bang, S.S. and Woolkalis, M.J. (1980). Re-evaluation of the taxonomy of *Vibrio*, *Beneckea* and *Photobacterium*: abolition of the genus *Beneckea*. *Current Microbiology*, **4**, 127-33.

Bayon, C. (1980). Volatile fatty acids and methane production in relation to anaerobic carbohydrate fermentation in *Oryctes nasicornis* larvae (Coleoptera: Scarabaeidae). *Journal of Insect Physiology*, **26**, 819-28.

Bednar, T.W. and Juniper, B.E. (1965). Microfibrillar structure in the fungal portion of the lichen *Xanthoria parietina* (L) Th. Fr. *Experimental Cell Research*, **36**, 680-3.

Belay, N., Sparling, R. and Daniels, C. (1984). Dinitrogen fixation by a thermophilic bacterium. *Nature*, **312**, 286-8.

Bentley, B.L. (1984). Nitrogen fixation in termites: fate of newly fixed nitrogen. *Journal of Insect Physiology*, **30**, 653-5.

Berger, J. (1980). Feeding behaviour of *Didinium nasutum* on *Paramecium bursaria* with normal or apochlorotic zoochlorellae. *Journal of General Microbiology*, **118**, 397-404.

Bergerson, F.J. (1971). The central reactions in nitrogen fixation. In: *Biological nitrogen fixation in natural and agricultural habitats*. (eds T.A. Lie and E.G. Mulder). *Plant and Soil* (special vol.), pp. 511-24.

Bergerson, F.J. (1980). Leghaemoglobin, oxygen supply and nitrogen fixation: studies with soybean nodules. In *Nitrogen Fixation* (W.D.P. Stewart and T. Gallon, eds) pp. 139-60. Academic Press, London.

Bergerson, F.J., Kennedy, G.S. and Wittmann, W. (1965). Nitrogen fixation in coralloid roots of *Macrozamia communis*. *Australian Journal of Biological Sciences*, **18**, 1135-42.

Beringer, J.E., Brewin, N., Johnston, A.W.B., Schulman, H.M. and Hopwood, D.A. (1979). The *Rhizobium*-legume symbiosis. *Proceedings of the Royal Society of London, Series B*, **204**, 219-33.

Beschel, R. (1955). Individuum und Alter bei Flechten. *Phyton (Horn, N.O.)*, **6**, 60-8.

Bignell, D.E. (1977). An experimental study of cellulose and hemicellulose degradation in the alimentary canal of the American cockroach. *Canadian Journal of Zoology*, **55**, 579-89.

Bignell, D.E. (1984). The arthropod gut as an environment for microorganisms. In *Invertebrate-Microbial Interactions* (J.M. Anderson, A.D.M. Rayner and D.W.H. Walton, eds) pp. 205-28. Cambridge University Press.

Bignell, D.E., Oskarsson, H. and Anderson, J.M. (1980). Colonization of the epithelial face of the peritrophic membrane and ectoperitrophic space by actinomycetes in a soil-feeding termite. *Journal of Invertebrate Pathology*, **36**, 426-8.

Bjorkman, E. (1960). *Monotropa hypopytis*. L. an epiparasite on tree roots. *Physiologia Plantarum*, **13**, 308-27.

Blackbourn, D.J., Taylor, F.J.R. and Blackbourn, J. (1973). Foreign organelle-retention by ciliates. *Journal of Protozoology*, **20**, 286-8.

Blank, R.J. and Trench, R.K. (1985). Speciation and symbiotic dinoflagellates. *Science*, **229**, 656-8.

Bohlool, B.B. and Schmidt, E.L. (1974). Lectins: a possible basis for specificity in the *Rhizobium*-legume root nodule symbiosis. *Science*, **185**, 269-71.

Bonnett, H.T. and Silvester, W.B. (1981). Specificity in the *Gunnera-Nostoc* endosymbiosis. *New Phytologist*, **89**, 121–8.

Borst, P. and Grivell, L.A. (1978). The mitochondrial genome of yeast. *Cell*, **15**, 705–23.

Boucher, D.H. (ed.) (1985). *The Biology of Mutualism: Ecology and Evolution.* Croom-Helm, London. 358pp.

Boucher, D.H., James, S. and Keeler, K.H. (1982). The ecology of mutualism. *Annual Review of Ecology and Systematics*, **13**, 315–47.

Bowen, G.D. and Theodoru, C. (1967). Studies on phosphate uptake by mycorrhizas. *14 IUFRO Congress*, **5**, 116–38.

Boyle, J.E. and Smith, D.C. (1975). Biochemical interactions between the symbionts of *Convoluta roscoffensis*. *Proceedings of the Royal Society of London Series B*, **189**, 121–35.

Bracke, J.W., Cruden, D.L. and Markovetz, A.J. (1978). Effect of metronidazole on the intestinal microflora of the American cockroach *Periplaneta americana*. *Antimicrobial Agents and Chemotherapy*, **13**, 115–20.

Bracke, J.W., Cruden, D.L. and Markovetz, A.J. (1979). Intestinal microbial flora of the American cockroach *Periplaneta americana* L. *Applied and Environmental Microbiology*, **38**, 945–55.

Bracke, J.W. and Markovetz, A.J. (1980). Transport of bacterial end products from the colon of *Periplaneta americana*. *Journal of Insect Physiology*, **26**, 85–9.

Bradley, R., Burt, A.J. and Read, D.J. (1982). The biology of mycorrhiza in the Ericaceae. VIII. The role of mycorrhizal infection in heavy metal resistance. *New Phytologist*, **91**, 197–201.

Breznak, J.A. (1982). Intestinal microbiota of termites and other xylophagous insects. *Annual Review of Microbiology*, **36**, 323–43.

Breznak, J.A. (1984). Biochemical aspects of symbiosis between termites and their intestinal microbiota. In *Invertebrate-Microbial Interactions* (J.M. Anderson, A.D.M. Rayner and D.W.H. Walton, eds) pp. 173–204. Cambridge University Press.

Breznak, J.A., Brill, W.J., Mertins, J.W. and Coppel, H.C. (1973). Nitrogen fixation in termites. *Nature*, **244**, 577–9.

Brian, P.W. (1966). Obligate parasitism in fungi. *Proceedings of the Royal Society of London Series B*, **168**, 101–18.

Brock, T.D. (1975). The effect of water potential on photosynthesis in whole lichens and in their liberated algal components. *Planta*, **124**, 13–23.

Brooks, M.A. (1963). Symbiosis and aposymbiosis in arthropods. *Symposia of the Society for General Microbiology*, **13**, 200–31.

Brooks, M.A. (1970). Comments on the classification of intracellular symbiotes of cockroaches and a description of the species. *Journal of Invertebrate Pathology*, **16**, 249–58.

Brown, D.H. (ed.) (1986). *Lichen Physiology and Cell Biology* 362 pp. Plenum, New York.

Bruggen, J.J.A. van., Stumm, C.K. and Vogels, G.D. (1983). Symbiosis of methanogenic bacteria and sapropelic protozoa. *Archives of Microbiology*, **136**, 89–95.

Bruggen, J.J.A. van., Zwart, K.B., van Assema, R.M., Stumm, C.K. and Vogels, G.D. (1984). *Methanobacterium formicicum*, an endosymbiont of the anaerobic ciliate *Metopus striatus* McMurrich. *Archives of Microbiology*, **139**, 1–7.

Buchner, P. (1966). *Endosymbiosis of Animals with Plant Microorganisms.* 909 pp. John Wiley, New York.

Burger-Wiersma, T., Veenhuis, M., Korthals, H.J., Van de Wiel, C.C.M., and Mur,

L.R. (1986). A new prokaryote containing chlorophylls *a* and *b*. *Nature*, **320**, 262–4.

Butler, J.H.A. and Buckerfield, J.C. (1979). Digestion of lignin by termites. *Soil Biology and Biochemistry*, **11**, 507–11.

Buwalda, J.G., Stribley, D.P. and Tinker, P.B. (1984). The development of ecto-mycorrhizal root systems. V. The detailed pattern of development of infection and the control of infection level by host in young leek plants. *New Phytologist*, **96**, 411–27.

Callaham, D., Del Tredici, P. and Torrey, J.G. (1978). Isolation and cultivation *in vitro* of the actinomycete causing root nodulation in *Comptonia*. *Science*, **199**, 899–902.

Campbell, B.C. and Nes, W.D., (1983). A reappraisal of sterol biosynthesis and metabolism in aphids. *Journal of Insect Physiology*, **29**, 149–56.

Carroll, S. and Blanquet, R.S. (1984). Alanine uptake by isolated zooxanthellae of the mangrove jellyfish *Cassiopeia xamachana*. II. Inhibition by host homogenate fraction. *Biological Bulletin*, **166**, 419–26.

Cates, J.N. and McLaughlin, J.J.A. (1976). Differences of ammonia metabolism in symbiotic and aposymbiotic *Condylactis* and *Cassiopaea* spp. *Journal of experimental Marine Biology and Ecology*, **21**, 1–5.

Cavalier-Smith, T. (1975). The origin of nuclei and of eukaryotic cells. *Nature*, **256**, 463–8.

Cavanaugh, C.M. (1983). Symbiotic chemoautotrophic bacteria in marine invertebrates from sulphide-rich habitats. *Nature*, **302**, 58–61.

Cernichiari, E., Muscatine, L. and Smith, D.C. (1969). Maltose excretion by the symbiotic algae of *Hydra viridis*. *Proceedings of the Royal Society of London Series B*, **173**, 557–76.

Chandler, M.R., Date, R.A. and Roughley, R.J. (1982). Infection and root-nodule development in *Stylosanthes* species by *Rhizobium*. *Journal of Experimental Botany*, **33**, 47–57.

Chang, K-P. (1975). Haematophagous insect and haemoflagellate as hosts for prokaryotic endosymbionts. *Symposia of the Society for Experimental Biology*, **29**, 407–28.

Chang, K-P., Chang, C.S. and Sassa, S. (1975). Haeme biosynthesis in bacterium–protozoon symbioses: enzymic defects in host haemoflagellates and complemental role of the intracellular symbiotes. *Proceedings of the National Academy of Sciences U.S.A.*, **72**, 2979–83.

Chang, K-P., and Trager, W. (1974). Nutritional significance of symbiotic bacteria in two species of haemoflagellates. *Science*, **183**, 531–2.

Chapman-Andresen, C. and Hamburger, K. (1981). Respiratory studies on the giant amoeba *Pelomyxa palustris*. *Journal of Protozoology*, **28**, 433–44.

Clark, K.B. and Busacca, M. (1978). Feeding specificity and chloroplast retention in four tropical Ascoglossa, with a discussion of the extent of chloroplast symbiosis and the evolution of the order. *Journal of Molluscan Studies*, **44**, 272–82.

Clarke, R.T.J. (1977). The gut and its microorganisms. In *Microbial Ecology of the Gut* (R.T.J. Clarke and T. Bauchop, eds) pp. 36–72. Academic Press, London.

Cleveland, L.R. (1925). The effects of oxygenation and starvation on the symbiosis between the termite, *Termopsis*, and its intestinal flagellates. *Biological Bulletin*, **48**, 309–26.

Cleveland, L.R., Burke, A.W. and Karlson, P. (1960). Ecdysone induced modifications in the sexual cycles of the protozoa of *Cryptocercus*. *Journal of Protozoology*, **7**, 229–39.

Cleveland, L.R. and Grimstone, A.V. (1964). The fine structure of the flagellate

Mixotricha paradoxa and its associated microorganisms. *Proceedings of the Royal Society of London Series B.*, **159**, 668-86.

Coates, M.E. and Fuller, R. (1977). The gnotobiotic animal in the study of gut microbiology. In *Microbial Ecology of the Gut* (R.T.J. Clarke and T. Bauchop, eds) pp. 311-46. Academic Press, London.

Cochran, D.G., Mullins, D.E. and Mullins, K.J. (1979). Cytological changes in the fat body of the American cockroach *Periplaneta americana* in relation to dietary nitrogen levels. *Annals of the Entomological Society of America*, **72**, 197-205.

Coleman, G.S. (1979). Rumen ciliate protozoa. In *Biochemistry and Physiology of Protozoa*. II. (M. Levandowsky and S.H. Hutner, eds) pp. 381-408. Academic Press, London.

Collins, C.R. and Farrar, J.F. (1978). Structural resistance to mass transfer in the lichen *Xanthoria parietina*. *New Phytologist*, **81**, 71-83.

Cooke, R.C. and Whipps, J.M. (1980). The evolution of modes of nutrition in fungi parasitic on terrestrial plants. *Biological Reviews*, **55**, 341-62.

Culberson, C.F. (1969). *Chemical and Botanical Guide to Lichen Products* 628 pp. The University of North Carolina Press, Chapel Hill.

Culberson, C.F. (1970). Supplement to *Chemical and Botanical Guide to Lichen Products*. *Bryologist*, **73**, 177-377.

Culberson, C.F. and Ahmadjian, V. (1980). Artificial reestablishment of lichens. II. Secondary products of resynthesized *Cladonia cristatella* and *Lecanora chrysoleuca*. *Mycologia*, **72**, 90-109.

Culberson, C.F., Culberson, W.L. and Johnson, C.F. (1977). *Second Supplement to Chemical and Botanical Guide to Lichen Products*. 400pp. The American Bryological and Lichenological Society, St. Louis.

Dando, P.R., Southward, A.J., Southward, E.C., Terwilliger, N.B. and Terwilliger, N.C. (1985). Sulphur-oxidising bacteria and haemoglobin in gills of the bivalve mollusc *Myrtea spinifera*. *Marine Ecology – Progress Series*, **23**, 85-98.

Dando, P.R., Southward, A.J. and Southward, E.C. (1986). Chemoautotrophic symbionts in the gills of the bivalve mollusc *Lucinoma borealis* and the sediment chemistry of its habitat. *Proceedings of the Royal Society of London B*, **227**, 227-47.

Dasch, G.A., Weiss, E. and Chang, K-P. (1984). Endosymbionts of insects. In *Bergey's Manual of Systematic Bacteriology*. (N.R. Krieg, ed.) pp. 811-33. Williams and Wilkins, Baltimore.

Dayhoff, M.O. and Schwartz, R.M. (1981). Evidence on the origin of eukaryotic mitochondria from protein and nucleic acid sequences. *Annals of the New York Academy of Sciences*, **361**, 92-103.

Dazzo, F.B. and Brill, W.J. (1978). Regulation by fixed nitrogen of host-symbiont recognition in the *Rhizobium*-clover symbiosis. *Plant Physiology*, **62**, 18-21.

Dazzo, F.B. and Hubbell, D.H. (1975). Cross-reactive antigens and lectin as determinants of symbiotic specificity in the *Rhizobium*-clover association. *Applied Microbiology*, **30**, 1017-33.

Dazzo, F.B. and Truchet, G.L. (1984). Attachment of nitrogen-fixing bacteria to roots of host plants. In *Current Developments in Biological Nitrogen Fixation* pp. 65-100 (N.S. Subba Rao, ed.). Edward Arnold, London.

Dijk, C. van and Merkus, E. (1976). A microscopical study of the development of a spore-like stage in the life cycle of the root nodule endophyte of *Alnus glutinosa* (L.) Gaertn. *New Phytologist*, **77**, 73-91.

Doolittle, W.F. (1982). Molecular evolution. In *The Biology of Cyanobacteria* (N.G. Carr and B.A. Whitton, eds), pp. 307-31. Blackwell Scientific Publications, UK.

Douglas, A.E. (1983a). Establishment of the symbiosis in *Convoluta roscoffensis*. *Journal of the Marine Biological Association UK*, **63**, 419–34.

Douglas, A.E. (1983b). Uric acid utilization in *Platymonas convolutae* and symbiotic *Convoluta roscoffensis*. *Journal of the Marine Biological Association UK*, **63**, 435–47.

Douglas, A.E. and Gooday, G.W. (1982). The behaviour of algal cells towards egg capsules of *Convoluta roscoffensis* and its role in the persistence of the *Convoluta*-alga symbiosis. *British Phycological Journal*, **17**, 383–8.

Douglas, A.E., and Huss, V.A.R. (1986). On the characteristics and taxonomic identity of symbiotic *Chlorella*. *Archives of Microbiology*, **145**, 80–4.

Douglas, A.E., and Smith, D.C. (1983). The cost of symbionts to the host in the green hydra symbiosis. In *Endocytobiology, Endosymbiosis and Cell Biology* II. (Schwemmler, W. and Schenk, H.E.A., eds) pp. 631–48. Walter de Gruyter and Co., Berlin.

Douglas, A.E. and Smith, D.C. (1984). The green hydra symbiosis. VIII. Mechanisms in symbiont regulation. *Proceedings of the Royal Society of London Series B*, **221**, 291–319.

Drew, E.A. and Smith, D.C. (1967). Studies in the physiology of lichens. VII. The physiology of the *Nostoc* symbionts of *Peltigera polydactyla* compared with cultured and free-living forms. *New Phytologist*, **66**, 379–88.

Droop, M.R. (1963). Algae and invertebrates in symbiosis. *Symposia of the Society for General Microbiology*, **13**, 171–99.

Duckett, J.G., Prasad, A.K., Davies, D.A. and Walker, S. (1977). A cytological analysis of the *Nostoc*–bryophyte relationship. *New Phytologist*, **79**, 349–62.

Duckett, J.G., Toth, R. and Soni, S.L. (1975). An ultrastructural study of the *Azolla, Anabaena azollae* relationship. *New Phytologist*, **75**, 111–18.

Duddridge, J.A. (1985). A comparative ultrastructural analysis of the host-fungus, interface in mycorrhizal-parasitic associations. In *Developmental Biology of Higher Fungi*. British Mycological Society Symposium. Vol. 10. (eds D. Moore, L.A. Casselton, D.A. Wood and J.C. Frankland). pp. 141–73. Cambridge University Press.

Duddridge, J.A., Malibari, A., and Read, D.J. (1980). Structure and function of mycorrhizal rhizomorphs with special reference to their role in water transport. *Nature*, **287**, 834–6.

Duddridge, J.A., and Read, D.J. (1982). An ultrastructural analysis of the development of mycorrhizas in *Monotropa hypopitys*. *New Phytologist*, **92**, 203–14.

Duve, C.-de. (1969). Evolution of the peroxisome. *Annals of the New York Academy of Sciences*, **168**, 369–81.

Dykens, J.A. and Shick, J.M. (1982). Oxygen production by endosymbiotic algae controls superoxide dismutase activity in their animal host. *Nature*, **297**, 579–80.

Eadie, J.M. and Gill, J.C. (1971). The effect of the absence of rumen ciliate protozoa on growing lambs fed on a roughage-concentrate diet. *British Journal of Nutrition*, **26**, 155–67.

Eaton, J.W. and Young, J.O. (1975). Studies on the symbiosis of *Phaenocora typhlops* (Vejdovsky) (Turbellaria; Neorhabdocoela) and *Chlorella vulgaris* Fott and Novakova (Chlorococcales). I. Field and laboratory observations on the symbiotic relationship. *Archives of Hydrobiology*, **75**, 50–75.

Eberle, M.W. and McLean, D.L. (1983). Observations of symbiote migration in human body lice with scanning and transmission electron microscopy. *Canadian Journal of Microbiology*, **29**, 755–62.

Ehrhardt, P. (1968). Einfluss von Ernahrungsfaktoren auf die Entwicklung von Safte saugenden Insekten unter besonderer Berucksichtigung von Symbionten. *Zeitschift fur Parasitenkunde*, **31**, 38–66.

Enderlin, C.S. and Meeks, J.C. (1983). Pure culture and reconstitution of the *Anthoceros-Nostoc* symbiotic association. *Planta*, **158**, 157–65.

Etzler, M.E. (1985). Plant lectins: molecular and biological aspects. *Annual Review of Plant Physiology*, **36**, 209–34.

Evans, H.J., Bottomley, P.J. and Newton, W.E. (eds). (1985). Nitrogen Fixation research progress. *Proceedings of the 6th International Congress on Nitrogen Fixation*. 731pp. Martinus Nijhoff, Dordrecht.

Evans, H.J., Emerich, W., Lepo, J.E., Maier, K.R., Carter, K.R., Hanus, F.J. and Russell, S.A. (1980). The role of hydrogenase in nodule bacteroids and free-living rhizobia. In *Nitrogen Fixation*, (W.D.P. Stewart and J.L. Gallon, eds) pp. 55–81. Academic Press, London.

Farrar, J.F. (1976a). Ecological physiology of the lichen *Hypogymnia physodes*. II. Effects of wetting and drying cycles and the concept of physiological buffering. *New Phytologist*, **77**, 105–13.

Farrar, J.F. (1976b). Ecological physiology of the lichen *Hypogymnia physodes*. III. The importance of the rewetting phase. *New Phytologist*, **77**, 115–25.

Felbeck, H. (1983). Sulphide oxidation and carbon fixation by the gutless clam *Solemya reidi*: an animal-bacteria symbiosis. *Journal of Comparative Physiology B*, **152**, 3–11.

Felbeck, H., Childress, J.J. and Somero, G.N. (1981). Calvin-Benson cycle and sulphide oxidation enzymes in animals from sulphide-rich habitats. *Nature*, **293**, 291–3.

Fell, P.E. (1983). Porifera. In: *Reproductive Biology of Invertebrates. I. Oogenesis, Oviposition and Oosorption* (K.G. Adiyodi and R.G. Adiyodi, eds) pp. 1–29. John Wiley and Sons, UK.

Fenchel, T., Perry, T. and Thane, A. (1977). Anaerobiosis and symbiosis with bacteria in free-living ciliates. *Journal of Protozoology*, **24**, 154–63.

Finlay, R.D. and Read, D.J. (1986). The structure and function of the vegetative mycelium of ectomycorrhizal plants. I. Translocation between plants interconnected by a common mycelium. *New Phytologist*, **103**, 143–56.

Fischelson, L., Montgomery, L. and Myrberg, A. (1985). A unique symbiosis in the gut of tropical herbivorous surgeonfish (Acanthuridae: Teleostei) from the Red Sea. *Science*, **229**, 49–51.

Fisher, C.R. and Trench, R.K. (1980). In vitro carbon fixation by *Prochloron* sp. isolated from *Diplosoma virens*. *Biological Bulletin*, **159**, 636–48.

Fitt, W.K. and Trench, R.K. (1981). Spawning, development and acquisition of zooxanthellae by *Tridacna squamosa* (Mollusca, Bivalvia). *Biological Bulletin*, **161**, 213–35.

Floener, L. and Bothe, H. (1980). Nitrogen fixation in *Rhopalodia gibba*, a diatom containing blue-greenish inclusions symbiotically. In *Endocytobiology, Endosymbiosis and Cell Research*. Vol. I. (H.E.A. Schenk and W. Schwemmler, eds), pp. 541–52. Walter de Gruyter, Berlin.

Floener, L., Danneberg, G. and Bothe, H. (1982). Metabolic activities in *Cyanophora paradoxa* and its cyanelles. II. Photosynthesis and respiration. *Planta*, **156**, 78–83.

Fortin, J.A., Piche, Y., and Lalonde, M. (1980). Technique for observation of early morphological changes during ectomycorrhizal formation. *Canadian Journal of Botany*, **58**, 361–5.

Francis, R., Finlay, R.D. and Read, D.J. (1986). Vesicular–arbuscular mycorrhiza in natural vegetation systems. IV. Transfer of nutrients in inter- and intra-specific combinations of host plants. *New Phytologist*, **102**, 103–11.

Francis, R. and Read, D.J. (1984). Direct transfer of carbon between plants connected by vesicular-arbuscular mycorrhizal mycelium. *Nature*, **307**, 53–6.

Gallop, A. (1974). Evidence for the presence of a 'factor' in *Elysia viridis* which stimulates photosynthate release from its symbiotic chloroplasts. *New Phytologist*, **73**, 1111–17.

Gallop, A., Bartrop, J. and Smith, D.C. (1980). The biology of chloroplast acquisition by *Elysia viridis*. *Proceedings of the Royal Society of London Series B*, **207**, 335–49.

Galun, M. (1987). Selectivity in lichens and other symbiotic associations. In *Progress and Problems in Lichenology in the Eighties*. (E. Peveling, A. Henssen, O.L. Lange and C. Leuckert, eds). J. Cramer (in press).

Galun, M. and Bubrick, P. (1984). Physiological interactions between the partners of the lichen symbiosis. In *Cellular Interactions, Encyclopedia of Plant Physiology Vol. 17* (Linskens, H.F. and Heslop-Harrison, J., eds), pp. 362–401. Springer, Berlin.

Gasaway, W.C. (1976). Volatile fatty acids and metabolizable energy derived from caecal fermentation in the willow ptarmigan. *Comparative Biochemistry and Physiology*, **53A**, 115–21.

Gibbs, S.P. (1981). The chloroplasts of some algal groups may have evolved from eukaryotic algae. *Annals of the New York Academy of Sciences*, **361**, 193–208.

Giere, O. (1981). The gutless marine oligochaete *Phallodrilus leukodermatus*. Structural studies on an aberrant tubificid associated with bacteria. *Marine Ecology Progress Series*, **5**, 353–7.

Godbout, C. and Fortin, J.A. (1985). Synthesised ectomycorrhizae of aspen: fungal genus level of structural characterisation. *Canadian Journal of Botany*, **63**, 252–62.

Gordon, A.J., Ryle, G.J.A., Mitchell, D.F. and Powell, C.E. (1985). The flux of ^{14}C-labelled photosynthate through soybean root nodules during N_2 fixation. *Journal of Experimental Botany*, **36**, 756–69.

Goreau, T.F. (1959). The physiology of skeleton formation in corals. I. A method for measuring the rate of calcium deposition by corals under different conditions. *Biological Bulletin*, **116**, 59–75.

Goreau, T.F. (1961). Problems of growth and calcium deposition in reef corals. *Endeavour*, **20**, 32–9.

Goreau, T.F., Goreau, N.I. and Yonge, C.M. (1973). On the utilisation of photosynthetic products from zooxanthellae and of a dissolved amino acid in *Tridacna maxima* f. *elongata*. *Journal of Zoology London*, **169**, 417–54.

Gortz, H.D. (1982). Infection of *Paramecium bursaria* with bacteria and yeasts. *Journal of Cell Science*, **58**, 445–53.

Graham, P.H. (1964). The application of computer techniques to the taxonomy of the root-nodule bacteria of legumes. *Journal of General Microbiology*, **35**, 511–17.

Granhall, U. and Hofsten, A.V. (1976). Nitrogenase activity in relation to intracellular organisms in *Sphagnum* mosses. *Physiologia Plantarium*, **36**, 88–94.

Gray, M.W. and Doolittle, W.F. (1982). Has the endosymbiont hypothesis been proven? *Microbiological Reviews*, **46**, 1–42.

Grilli Caiola, M. (1980). On the phycobionts of the cycad coralloid roots. *New Phytologist*, **85**, 537–44.

Hale, M.E. (1983). *The Biology of Lichens* (3rd Edition). 190 pp. Edward Arnold, London.

Halliday, J. and Pate, J.S. (1976). Symbiotic nitrogen fixation by coralloid roots of the cycad *Macrozamia riedlei*: physiological characteristics and ecological significance. *Australian Journal of Plant Physiology*, **3**, 349–58.

Haneda, Y. and Tsuji, F.I. (1971). Light production in the luminous fishes *Photoblepharon* and *Anomalops* from the Banda Islands. *Science*, **173**, 143–5.

Harley, J.L. (1969). *The Biology of Mycorrhiza*, 2nd Edition. 334 pp. Leonard Hill, London.

Harley, J.L. (1984). The Mycorrhizal Association. In *Cellular Interactions. Encyclopedia of Plant Physiology New Series*, Vol. 17, (Linskens, H.F. and Heslop-Harrison, J., eds) pp. 148–86.

Harley, J.L. and Harley, E.L. (1986). A check list of mycorrhiza in the British Flora. *New Phytologist*, 104 (supplement), (in press).

Harley, J.L. and Smith, S.E. (1983). *Mycorrhizal Symbiosis*. 483 pp. Academic Press, London.

Harris, D., Pacovsky, S. and Paul, E.A. (1985). Carbon economy of Soybean – *Rhizobium–Glomus* associations. *New Phytologist*, **101**, 427–40.

Harris, G.P. and Kershaw, K.A. (1971). Thallus growth and the distribution of stored metabolites in the phycobionts of the lichens *Parmelia sulcata* and *Parmelia physodes*. *Canadian Journal of Botany*, **49**, 1367–72.

Haselkorn, R., Mazur, B., Orr, J., Rice, D., Wood, N. and Rippka, R. (1980). Heterocyst differentiation and nitrogen fixation in cyanobacteria (blue-green algae). In *Nitrogen Fixation*, Vol. 2, (U.E. Newton and W.H. Orme-Johnson, eds), pp. 259–78. University Park Press, Baltimore, USA.

Hastings, J.W. (1978). Bacterial and dinoflagellate luminescent systems. In: *Bioluminescence in Action* (P.J. Herring, ed.), pp. 129–70. Academic Press, London.

Hastings, J.W. and Nealson, K.H. (1981). The symbiotic luminous bacteria. In *The Prokaryotes – A Handbook of Habitats, Isolation and Identification of Bacteria*. I. (M.P. Starr, H. Stolp, H.G. Truger, A. Balows and H.G. Schlegel, eds), pp. 1332–45. Springer-Verlag, Berlin.

Hastings, J.W., Potrikus, C.J., Gupta, S.C., Kurfurst, M. and Makemson, J.C. (1985). Biochemistry and physiology of bioluminescent bacteria. *Advances in Microbial Physiology*, **26**, 235–91.

Hatch, A.B. (1937). The physical basis of mycotrophy in the genus *Pinus*. *Black Rock Forest Bulletin*, **6**, 168 pp.

Hawksworth, D.L. and Hill, D.J. (1984). *The Lichen-forming Fungi*. 158pp. Blackie, Glasgow and London.

Hawksworth, D.L. and Rose, F. (1976). *Lichen as Pollution Monitors*. Studies in Biology. No. 66. Edward Arnold, London.

Heath, I.B. (1980). Variant mitoses in lower eukaryotes: indicators of the evolution of mitosis? *International Review of Cytology*, **64**, 1–80.

Heinhorst, S. and Shively, J.M. (1983). Encoding of both subunits of ribulose-1,5-bisphosphate carboxylase by organelle genome of *Cyanophora paradoxa*. *Nature*, **304**, 373–4.

Henry, S.M. (1962). The significance of microorganisms in the nutrition of insects. *Transactions of the New York Academy of Science*, **24**, 676–83.

Herd, R.M. and Dawson, T.J. (1984). Fibre digestion in the emu, *Dromaius novaehollandiae*, a large bird with a simple gut and high rates of passage. *Physiological Zoology*, **57**, 70–84.

Herdman, M. and Stanier, R.Y. (1977). The cyanelle: chloroplast or endosymbiotic prokaryote? *FEMS Letters*, **1**, 7–12.

Herring, P.J. (1977). Luminescence in cephalopods and fish. *Symposia of the Zoological Society of London*, **38**, 127–59.

Hespell, R.B. and Bryant, M.P. (1981). The genera *Butyrovibrio, Succinivibrio, Succinimonas, Lachnospira* and *Selenomonas*. In *The Prokaryotes – a Hand-*

book of Habitats, Isolation and Identification of Bacteria (M.P. Starr, H. Stolp, H.G. Truger, A. Balows and H.G. Schlegel, eds) pp. 1450-63. Springer-Verlag, Berlin.

Hickling, C.F. (1966). On the feeding process in the white amur *Ctenopharyngodon idella*. *Journal of Zoology, London*, **148**, 408-19.

Hill, D.J. (1972). The movement of carbohydrate from the alga to the fungus in the lichen *Peltigera polydactyla*. *New Phytologist*, **71**, 31-9.

Hill, D.J. (1977). The role of *Anabaena* in the *Azolla-Anabaena* symbiosis. *New Phytologist*, **78**, 611-16.

Hinde, R. (1971). Maintenance of aphid cells and the intracellular symbiotes of aphids in vitro. *Journal of Invertebrate Pathology*, **17**, 333-8.

Hinde, R. (1978). The metabolism of photosynthetically fixed carbon by isolated chloroplasts from *Codium fragile* (Chlorophyta: Siphonales) and by *Elysia viridis* (Mollusca: Sacoglossa). *Biological Journal of the Linnean Society*, **10**, 329-42.

Hinde, R. (1980). Chloroplast 'symbiosis' in sacoglossan molluscs. In *Endocytobiology, Endosymbiosis and Cell Biology*. Vol. I. (W. Schwemmler and H.E.A. Schenk eds) pp. 729-36. Walter de Gruyter, Berlin.

Hinde, R. (1983). Host release factors in symbioses between algae and invertebrates. In *Endocytobiology, Endosymbiosis and Cell Biology*. Vol. II. (H.E.A. Schenk and W. Schwemmler eds) pp. 709-26. Walter de Gruyter, Berlin.

Hinde, R. and Smith, D.C. (1974). 'Chloroplast symbiosis' and the extent to which it occurs in Sacoglossa (Gastropoda: Mollusca). *Biological Journal of the Linnean Society*, **6**, 349-56.

Hinde, R. and Smith, D.C. (1975). The role of photosynthesis in the nutrition of the mollusc *Elysia viridis*. *Biological Journal of the Linnean Society*, **7**, 161-71.

Hobson, P.N. (1977). *The Microflora of the Rumen*. 49 pp. Meadowfield Press Ltd., UK.

Hoegh-Guldberg, O. and Hinde, R. (1986). Studies on a nudibranch that contains zooxanthellae. I. Photosynthesis, respiration, and the translocation of newly fixed carbon by zooxanthellae in *Pteraeolidia ianthina*. *Proceedings of the Royal Society of London, Series B*. (in press).

Hoegh-Guldberg, O., Hinde, R. and Muscatine, L. (1986). Studies on a nudibranch that contains zooxanthellae. II. Contribution of zooxanthellae to animal respiration (CZAR) in *Pteraeolidia ianthina* with high and low densities of zooxanthellae. *Proceedings of the Royal Society of London, Series B*. (in press).

Hohman, T.C., McNeil, P.L., and Muscatine, L. (1982). Phagosome-lysosome fusion inhibited by algal symbionts of *Hydra viridis*. *Journal of Cell Biology*, **94**, 56-63.

Holligan, P.M. and Gooday, G.W. (1975). Symbiosis in *Convoluta roscoffensis*. *Symposia of the Society for Experimental Biology*, **29**, 205-227.

Honegger, R. (1984). Cytological aspects of the mycobiont-phycobiont relationship in lichens. *Lichenologist*, **16**, 111-27.

Honegger, R. (1986a). Fine structure of different types of symbiotic relationships in lichens. In *Lichen Physiology and Cell Biology* (D.H. Brown, ed.) pp. 287-302. Plenum, New York.

Honegger, R. (1986b). Ultrastructural studies in lichens. II. Mycobiont and photobiont cell wall surface layers and adhering crystalline lichen products in four Parmeliaceae. *New Phytologist*, **103**, 797-805.

Honegger, R. (1987). Questions about pattern formation in the algal layer of lichens with stratified (heteromerous) thalli. In *Progress and Problems in Lichenology in the Eighties.* (E. Peveling, A. Henssen, O.L. Lange and C. Leuckert, eds). J. Cramer (in press).

Honigberg, B.M. (1970). Protozoa associated with termites and their role in digestion. In *Biology of Termites.* II. (K. Krishna and F.M. Weesner, eds) pp. 1–36. Academic Press, London.

Hoover, W.H. and Heitmann, R.N. (1972). Effects of dietary fibre levels on weight gain, caecal volume and volatile fatty acid production in rabbits. *Journal of Nutrition,* **102**, 375–9.

Houk, E.J. and Griffiths, G.W. (1980). Intracellular symbiotes of the Homoptera. *Annual Review of Entomology,* **25**, 161–87.

Houpt, T.R. (1970). Urea and the ruminant: movement of endogenous urea nitrogen into the rumen. In *Urea and the Kidney* (B. Schmidt-Nielsen, ed.) pp. 105–13. Excerpta Medica Foundation, Amsterdam.

Hungate, R.E. (1966). *The Rumen and its Microbes.* Academic Press.

Ishikawa, H. (1984). Molecular aspects of intracellular symbiosis in the aphid mycetocyte. *Zoological Science,* **1**, 509–22.

Iverson, J.B. (1980). Colic modifications in iguanine lizards. *Journal of Morphology,* **163**, 79–93.

Jahns, H. (1987). New trends in developmental morphology of the thallus. In *Progress and Problems in Lichenology in the Eighties.* (E. Peveling, A. Henssen, O.L. Lange and C. Leuckert, eds). J. Cramer (in press).

Jannasch, H.W. and Taylor, C.D. (1984). Deep sea microbiology. *Annual Review of Microbiology,* **38**, 487–514.

Jaynes, J.M. and Vernon, L.P. (1982). The cyanelle of *Cyanophora paradoxa*: almost a cyanobacterial chloroplast. *Trends in Biochemical Sciences,* **7**, 22–4.

Jeon, K.W. (1972). Development of cellular dependence on infective organisms: Micrurgical studies in amoebas. *Science,* **179**, 1122–3.

Jeon, K.W. (1975). Selective effects of enucleation and transfer of heterologous nuclei on cytoplasmic organelles in *Amoeba proteus. Journal of Protozoology,* **22**, 402–5.

Jeon, K.W. (1980). Symbiosis of bacteria with *Amoeba.* In *Cellular Interactions in Symbiosis and Parasitism* (C.B. Cook, P.W. Pappas and E.D. Rudolph, eds), pp. 245–62. Ohio State University Press, Columbus, U.S.A.

Jeon, K.W. (1972) and Ahn, T.I. (1978). Temperature sensitivity: a cell character determined by obligate endosymbionts in amoebae. *Science,* **202**, 635–7.

Johannes, R.E., Coles, S.L. and Kuenzel, N.T. (1970). The role of zooplankton in the nutrition of some Scleractinian corals. *Limnology and Oceanography,* **15**, 579–86.

John, P. and Whatley, F.R. (1975). *Paracoccus denitrificans* and the evolutionary origin of the mitochondrion. *Nature,* **254**, 495–8.

Johnston, A.W.B., Beynon, J.L., Buchanan-Wollaston, A.V., Setchell, S.M., Hirsch, P.R. and Beringer, J.E. (1978). High frequency transfer of nodulating ability between strains and species of *Rhizobium. Nature,* **276**, 635–6.

Jolley, E. and Smith, D.C. (1978). The green hydra symbiosis. I. Isolation, culture and characteristics of the *Chlorella* symbionts of 'European' *Hydra viridis. New Phytologist,* **81**, 637–45.

Jolley, E. and Smith, D.C. (1980). The green hydra symbiosis. II. The biology of the establishment of the association. *Proceedings of the Royal Society of London Series B,* **207**, 311–33.

Jones, M.L. (1981). *Riftia pachyptila* Jones: observations on the vestimentiferan worm from the Galapagos Rift. *Science,* **213**, 333–6.

Jordan, D.C. (1984). Family III. Rhizobiaceae. In: *Bergeys Manual of Systematic*

Bacteriology, volume 1 (eds N.R. Krieg and J.G. Holt). pp. 234–44. Williams and Wilkins, Baltimore.

Jurzitza, G. (1979). The fungi symbiotic with anobiid beetles. In *Insect-Fungus Symbiosis* (L.R. Batra, ed.) pp. 65–76. John Wiley and Sons, New York.

Kaplan, D. and Peters, G.A. (1981). The *Azolla-Anabaena* relationship. X. $^{15}N_2$ fixation and transport in main stem axes. *New Phytologist*, **89**, 337–46.

Karakashian, M.W. (1975). Symbiosis in *Paramecium bursaria*. *Symposia of the Society for Experimental Biology*, **29**, 229–65.

Karl, D.M., Wirsen, C.O. and Jannasch, H.W. (1980). Deep-sea primary production at the Galapagos hydrothermal vents. *Science*, **207**, 1345–7.

Kawaguti, S. (1971). Blue-green algae in echiuroid worms. In *Aspects of the Biology of Symbiosis* (T.C. Chang, ed.), pp. 265–73. Butterworth, London.

Keeble, F. (1912). *Plant-Animals: A Study in Symbiosis*. Cambridge University Press.

Kemp, P., White, R.W. and Lander, D.J. (1975). The hydrogenation of unsaturated fatty acids by five bacterial isolates from the sheep rumen, including a new species. *Journal of General Microbiology*, **90**, 100–14.

Kershaw, K.A. (1985). *Physiological Ecology of Lichens*. Cambridge University Press. 293 pp.

Kessler, E. (1982). Chemotaxonomy in the Chlorococcales. *Progress in Phycological Research*, **1**, 111–35.

Kidston, R. and Lang, W.H. (1921). On Old Red Sandstone plants showing structure from the Rhynie Chert bed, Aberdeenshire. *Transactions of the Royal Society of Edinburgh*, **52**, 855–902.

Klug, M.J. and Kotarski, S. (1980). Bacteria associated with the gut tract of larval stages of the aquatic cranefly *Tipula abdominalis* (Diptera:Tipulidae). *Applied and Environmental Microbiology*, **40**, 408–16.

Koch, A. (1967). Insects and their endosymbionts. In *Symbiosis*. Vol. II (S.M. Henry, ed.) pp. 1–106. Academic Press, London.

Kott, P. (1980). Algal-bearing didemnid ascidians in the Indo-West Pacific. *Memoirs of the Queensland Museum*, **20**, 1–47.

Kott, P., Parry, D.L. and Cox, G.C. (1984). Prokaryotic symbionts with a range of ascidian hosts. *Bulletin of Marine Science*, **34**, 308–12.

Landis, W.G. (1981). The ecology, role of killer trait, and interactions of five species of the *Paramecium aurelia* complex inhabiting the littoral zone. *Canadian Journal of Zoology*, **59**, 1734–43.

Lange, O.L., Schulze, E.-D. and Koch, W. (1970). Experimentell-Okologische Untersuchungen an Flechten der Negev-Wuste. II. CO_2-Gaswechsel und Wasserhaushalt von *Ramalina maciformis* (Del.) Bory an naturlichen Standort Wahrend der Sommerlichen Trockenperiode. *Flora*, **159**, 38–62.

Lange, O.L. and Ziegler, H. (1986). Different limiting processes of photosynthesis in lichens. In *Biological Control of Photosynthesis*. (R. Marcelle, H. Clijsters and M. Van Poucke, eds). pp. 147–61. Nijhoff, Dordrecht.

Larson, O.W. (1987). The absorption and release of water by lichens. In *Progress and Problems in Lichenology in the Eighties*. (E. Peveling, ed.). (in press).

Law, R. and Lewis, D.H. (1983). Biotic environments and the maintenance of sex – some evidence from mutualistic symbioses. *Biological Journal of the Linnean Society*, **20**, 249–76.

Lawrey, J.D. (1984). *Biology of Lichenized Fungi*. 407 pp. Praeger, New York.

Lechowicz, M.J. (1981). The effects of climatic pattern on lichen productivity: *Cetraria cucullata* (Bell.) Ach. in the arctic tundra of Northern Alaska. *Oecologia*, **50**, 210–16.

Lee, J.J. and McEnery, M.E. (1983). Symbiosis in foraminifera. In *Algal Symbiosis:*

a Continuum of Interaction Strategies (L.J. Goff ed.), pp. 37–68. Cambridge University Press.

Legocki, R.P. and Verma, D.P.S. (1980). Identification of 'Nodule-Specific' host proteins (nodulins) involved in the development of *Rhizobium*-legume Symbiosis. *Cell*, **20**, 153–63.

Leiner, M., Schweikhardt, F., Blaschke, G., Konig, K. and Fischer, M. (1968). Die Gärung und Atmung von *Pelomyxa palustris* Greeff. *Biologisches Zentralblatt*, **87**, 567–91.

Leisman, G., Cohn, D.H. and Nealson, K.H. (1980). Bacterial origin of luminescence in marine animals. *Science*, **208**, 1271–3.

Levenson, S.M., Tenant, B., Geeves, E., Laundy, R. and Daft, F. (1962) *Archives of Internal Medicine*, **110**, 693–702.

Lewis, D.H. (1973). Concepts in fungal nutrition and the origin of biotrophy. *Biological Reviews*, **48**, 261–78.

Lewis, D.H. (1985). Symbiosis and mutualism: crisp concepts and soggy semantics. pp. 29–39 in *The Biology of Mutualism: Ecology and Evolution* (ed. D.H. Boucher), Croom-Helm, London.

Lewis, D.H. and Harley, J.L. (1965). Carbohydrate physiology of mycorrhizal roots of beech. III. Movement of sugars between host and fungus. *New Phytologist*, **64**, 256–69.

Locker, J., Synenki, R.M., Merten, S. and Rabonowitz, M (1981). Eukaryotic features of mitochondrial transcription and gene structure in yeast. *Annals of the New York Academy of Sciences*, **361**, 105–18.

Lockhart, C.M., Rowell, P. and Stewart, W.D.P. (1978). Phytohaemmagglutins from the nitrogen-fixing lichens *Peltigera canina* and *P. polydactyla*. *FEMS Microbiology Letters*, **3**, 127–30.

Long, S.R. (1984). Genetics of *Rhizobium* nodulation. In *Plant-Microbe Interactions Volume 1*. (T. Kosuge and E.W. Nester, eds). pp. 265–306. MacMillan, New York.

Luehrsen, K.R., Nicholson, D.E., Eubanks, D.C. and Fox, G.E. (1981). An archaebacterial 5S rRNA contains a long insertion sequence. *Nature*, **293**, 755–6.

Lumpkin, T.A. and Plucknett, D.L. (1980). *Azolla*: botany, physiology and use as a green manure. *Economic Botany*, **34**, 111–53.

McAuley, P.J. (1982). Temporal relationships of host cell and algal mitosis in the green hydra symbiosis. *Journal of Cell Science*, **58**, 423–31.

McAuley, P.J. (1985). The cell cycle of symbiotic *Chlorella*. I. The relationship between host feeding and algal cell growth and division. *Journal of Cell Science*, **77**, 225–39.

McAuley, P.J. and Smith, D.C. (1982a). The green hydra symbiosis. V. Stages in the intracellular recognition of algal symbionts by digestive cells. *Proceedings of the Royal Society of London Series B*, **216**, 7–23.

McAuley, P.J. and Smith, D.C. (1982b). The green hydra symbiosis. VII. Conservation of the host cell habitat by the symbiotic algae. *Proceedings of the Royal Society of London Series B*, **216**, 415–26.

McBee, R.H. (1977). Fermentation in the hindgut. In *Microbial Ecology of the Gut* (R.T.J. Clarke and T. Bauchop, eds) pp. 185–222. Academic Press, London.

McFarlane, A.E. (1982). *Ultrastructural and Immunological Studies of the Symbiosis between* Convoluta roscoffensis *and Prasinophyceae Algae*. Ph.D. Thesis, University of Bristol.

Macfarlane, J.D. and Kershaw, K.A. (1982). Physiological-environmental interactions in lichens. XIV. The environmental control of glucose movement from alga to fungus in *Peltigera polydactyla*, *P. rufescens* and *Collema furfuraceum*. *New Phytologist*, **91**, 93–101.

McLelland, J. (1979). Digestive system. In *Form and Function in Birds*. I. (A.S. King and J. McLelland, eds) pp. 69–181. Academic Press, London.

McNab, J.M. (1973). The avian caeca: a review. *World Poultry Science Journal*, 29, 251–63.

McNeil, P.L., Hohman, T.C. and Muscatine, L. (1981). Mechanisms of nutritive endocytosis. II. The effect of charged agents on phagocytic recognition by digestive cells. *Journal of Cell Science*, 52, 243–69.

Mackie, G.O. and Bone, Q. (1978). Luminescence and associated effector activity in *Pyrosoma* (Tunicata: Pyrosomida). *Proceedings of the Royal Society of London Series B*, 202, 483–95.

Macy, J.M. (1981). Nonpathogenic members of the genus *Bacteriodes*. In *The Prokaryotes – a Handbook of Habitats, Isolation and Identification of Bacteria*. (M.P. Starr, H. Stolp, H.G. Truger, A. Balows and H.G. Schlegel, eds). pp. 1450–63. Springer–Verlag, Berlin.

Mague, T.H., Weare, N.M. and Holm-Hansen, O. (1974). Nitrogen fixation in the North Pacific Ocean. *Marine Biology*, 24, 109–19.

Malachowski, J.A., Baker, K.K. and Hooper, G.R. (1980). Anatomy and algal–fungus interactions in the lichen *Usnea cavernosa*. *Journal of Phycology*, 16, 346–54.

Malke, H. and Schwartz, W. (1966). Untersuchungen uber die Symbiose von Tieren mit Pilsen und Baktierein. XII. Die Bedeutung der Blattiden-Symbiose. *Zeitschift fur Allgemeine Mikrobiologie*, 6, 34–68.

Margulis, L. (1970). *Origin of Eukaryotic Cells*. Yale University Press, New Haven and London.

Margulis, L. (1976). Genetic and evolutionary consequences of symbiosis. *Experimental Parasitology*, 39, 277–349.

Margulis, L. (1980). Symbiosis as parasexuality. In *Cellular Interactions in Symbiosis and Parasitism* (C.B. Cook, P.W. Pappas and E.D. Rudolph, eds), pp. 263–73. Ohio State University Press.

Margulis, L. (1981). *Symbiosis in Cell Evolution*. Freeman, San Fransisco.

Margulis, L., Chase, D. and To, L.P. (1979). Possible evolutionary significance of spirochaetes. *Proceedings of the Royal Society of London Series B*, 204, 189–98.

Margulis, L., To, L.P. and Chase, D. (1978). Microtubules in prokaryotes. *Science*, 200, 1118–24.

Margulis, L., To, L.P. and Chase, D. (1981). Microtubules, undulipodia and *Pillotina* spirochaetes. *Annals of the New York Academy of Sciences*, 361, 356–68.

Marton, K. and Galun, M. (1976). In vitro dissociation and reassociation of the symbionts in the lichen *Heppia echinulata*. *Protoplasma*, 87, 135–43.

Marx, C., Dexheimer, J., Gianinazzi-Pearson, V. and Gianinazzi, S. (1982). Enzymatic studies on the metabolism of vesicular-arbuscular mycorrhizas. IV. Ultracytoenzymological evidence (ATPase) for active transfer processes in the host arbuscular interface. *New Phytologist*, 90, 37–43.

Marx, M., and Peveling, E. (1983). Surface receptors in lichen symbionts visualized by fluorescence microscopy after use of lectins. *Protoplasma*, 114, 52–61.

Mauldin, J.K., Rich, N.M. and Cook. D.W. (1978). Amino acid synthesis from ^{14}C-acetate by normally and abnormally faunated termites, *Coptotermes formosanus*. *Insect Biochemistry*, 8, 105–9.

Meier, R., Lefort-Tran, M., Pouphila, M., Reisser, W. and Wiessner, W. (1984). Comparative freeze-fracture study of perialgal and digestive vacuoles in *Paramecium bursaria*. *Journal of Cell Science*, 71, 121–40.

Melin, E. (1958). Translocation of nutritive elements through mycorrhizal mycelia to pine seedlings. *Botaniska Notiser*, 111, 251–6.

Mews, L.K. (1980). The green hydra symbiosis. III. The biotrophic transport of carbohydrate from alga to animal. *Proceedings of the Royal Society of London Series B*, **209**, 377–401.

Mews, L. and Smith, D.C. (1982). The green hydra symbiosis. VI. What is the role of maltose transfer from alga to animal? *Proceedings of the Royal Society of London B*, **216**, 397–413.

Meyer, F.H. (1973). Distribution of ectomycorrhizae in native and man-made forests. In *Ectomycorrhizae* (eds G.C. Marks and T.T. Kozlowski), pp. 79–105, Academic Press, New York and London.

Meyer, H. Provasoli, L. and Meyer, F. (1979). Lipid biosynthesis in the marine flatworm *Convoluta roscoffensis* and its algal symbiont *Platymonas convolutae*. *Biochimica et Biophysica Acta*, **573**, 464–80.

Millbank, J.W. (1984). Nitrogen fixation by lichens. In *Current Developments in Nitrogen Fixation* (N.S. Subba Rao, ed.). pp. 197–218. Edward Arnold, London..

Millbank, J.W. and Kershaw, K.A. (1969). Nitrogen metabolism in lichens. I. Nitrogen fixation in the cephalodia of *Peltigera aphthosa*. *New Phytologist*, **68**, 721–9.

Minchin, F.R. and Pate, J.S. (1973). The carbon balance of a legume and the functional economy of its root nodules. *Journal of Experimental Botany*, **24**, 259–71.

Minchin, F.R., Sheehy, J.E., Minguez, M.I. and Witty, J.F. (1985). Characterisation of the resistance to oxygen diffusion in legume nodules. *Annals of Botany*, **55**, 53–60.

Minchin, F.R., Summerfield, D.J., Hadley, P., Roberts, E.H. and Rawsthorne, S. (1981). Carbon and nitrogen nutrition of nodulated roots of grain legumes. *Plant, Cell and Environment*, **4**, 5–26.

Minchin, F.R., Witty, J.F., Sheehy, J.E. and Muller, M. (1983). A major error in the acetylene reduction assay: decreases in nodular nitrogenase activity under assay conditions. *Journal of Experimental Botany*, **34**, 641–9.

Mittler, T.E. (1971). Dietary amino acid requirement of the aphid *Myzus persicae* affected by antibiotic uptake. *Journal of Nutrition*, **101**, 1023–8.

Molina, R., Trappe, J.M. and Stickler, G.S. (1978). Mycorrhizal fungi associated with *Festuca* in Western United States and Canada. *Canadian Journal of Botany*, **56**, 1691–5.

Moller, C.M., Muller, D. and Nielsen, J. (1954). The dry matter production of european beech. *Forstlige Forsogsvaesen, Denmark*, **21**, 253–335.

Morrall, S. and Greenwood, A.D. (1982). Ultrastructure of nucleomorph division in species of Cryptophyceae and its evolutionary implications. *Journal of Cell Science*, **54**, 311–28.

Morrison, T.M. (1962). Absorption of phosphorus from soils by mycorrhizal plants. *New Phytologist*, **61**, 10–20.

Morton, E.S. (1978). Avian arboreal folivores: why not? In *The Ecology of Arboreal Folivores*. (G.G. Montgomery ed.) pp. 123–30. Smithsonian Institute, Washington DC, USA.

Mosse, B., Powell, C. L. and Hayman, D.S. (1976). Plant growth responses to vesicular-arbuscular mycorrhizas. IX. Interactions between VA mycorrhiza, rock phosphate and symbiotic nitrogen. *New Phytologist*, **76**, 331–42.

Moulder, J.W. (1979). The cell as an extreme environment. *Proceedings of the Royal Society of London Series B*, **204**, 199–210.

Muller, M. (1980). The hydrogenosome. *Symposia of the Society for General Microbiology*, **30**, 127–42.

Mullins, D.E. and Cochran, D.G. (1975). Nitrogen metabolism in the American cockroach. *Comparative Biochemistry and Physiology*, **50A**, 489-510.

Murray, P.A. and Zinder, S.H. (1984). Nitrogen fixation by a methanogenic archaebacterium. *Nature (London)*, **312**, 284-6.

Muscatine, L. (1965). Symbiosis of hydra and algae. III. Extracellular products of the algae. *Comparative Biochemistry and Physiology*, **16**, 77-92.

Muscatine, L. (1967). Glycerol excretion by symbiotic algae from corals and *Tridacna* and its control by the host. *Science*, **156**, 516-19.

Muscatine, L. (1973). Nutrition of Corals. In *Biology and Geology of Coral Reefs*. Vol. II, pp. 77-115. Academic Press, New York.

Muscatine, L. (1980). Uptake, retention and release of dissolved inorganic nutrients by marine alga-invertebrate associations. In *Cellular Interactions in Symbiosis and Parasitism*. (C.B. Cook, P.W. Pappas and E.D. Rudolph, eds), pp. 229-40. Ohio State University Press.

Muscatine, L., Boyle, J.E. and Smith, D.C. (1974). Symbiosis of the acoel flatworm *Convoluta roscoffensis* with the alga *Platymonas convolutae*. *Proceedings of the Royal Society of London B.*, **187**, 221-34.

Muscatine, L., Cook, C.B., Pardy, R.L. and Pool, R.R. (1975). Uptake, recognition and maintenance of symbiotic *Chlorella* by *Hydra viridis*. *Symposia of the Society for Experimental Biology*, **29**, 175-203.

Muscatine, L., Falkowski, P., Porter, J. and Dubinsky, Z. (1984). Fate of photosynthetically-fixed carbon in light and shade-adapted colonies of the symbiotic coral *Stylophora pistillata*. *Proceedings of the Royal Society of London Series B*, **222**, 181-202.

Muscatine, L. and Lenhoff, H.M. (1965). Symbiosis of hydra with algae. II. Effects of limited food and starvation on growth of symbiotic and aposymbiotic hydra. *Biological Bulletin*, **129**, 316-28.

Muscatine, L. and McAuley, P.J. (1982). Transmission of symbiotic algae to eggs of green hydra. *Cytobios*, **33**, 111-24.

Muscatine, L. and Porter, J.W.P. (1977). Reef corals: mutualistic symbioses adapted to nutrient-poor environments. *Bioscience*, **27**, 454-60.

Nealson, K.H. (1979). Alternative strategies of symbiosis of marine luminous fishes harbouring light-emitting bacteria. *Trends in Biochemical Sciences*, **3**, 105-10.

Neckelmann, N. and Muscatine, L. (1983). Regulatory mechanisms maintaining the *Hydra-Chlorella* symbiosis. *Proceedings of the Royal Society of London Series B*, **219**, 193-210.

Nelson, C.P. (1964). The production and translocation of photosynthate C^{14} in conifers. In *Formation of Wood in Forest Trees* (ed. M.H. Zimmerman), pp. 235-57, Maria Mons Cabot Foundation, New York.

Nogge, G. (1976). Sterility in tsetse flies (*Glossina morsitans* Westwood) caused by loss of symbionts. *Experientia*, **32**, 995-6.

Nutman, P.S. (1963). Factors influencing balance of mutual advantage in legume symbiosis. *Symposia of the Society for General Microbiology*, **13**, 51-71.

Nutman, P.S. and Ross, G.J.S. (1969). *Rhizobium* in the soils of the Rothamsted and Woburn farms. *Report of Rothamsted Experimental Station* 1969, 148-67.

Nye, P.H. and Tinker, P.B. (1977). *Solute Movement in the Soil-Root System*. Blackwell Scientific Publications, Oxford.

O'Brien, T. (1978). An ultrastructural study of zoochlorellae in a marine coelenterate. *Transactions of the American Microscopical Society*, **97**, 320-9.

Obukowicz, M., Schaller, M. and Kennedy, G.S. (1981). Ultrastructure and phenolic histochemistry of the *Cycas-Anabaena* symbiosis. *New Phytologist*, **87**, 751-9.

Odelson, D.A. and Breznak, J.A. (1983). Volatile fatty acid production by the hindgut microbiota of xylophagous insects. *Applied and Environmental Microbiology*, **45**, 1602-13.

Odum, E.P. (1959). *Fundamentals of Ecology*. W.B. Saunders, Philadelphia.

O'Gara, F. and Shanmugam, K.T. (1976). Regulation of nitrogen fixation by *Rhizobium*; export of fixed N_2 as NH_4^+. *Biochimica et Biophysica Acta*, **437**, 313-21.

Orpin, C.G. (1981). Isolation of cellulolytic phycomycete fungi from the caecum of the horse. *Journal of General Microbiology*, **123**, 287-96.

Ott, J., Rieger, G., Rieger, R. and Enderes, F. (1982). New mouthless interstitial worms from the sulphide system: symbiosis with prokaryotes. *Marine Ecology*, **3**, 313-33.

Ott, S. (1987). Reproductive strategies in lichens. In *Progress and Problems in Lichenology in the Eighties*. (E. Peveling, A. Henssen, O.L. Lange and C. Leuckert, eds). J. Cramer (in press).

Paerl, H.W. (1982). Interactions with bacteria. In *The Biology of Cyanobacteria* (N.G. Carr and B.A. Whitton, eds), pp. 441-61. Blackwell Scientific Publications, UK.

Paerl, H.W. (1984). N_2 fixation (nitrogenase activity) attributable to a specific *Prochloron* (Prochlorophyta)-ascidian association in Palau, Micronesia. *Marine Biology*, **81**, 251-4.

Pardy, R.L. (1980). Symbiotic algae and ^{14}C incorporation in the freshwater clam, *Anodonta*. *Biological Bulletin*, **158**, 349-55.

Pardy, R.L. and Heacox, A.E. (1976). Growth of algal symbionts in regenerating hydra. *Nature*, **260**, 809-10.

Patterson, G.M. and Withers, N.W. (1982). Laboratory cultivation of *Prochloron*, a tryptophan auxotroph. *Science*, **217**, 1934-5.

Peters, G.A. and Calvert, H.E. (1983). The *Azolla-Anabaena azollae* symbiosis. In *Algal Symbiosis - A Continuum of Interaction Strategies*. (L.J. Goff, ed.), pp. 109-46. Cambridge University Press.

Peters, G.A., Toia, R.E., Raweed, D. and Levine, N.J. (1978). The *Azolla-Anabaena azollae* relationship. VI. Morphological aspects of the association. *New Phytologist*, **71**, 561-7.

Peveling, E. (ed.). (1987). *Progress and Problems in Lichenology in the Eighties*. (in press).

Pickett-Heaps, J. (1974). The evolution of mitosis and the eukaryotic condition. *Biosystems*, **6**, 37-48.

Pirozynski, K.A. and Malloch, D.W. (1975). The origins of land plants: a matter of mycotrophism. *Biosystems*, **6**, 153-64.

Postgate, J. (1978). *Nitrogen Fixation*, 67 pp. Studies in Biology no. 92, Edward Arnold, London.

Postgate, J.R. (1982). *The Fundamentals of Nitrogen Fixation*. 252 pp. Cambridge University Press, Cambridge.

Potrikus, C.J. and Breznak, J.A. (1980a). Uric acid in wood-eating termites. *Insect Biochemistry*, **10**, 19-27.

Potrikus, C.J. and Breznak, J.A. (1980b). Uric acid-degrading bacteria in the guts of termites (*Reticulitermes flavipes* Kollar). *Applied and Environmental Microbiology*, **40**, 117-24.

Potrikus, C.J. and Breznak, J.A. (1981). Gut bacteria recycle uric acid nitrogen in termites: a strategy for nutrient conservation. *Proceedings of the National Academy of Sciences*, **78**, 4601-5.

Prakash, R.K. and Schilperoort, R.A. (1982). Relationship between *nif* plasmids of fast growing *Rhizobium* species and Ti plasmids of *Agrobacterium tumefaciens*. *Journal of Bacteriology*, **149**, 1129-34.

Preer, L.B. (1981). Prokaryotic symbionts of *Paramecium*. In *The Prokaryotes - A Handbook of Habitats, Isolation and Identification of Bacteria*. Vol. II. (M.P. Starr, H. Stolp, H.G. Truger, A. Balows and H.G. Schlegel, eds). pp. 2127–36. Springer–Verlag, Berlin.

Preer, J.R., Preer, L.B. and Jurand, A. (1974). *Kappa* and other endosymbionts of *Paramecium aurelia*. *Bacteriological Reviews*, **38**, 113–63.

Prins, R.A. (1977). Biochemical activities of gut micro-organisms. In *Microbial Ecology of the Gut* (R.T.J. Clarke and T. Bauchop, eds) pp. 73–183. Academic Press, London.

Prins, R.A. and Clarke, R.T.J. (1980). Microbial ecology of the rumen. In *Digestive Physiology and Metabolism in Ruminants* (Y. Ruckebusch and P. Thivend, eds) pp. 179–204. MTP Press Ltd., UK.

Provasoli, L., Yamasu, T. and Manton, I. (1968). Experiments on the resynthesis of symbiosis in *Convoluta roscoffensis* with different flagellate cultures. *Journal of the Marine Biological Association UK.*, **48**, 465–79.

Quispel, A. (1943). The mutual relations between algae and fungi in lichens. *Recueil Travaux botanique Neerlandaise*, **40**, 413–541.

Raff, R.A. and Mahler, H.R. (1975). The symbiont that never was: an enquiry into the evolutionary origin of the mitochondrion. *Symposia of the Society for Experimental Biology*, **29**, 41–92.

Rai, A.N., Rowell, P. and Stewart, W.D.P. (1981). ^{15}N incorporation and metabolism in the lichen *Peltigera aphthosa* Willd. *Planta*, **152**, 544–52.

Rai, A.N., Rowell, P. and Stewart, W.D.P. (1983). Interactions between cyanobacterium and fungus during $^{15}N_2$-incorporation and metabolism in the lichen *Peltigera canina*. *Archives of Microbiology*, **134**, 136–42.

Rau, G.H. (1981). Hydrothermal vent clam and tube worm $^{13}C/^{12}C$: further evidence of nonphotosynthetic food sources. *Science*, **213**, 338–40.

Rawsthorne, S., Minchin, F.R., Summerfield, R.J., Cookson, C. and Coombs, J. (1980). Carbon and nitrogen metabolism in legume nodules. *Phytochemistry*, **19**, 341–55.

Ray, T.B., Peters, G.A., Toia, R.E. and Mayne, B.C. (1978). *Azolla-Anabaena* relationship. VII. Distribution of ammonia-assimilating enzymes, protein and chlorophyll between host and symbiont. *Plant Physiology*, **62**, 463–7.

Read, C.P. (1970). *Parasitism and Symbiology*. 316 pp. Ronald Press: New York.

Read, D.J. (1974). *Pezizella ericae* sp. nov. the perfect state of a typical mycorrhizal endophyte of Ericaceae. *Transactions of the British Mycological Society*, **65**, 381–3.

Read, D.J. (1983). The biology of mycorrhiza in the Ericales. *Canadian Journal of Botany*, **61**, 985–1004.

Read, D.J. and Armstrong, W. (1972). A relationship between oxygen transport and the formation of the ectotrophic mycorrhizal sheath in conifer seedlings. *New Phytologist*, **71**, 49–53.

Read, D.J. and Stribley, D.P. (1973). Effect of mycorrhizal infection on nitrogen and phosphorus nutrition of ericaceous plants. *Nature*, **244**, 81.

Rees. T.A.V. (1986). The green hydra symbiosis and ammonium. I. The role of the host in ammonium assimilation and its possible regulatory significance. *Proceedings of the Royal Society Series B*, (in press).

Reisser, W. (1984). Endosymbiotic cyanobacteria and cyanellae. In *Cellular Interactions. Encyclopedia of Plant Physiology, New Series*, Volume 17. (A. Pirson and M.H. Zimmermann, eds), pp. 91–112. Springer–Verlag Berlin.

Richardson, D.H.S., Hill, D.J. and Smith, D.C. (1968). Lichen physiology. XI. The role of the alga in determining the pattern of carbohydrate movement between the lichen symbionts. *New Phytologist*, **67**, 469–86.

Richmond, M.H. (1979). 'Cells' and 'organisms' as a habitat for DNA. *Proceedings of the Royal Society of London Series B*, **204**, 235–50.

Robertson, J.G., Wells, B., Bisseling, T., Farnden, K. and Johnston, A.W.B., (1984). Immunogold localisation of leghaemoglobin in cytoplasm of nitrogen-fixing root-nodules of pea. *Nature*, **311**, 254–6.

Rodgers, G.A. and Stewart, W.D.P. (1977). The cyanophyte–hepatic symbiosis. I. Morphology and physiology. *New Phytologist*, **78**, 441–58.

Rommell, L.G. (1939). Barrskogens marksvampar och deras roll i skogens liv. *Svenska Skogsv. foren. Tidskrift*, **37**, 348–75.

Rook, J.A.F. and Thomas, P.C. (1983). *Nutritional physiology of farm animals*. Longman.

Roos, U.-P. (1984). From proto-mitosis to mitosis – an alternative hypothesis on the origin and evolution of the mitotic spindle. *Origins of Life*, **13**, 183–93.

Ruby, E.G., Greenberg, E.P. and Hastings, J.W. (1980). Planktonic marine luminous bacteria: species distribution in the water column. *Applied and Environmental Microbiology*, **39**, 302–6.

Ruby E.G. and Morin J.G. (1979). Luminous enteric bacteria of marine fishes in a study of their distribution, density and dispersion. *Applied and Environmental Microbiology*, **38**, 406–11.

Rudman, W.B. (1981). The anatomy and biology of alcyonarian-feeding aeolid opisthobranch molluscs and their development of symbiosis with zooxanthellae. *Zoological Journal of the Linnean Society*, **72**, 219–62.

Rutter, J.C. and Cobb, A.H. (1983). Translocation of orthophosphate and glucose-6-phosphate in *Codium fragile* chloroplasts. *New Phytologist*, **95**, 559–68.

Ryle, G.J.A., Arnott, R.A., Powell, C.E. and Gordon, A.J. (1984). N_2 fixation and the respiratory costs of nodules, nitrogenase activity and nodule growth and maintenance of Fiskeby Soyabean. *Journal of Experimental Botany*, **35**, 1150–65.

Sagan, L. (L. Margulis) (1967). On the origin of mitosing cells. *Journal of Theoretical Biology*, **14**, 225–75.

Sanders, F.E. and Tinker, P.B. (1973). Phosphate flow into mycorrhizal roots. *Pesticide Science*, **4**, 385–95.

Sara, M. (1971). Ultrastructural aspects of the symbiosis between two species of the genus *Aphanocapsa* (Cyanophyceae) and *Ircinia variabilis*. *Marine Biology*, **11**, 214–221.

Savage, D.C. (1977). Interactions between the host and its microbes. In *Microbial Ecology of the Gut* (R.T.J. Clarke and T. Bauchop, eds) pp. 277–310. Academic Press, London.

Schaedler, R.W. (1973). The relationship between the host and its intestinal microflora. *Proceedings of the Nutrition Society*, **32**, 41–7.

Schnepf, E. and Deichgraber, G. (1984). 'Myzocytosis', a kind of endocytosis with implications to compartmentation in endosymbiosis. *Naturwissenschaften*, **71**, 5–218.

Schoenberg, D.A. and Trench, R.K. (1980). Genetic variation in *Symbiodinium* (= *Gymnodinium*) *microadriaticum* Freudenthal, and specificity in its symbiosis with marine invertebrates. *Proceedings of the Royal Society of London Series B*, **207**, 405–60.

Schwabe, G.H. and Mollenhauer, R. (1967). Uber den Einfluss der Begleitbakterien auf das Lagerbild von *Nostoc sphaericum*. *Nova Hedwigia*, **13**, 77–80.

Schwartz, R.M. and Dayhoff, M.O. (1981). Chloroplast origins: inferences from protein and nucleic acid sequences. *Annals of the New York Academy of Sciences*, **361**, 260–72.

Schwemmler, W. (1973). Beitrag zur Analyse des Endosymbiosezyklus von *Euscelis plebijus* F. mittels *in vitro* beobachtung. *Biologisches Zentralblatt*, **92**, 749–72.

Schwemmler, W. (1974). Endosymbionts: factors of egg pattern formation. *Journal of Insect Physiology*, **20**, 1467–74.

Schwendener, S. (1867). Ueber den Bau des Flechtenthallus. *Verhandlung Schweizerischen Naturforschung Gesellschaft Aarau*, 88–90.

Searcy, D.G., Stein, D.B. and Green, G.R. (1978). Phylogenetic affinities between eukaryotic cells and a thermophilic mycoplasma. *Biosystems*, **10**, 19–28.

Searcy, D.G., Stein, D.B. and Searcy, K.B. (1981). A mycoplasma-like archaebacterium possibly related to the nucleus and cytoplasm of eukaryotic cells. *Annals of the New York Academy of Sciences*, **361**, 312–23.

Sheehy, J.E., Minchin, F.R., and Witty, J.F. (1985). Control of nitrogen fixation in a legume nodule: an analysis of the role of oxygen diffusion in relation to nodule structure. *Annals of Botany*, **55**, 549–62.

Silsbury, J.H. (1977). Energy requirement for symbiotic nitrogen fixation. *Nature*, **267**, 149–50.

Silvester, W.B. (1976). Endophyte adaptation in *Gunnera-Nostoc* symbiosis. In *Symbiotic Nitrogen Fixation in Plants*. (P.S. Nutman, ed.), pp. 521–38. Cambridge University Press.

Silvester, W.B. and McNamara, P.J. (1976). The infection process and ultrastructure of the *Gunnera-Nostoc* symbiosis. *New Phytologist*, **77**, 135–41.

Silvester, W.B. and Smith, D.R. (1969). Nitrogen fixation by *Gunnera-Nostoc* symbiosis. *Nature*, **224**, 1231.

Slocum, R.D., Ahmadjian, V. and Hildreth, K.C. (1980). Zoosporogenesis in *Trebouxia gelatinosa*: ultrastructure, potential for zoospore release and implications for the lichen association. *Lichenologist*, **12**, 173–87.

Smith, A.L. (1927). *Lichens*. 464 pp. Cambridge.

Smith, D.C. (1961). The physiology of *Peltigera polydactyla* (Neck.) Hoffm. *Lichenologist*, **1**, 209–26.

Smith, D.C. (1962). The biology of lichen thalli. *Biological Reviews*, **37**, 537–70.

Smith, D.C. (1974). Transport from symbiotic algae and symbiotic chloroplasts to host cells. *Symposia of the Society for Experimental Biology*, **28**, 437–508.

Smith, D.C. (1975). Symbiosis and the biology of lichenised fungi. *Symposia of the Society for Experimental Biology*, **29**, 373–405.

Smith, D.C. (1979). Is a lichen a good model of biological interactions in nutrient-limited environments? In *Strategies of Microbial Life in Extreme Environments* (M. Shilo, ed.) pp. 291–303. Dahlem Konferenzen, Berlin.

Smith, D.C. (1980). Mechanisms of nutrient movement between lichen symbionts. In *Cellular Interactions in Symbiosis and Parasitism* (Cook, C.B., Pappas, P.W. and Rudolph, E.D., eds) pp. 197–227. Ohio State University Press, Columbus.

Smith, D.C. (1981). The role of nutrient exchange in recognition between symbionts. *Berichte Deutsche Botanische Gesellschaft*, **94**, supplement 517–28.

Smith, D.C., and Molesworth, S. (1973). Lichen physiology. XIII. Effects of rewetting dry lichens. *New Phytologist*, **72**, 525–33.

Smith, D.C., Muscatine, L. and Lewis, D.H. (1969). Carbohydrate movement from autotrophs to heterotrophs in parasitic and mutualistic symbiosis. *Biological Reviews*, **44**, 17–70.

Smith, S.E. (1967). Carbohydrate translocation in orchid mycorrhizal fungi. *New Phytologist*, **66**, 371–8.

Smith, S.E., St. John, B.J., Smith, F.A. and Nicholas, D.J.D. (1985). Activity of glutamine synthetase and glutamate dehydrogenase in *Trifolium subterraneum* L. and *Allium cepa* L.: effects of mycorrhizal infection and phosphate nutrition. *New Phytologist*, **99**, 211–27.

Snelgar, W.P., Green, T.G.A. and Wilkins, A.L. (1981). Carbon dioxide exchange in lichens: resistances to CO_2 uptake at different thallus water contents. *New Phytologist*, **88**, 353–61.

Soldo, A.T., Godey, G.A. and Bickson, S.A. (1982). Growth requirements of symbiont-free and symbiont *lambda*-bearing *Paramecium octaurelia* 299 for folic acid and biopterin. *Journal of Protozoology*, **29**, 612–15.

Southward, E.C. (1982). Bacterial symbionts in Pogonophora. *Journal of the Marine Biological Association UK*, **62**, 889–906.

Southward, A.J., Southward, E.C., Dando, P.R., Rau, G.H., Felbeck, H. and Flugel, H. (1981). Bacterial symbionts and low $^{13}C/^{12}C$ ratios in tissues of Pogonophora indicate unusual nutrition and metabolism. *Nature*, **293**, 616–20.

Southward, A.J., Southward, E.C., Dando, P.R., Barrett, R.L. and Ling, R. (1986). Chemoautotrophic function of bacterial symbionts in small pogonophora. *Journal of the Marine Biological Association of the United Kingdom*, **66**, 415–37.

Sprent, J.I. (1979). *The Biology of Nitrogen-Fixing Organisms*. 196 pp. McGraw-Hill, London.

Sprent, J.I. (1980). Root nodule anatomy, type of export product and evolutionary origin in some Leguminoseae. *Plant, Cell and Environment*, **3**, 35–43.

Stahl, D.A., Lane, D.J., Olsen, G.J. and Pace, N.R. (1984). Analysis of hydrothermal vent-associated symbionts by ribosomal RNA sequences. *Science*, **224**, 409–11.

Stanier, R.Y., Adelberg, E.A. and Ingraham, J.L. (1977). *General Microbiology* (fourth edition). MacMillan, London.

Starr, M.B. (1975). A generalized scheme for classifying organismic associations. *Symposia of the Society for Experimental Biology*, **29**, 1–20.

Steele, R.D. (1976). Light intensity as a factor in the regulation of the density of symbiotic zooxanthellae in *Aiptasia tagetes* (Coelenterata, Anthozoa). *Journal of Zoology London*, **179**, 387–405.

Sterrer, W. and Rieger, R. (1974). *Retronectidae* – a new cosmopolitan marine family of *Catenulida* (Turbellaria). In *Biology of Turbellaria* (N. Rieser and M. Morse, eds), pp. 63–92. McGraw-Hill, New York.

Stevens, C.E. (1977). Comparative physiology of the digestive system. In *Dukes' Physiology of Domestic Animals* (M.J. Swanson, ed.), pp. 216–32. Cornell University Press, Ithaca, U.S.A.

Stewart, K.D. and Mattox, K.R. (1984). The case for a polyphyletic origin of mitochondria; morphological and molecular comparison. *Journal of Molecular Evolution*, **21**, 54–7.

Stewart, W.D.P. and Rodgers, G.A. (1977). The cyanophyte–hepatic symbiosis. II. Nitrogen fixation and the interchange of nitrogen and carbon. *New Phytologist*, **78**, 459–71.

Stewart, W.D.P., Rowell, P. and Rai, A.N. (1983). Cyanobacteria-eukaryotic plant symbioses. *Annals of Microbiology*, **134B**, 205–28.

Stolp, H. (1979). Interactions between *Bdellovibrio* and its host cell. *Proceedings of the Royal Society of London Series B*, **204**, 211–17.

Tamm, S.L. (1980). The ultrastructure of prokaryote–eukaryote cell junctions. *Journal of Cell Science*, **44**, 335–52.

Tapper, R. (1981). Direct measurement of translocation of carbohydrate in the lichen

Cladonia convoluta, by quantitative autoradiography. *New Phytologist*, **89**, 429–37.

Taylor, F.J.R. (1979). Symbionticism revisited: a discussion of the evolutionary impact of the intracellular symbioses. *Proceedings of the Royal Society of London Series B*, **204**, 267–86.

Taylor, R. and Beringer, J.E. (1981). Populations of *Rhizobium* in the soil. In *Rothamsted Experimental Station Report* p. 213.

Thorington, G. and Margulis, L. (1981). *Hydra viridis*: transfer of metabolites between *Hydra* and symbiotic algae. *Biological Bulletin*, **160**, 175–88.

Tinker, P.B. (1984). The role of microorganisms in nutrient uptake. *Plant and Soil*, **76**, 77–91.

Trench, R.K. (1971). The physiology and biochemistry of zooxanthellae symbiotic with marine coelenterates. *Proceedings of the Royal Society of London Series B*, **177**, 225–64.

Trench, R.K. (1986). Dinoflagellates in non-parasitic symbiosis. In *The Biology of Dinoflagellates* (F.J.R. Taylor, ed.). (in press). Blackwell Scientific.

Trench, R.K., Boyle, J.E. and Smith, D.C. (1973). The association between chloroplasts of *Codium fragile* and the mollusc *Elysia viridis*. *Proceedings of the Royal Society of London Series B*, **184**, 51–81.

Trench, R.K., Greene, R.W. and Bystrom, B.G. (1969). Chloroplasts as functional organelles in animal tissues. *Journal of Cell Biology*, **42**, 404–17.

Trench, R.K., Pool, R.R., Logan, M. and Engelland, A. (1978). Aspects of the relationship between *Cyanophora paradoxa* (Korschikoff) and its endosymbiotic cyanelles *Cyanocyta korschikoffiana* (Hall and Claus). *Proceedings of the Royal Society of London Series B*, **202**, 423–43.

Trench, R.K., Wethey, D.S. and Porter, J.W. (1981). Some observations on the symbiosis with zooxanthellae among the tridacnidae. *Biological Bulletin*, **161**, 180–98.

Trinick, M.J. (1973). Symbiosis between *Rhizobium* and the non-legume *Trema aspera*. *Nature*, **244**, 459–60.

Trinick, M.J. (1982). Biology. In *Nitrogen Fixation Volume 2: Rhizobium* (W.J. Broughton, ed.) pp. 76–146, Oxford University Press.

Troyer, K. (1982). Transfer of fermentative microbes between generations in a herbivorous lizard. *Science*, **216**, 540–2.

Tschermak, E. (1941). Untersuchungen uber die Beziehungen von Pilz und Alge in den Flechten. *Osterreich Botanische Gesellschaft*, **90**, 234–307.

Tschermak-Woess, E. (1978). *Myrmecia reticulata* as a phycobiont and free-living; free-living *Trebouxia* – the problem of *Stenocybe septata*. *The Lichenologist*, **10**, 69–79.

Vacelet, J. and Donaday, C. (1977). Electron microscope study of the association between some sponges and bacteria. *Journal of Experimental and Marine Biology and Ecology*, **30**, 301–14.

Vincent, J.M., Nutman, P.S. and Skinner, F.A. (1979). The identification and classification of *Rhizobium*. In *Identification Methods for Microbiologists* (F.A. Skinner, ed.). 2nd Edition, pp. 49–69. Society for Applied Biology Technical Series, 14, Academic Press, London.

Vogels, G.D., Hoppe, W.F. and Stumm, C.K. (1980). Association of methanogenic bacteria with rumen ciliates. *Applied and Environmental Microbiology*, **40**, 608–12.

Vogt, K.A., Grier, C.C., Meier, C.E. and Edmunds, R.L. (1982). Mycorrhizal role in net primary production and nutrient cycling in *Abies amabilis* (Dougl.) Forbes ecosystems in Western Washington, *Ecology*, **63**, 370–80.

Wallace, R.J., Cheng, K.J., Dinsdale, D. and Orskov, E.R. (1979). An independent microbial flora of the epithelium and its role in the ecomicrobiology of the rumen. *Nature*, **279**, 424–6.

Weis, D.S. (1979). Correlation of sugar release and concanavalin A agglutinability with infectivity of symbiotic algae from *Paramecium bursaria* for aposymbiotic *P. bursaria*. *Journal of Protozoology*, **26**, 117–19.

Weiss, E. and Dasch, G.A. (1981). The family Rickettsiaceae: pathogens of domestic animals and invertebrates; nonpathogenic arthropod symbiotes. In *The Prokaryotes – A Handbook of Habitats, Isolation and Identification of Bacteria*. II. (M.P. Starr, H. Stolp, H.G. Truger, A. Balows and H.G. Schlegel, eds), pp. 2161–71. Springer-Verlag, Berlin.

Whatley, F.R. and Whatley, J.M. (1983). *Pelomyxa palustris*. In *Endocytobiology, Endosymbiosis and Cell Research*. II. (H.E.A. Schenk and W. Schwemmler, eds.), pp. 413–26. Walter de Gruyter, Berlin.

Whatley, J.M., John, P. and Whatley, F.R. (1979). From extracellular to intracellular: the establishment of mitochondria and chloroplasts. *Proceedings of the Royal Society of London Series B*, **204**, 165–87.

Whatley, J.M. and Whatley, F.R. (1984). Evolutionary aspects of the eukaryotic cell and its organelles. In *Cellular Interactions. Encyclopedia of Plant Physiology*, Vol. 17, (H.F. Linskens and J. Heslop-Harrison, eds), pp. 18–58. Springer-Verlag, Berlin and Heidelberg.

Wheeler, C.T. (1984). *Frankia* and its symbiosis in non-legume (actinorhizal) root nodules. In *Current Development in Biological Nitrogen Fixation* (N.S. Subba Rao, ed.). Edward Arnold, London. pp. 173–96.

Whitfield, P.S. (1979). *The Biology of Parasitism: an Introduction to the Study of Associating Organisms*. Edward Arnold, London.

Whittaker, R.H. and Margulis, L. (1978). Protist classification and the kingdoms of organisms. *BioSystems*, **10**, 3–18.

Wicker, C. and Nardon, P. (1983). Differential vitamin requirements of symbiotic and aposymbiotic weevils, *Sitophilus oryzae*. In *Endosymbiosis, Endocytobiology and Cell Biology*. Vol. II. (H.E.A. Schenk and W. Schwemmler, eds), pp. 733–8. Walter de Gruyter, Berlin.

Wilkerson, F.P., Parker, G.M. and Muscatine, L. (1983). Temporal patterns of cell division in natural populations of symbiotic algae. *Limnology and Oceanography*, **28**, 1009–14.

Wilkinson, C.R. (1978). Microbial associations in sponges. II. Numerical analysis of sponge and water bacterial populations. *Marine Biology*, **49**, 169–76.

Wilkinson, C.R. (1983a). Phylogeny of bacterial and cyanobacterial symbionts in marine sponges. In *Endocytobiology, Endosymbiosis and Cell Biology*. Vol. II. (W. Schwemmler and H.E.A. Schenk, eds), pp. 993–1002. Walter de Gruyter and Co., Berlin.

Wilkinson, C.R. (1983b). Net primary productivity in coral reef sponges. *Science*, **219**, 410–12.

Wilkinson, C.R. and Fay, P. (1979). Nitrogen fixation in coral reef sponges with symbiotic cyanobacteria. *Nature*, **279**, 527–9.

Wilkinson, C.R. and Vacelet, J. (1979). Transplantation of marine sponges to different conditions of light and current. *Journal of Experimental and Marine Biology and Ecology*, **37**, 91–104.

Williams, A.G. (1986). Rumen holotrich ciliate protozoa. *Microbiological Reviews*, **50**, 25–49.

Windham, W.R. and Akin, D.E. (1984). Rumen fungi and forage fibre degradation. *Applied and Environmental Microbiology*, **48**, 473–6.

Witty, J.F., Minchin, F.R. and Sheehy, J.E. (1983). Carbon costs of nitrogenase activity in legume root nodules determined using acetylene and oxygen. *Journal of Experimental Botany*, **34**, 951-63.

Witty, J.F., Minchin, F.R., Sheehy, J.E. and Minguez, M.I. (1984). Acetylene-induced changes in the oxygen diffusion resistance and nitrogenase activity of legume root nodules. *Annals of Botany*, **53**, 13-20.

Woese, C.R., Magrum, L.J. and Fox, G.E. (1978). Archaebacteria. *Journal of Molecular Evolution*, **11**, 245-52.

Wujek, D.E. (1979). Intracellular bacteria in the blue-green alga *Pleurocapsa minor*. *Transactions of the American Microscopical Society*, **165**, 908-9.

Yamin, M.A. (1981). Cellulose metabolism by the flagellate *Trichonympha* from a termite is independent of endosymbiotic bacteria. *Science*, **211**, 58-9.

Yamin, M.A. and Trager, W. (1979). *Journal of general Microbiology*, **113**, 417-20.

Yang, M.G., Manoharan, K. and Mickelson, O. (1970). Nutritional contribution of volatile fatty acids from the caecum of rats. *Journal of Nutrition*, **100**, 545-50.

Yarlett, N., Coleman, G.S., Williams, A.G. and Lloyd, D. (1984). Hydrogenosomes in known species of rumen entodiniomorphid protozoa. *FEMS Letters*, **21**, 15-19.

Yarlett, N., Hann, A.C. and Lloyd, D. (1983). Hydrogenosomes in a mixed isolate of *Isotricha prostoma* and *Isotricha intestinalis* from ovine rumen contents. *Comparative Biochemistry and Physiology*, **74B**, 357-64.

Yonge, C.M. (1936). Mode of life, feeding, digestion and symbiosis with zooxanthellae in the Tridacnidae. *Scientific Reports of the Great Barrier Reef Expedition*, **1**, 283-321.

Young, J.O. and Eaton, J.W. (1975). Studies on the symbiosis of *Phaenocora typhlops* (Vejdovsky) (Turbellaria; Neorhabdocoela) and *Chlorella vulgaris* var. *vulgaris*, Fott and Novakova (Chlorococcales). II. An experimental investigation into the survival value of the relationship to host and symbiont. *Archives of Hydrobiology*, **75**, 225-39.

Index

Index